The Motorcycle & The Molecule

(mis)adventures in community

Dougie Lux

Ashland, Oregon

Follow @DougieLux on Facebook and Instagram and join his newsletter for more adventures at www.DougieLux.com

While this is a satirical work that is based on true events, some creative license has been taken. Conversations have been reconstructed from notes and memory, and names have been changed to protect the innocent… and more importantly the *not so* innocent.

Cover art by Lindsay Carron
Edited by Deirdre Stoelzle

ISBN: 978-0-578-65056-2

Dark Water Light Publishing
www.DarkWaterLight.com

This book is dedicated to my sweet mother, who gave me life,
creativity and independence. I love you dearly,
and we can talk about all this later.

CONTENTS

Prologue

The sun set on the Autumnal Equinox as Great Jaguar Paw, divine ruler of Tikal, gazed down upon his city from the Temple of the Moon.

"Goddamn, times are good!" he said to himself, smiling.

While historians and scholars might argue about what Great Jaguar Paw actually said to himself, whatever it was, it was probably something along those lines. After all, he was Chak Tok Ich'aak I, the great Mayan king, imbued with the power to communicate with the gods themselves, so humility wasn't really that necessary. What was necessary was looking absolutely divine as he postured from atop the immense temple, in front of his humble denizens.

The gleaming Mayan city of Tikal, hewn from the jungle itself, protruded high above the tree canopy. Tikal stood as a testament to Great Jaguar Paw's power and influence, an undeniably phallic statement of man's will, thrust upon nature. An assortment of temples, palaces and ball courts lay spread out across his field of view, each assembled by generation after generation of devotees. For centuries, countless humans had spent their lifetimes hauling seemingly inexhaustible amounts of limestone from Tikal's distant quarries, assembling them into structures that would challenge time itself.

Like the rulers before him, Great Jaguar Paw had leveraged his divine power over the people to manifest his dreams into reality. And why not? He was their direct connection to a greater realm, born and raised for this role, to assert his dominance upon the world. By continuing the work of his predecessors, Great Jaguar Paw had continued to transform the land from untamed jungle into a vast expanse of paved limestone, studded with monolithic structures and neatly manicured farmland beyond. His noble leadership directed the focus of an entire people toward a unified vision, ensuring the growth of his empire and his continued attainment of power and glory. This was his divine right and his people were grateful for his leadership. Without him, nature would be an inhospitable force and society would have no direction; the people would be forced to fend for themselves, alone in a harsh world, full of suffering and emotionally unpredictable deities. Instead, Great Jaguar Paw gave them purpose, he gave them security, and the people praised him for it. For indeed, their labor, their structures and their artwork were more than just a gift to a king, but a requirement that the gods themselves demanded.

"Ah, yes." Great Jaguar Paw spoke into the breeze. "What better way could there be to spend a life?"

And so it had mostly been for thousands of years. Food was plentiful, water was abundant and the weather was downright delightful. Neighboring cities, some of formidable size, were either supportive of mutual trade or at least mostly tolerant toward each other. Skirmishes still broke out, but besides the occasional kidnapping and public sacrifice there was more than enough space and plenty of resources for all to coexist. Times were indeed pretty damn good for Great Jaguar Paw and the Mayan people.

But then of course, nothing lasts forever.

Act 1: The Guatemala Part

1. Downfall At Tikal (Part 1)

"Humans are ridiculous!" I laughed to myself in the rain. This wasn't just your ordinary rain, either. This was the sort of tropical downpour that drenches the earth and the severe humidity was making it that much more intense. The inside of my cheap, plastic poncho had become my own personal steam room, but despite that, and despite the drips of perspiration seeping down my back into my already soaked underwear, I couldn't help but smile at the scene in front of me. I laughed to myself again.

A woman standing across from me shot me a glance. Had I actually laughed out loud this time? It was hard to tell in my current state. I was, after all—for the next few hours at least—psychologically impaired. But it didn't really matter anyway. She didn't know me. In fact, none of the other twenty tourists on the tour knew me, so as far as any of them might know I might just be the kind of guy who laughs at the downfall of a civilization. But I wasn't laughing at the downfall of the Maya. I was laughing at something darker, more subtle, that was emerging from just below the surface of this whole jolly escapade.

Rodrigo, our stout, dark-skinned tour guide, was standing in the rain, enlightening us with stories of the Maya.

"So, if you can imagine, even these pathways that connect the buildings were paved with limestone. Most of the temples are solid limestone, too. Early looters used dynamite and heavy machinery to try to get *inside* them, but they just found more rock. The sheer amount of effort it took to build this city is staggering. They didn't have beasts of burden. They didn't even have the wheel. But they had lots of manpower." Rodrigo then repeated it all in Spanish for the other half of the group. I opted for the budget tour package without realizing that we'd be part of such a large group that we had all barely squeezed into the tour bus. On the ride to Tikal, Rodrigo told us that he used to be a captain in the Guatemalan army but had defected to become an environmental activist-turned-jungle tour guide. It made sense; he brought the same seriousness that he'd no doubt honed in his military escapades into his new profession.

"But no matter how much they attained," Rodrigo continued, "no matter how much they built, it was never enough. Sound familiar?" His gaze fell upon me. Was this a rhetorical question? Was he referring to humanity at large or just Americans? I wasn't sure of the answer to either question so I just pursed my lips and gave him a slow nod.

During the bus journey to Tikal, Rodrigo had told us about the Mayan empire's rise to power. The earliest villages, he said, began to form around 2000 BC and over the centuries grew into the first towns and cities. Hundreds of years before Jesus Christ was running around and doing his thing the Maya were using writing systems and creating monumental structures. By 250 AD the Maya were connecting their city-states by great roads over which trade routes were established. Of these, Tikal and Calakmul rose to great prominence. Known for their hieroglyphic script, art, architecture, mathematics, calendars and astronomical system, the Mayan empire at the height of its power had spread through southern Mexico, Guatemala, Belize, Honduras and El Salvador.

"Among their great accomplishments," Rodrigo continued, "was the creation of what we believe to be the earliest version of basketball!" This fact was followed by some muted chuckles. "Teams would face off in large stone courts and use their elbows and hips to knock rubbery balls through vertically oriented hoops. Certain games were of enough importance that they'd end in human sacrifice, often with the decapitation of a team's captain. As was the case throughout much of Mayan culture, an emphasis was given to human sacrifice as a way to honor the gods. It was not seen as barbaric to the Maya, but instead they believed that the sacrificial victim would be elevated to a higher plane of existence."

"So which team's captain would get sacrificed?" a young Indian tourist asked.

"Well, there's some debate over whether the winning or losing captain would be sacrificed, but it's possible that different games called for different religious practices. Can you imagine the incentive of not wanting to lose for fear of sacrifice?!" Rodrigo asked, laughing for a moment before becoming serious again. "But on the other hand, imagine knowing that by *winning* the game YOU would be sacrificed. Imagine a world like *that*." He let the silence hang for a moment before continuing.

"Okay!" Rodrigo clapped. "You have twenty minutes to explore the great plaza and then we will head back to the bus. And don't be late!" Rodrigo paused for effect, before hissing, "The snakes come out when it gets dark." He repeated it in Spanish, which prompted squeals from the crowd. People scattered and began clambering off in every direction.

And that's when the full humor of the situation hit me. Here we were, in plastic ponchos every color of the rainbow, slipping and sliding on the ruins of a culture that had collapsed due to climate change, environmental degradation, overpopulation, overconsumption, brutal infighting and war-mongering, and finally the sheer weight of its own bloated, ineffective governance ... And that was all *before* the Spanish arrived to finish the job. *Sound familiar?* You're damn right it sounds familiar, Rodrigo! Here we are, raising our eyebrows over the exact same issues that we are facing in our own culture, and watching these amorphous blobs of purple, yellow, pink and blue staring wide-eyed and taking pictures like the whole scenario was so completely alien to them seemed pretty damn funny right now.

I'd come to Central America to explore communities, to find connections and to bring home some optimistic solutions for how to live together, but somehow I'd gotten off track. I was now surrounded by strangers and entirely unconvinced that modern humans could work it out before we met the same fate as the Maya before us.

I wondered what it was like for the Maya to experience the slow-motion cultural train wreck that led to the end of their empire. Like us, most of them were probably in denial, too. Day-to-day life probably just carried on like normal. Until it didn't. I might have felt depressed if I wasn't so out of my mind. So instead, thoroughly amused by the absurdity of it all, I just shook my head, definitely laughing out loud this time as I stumbled up the first, steep step of the Temple of the Moon.

But let's rewind for a moment to establish some context. My current problems, like with so many human altercations, had all begun with a beaver.

2. Goddamn Beaver

"Do you even *care* about the environment?" It was not meant as a question.

"Can you *please* try to be a little more realistic?" The response was also not meant as a question. The conversation, one that was unfolding at the Manzanita community deep in the woods of Oregon, was going in circles and had been for some time. The argument was centered around one *Castor canadensis*, better known as the North American Beaver. But before we dive into that furry debacle, let's establish how we all got here. And what better character to start with than that meddling little bastard, *Castor canadensis*.

Beaver originated in the mountains of the northwest United States, where there had been a strong and healthy population of these little mammals for millennia. Beaver spent its days enjoying a variety of beaver activities: building dams; repairing leaks; chewing trees; swimming around, and lounging in the sunshine. Beaver was an accomplished architect and devout family animal and apart from the occasional scuffle with its competition, Beaver was safe and conveniently close to his food sources. Those were happy days for Beaver.

In the 1800s, however, as the early settlers moved west across the Great Plains of the United States to seek their fortune, gold wasn't the only thing that they found. They quickly realized that beaver pelts could be hawked for a pretty penny on the fur market, and so trapping beaver became big business. Large furriers enlisted the help of local trappers to comb the wilderness and deliver huge amounts of beaver pelts for shipment. Hundreds of thousands of pelts were being shipped from northern America to Europe every year. Business was splendid for trappers, less so for Beaver.

One such trapper was Silas Brown. It was the late 1800s in North Carolina when his parents had passed on, and with no remaining family, Silas had struck out on his own and headed west with a dream to strike it rich. As a boy, Silas' father had taught him carpentry, how to hunt, and other useful homesteading skills in the wilderness of the Appalachian Mountains; as a young man he had honed his survival skills and was now ready for adventure. The nation was experiencing Gold Rush fever and after hearing about the promises of the West, Silas gathered his tools and what few possessions he had, loaded them onto his horse-drawn wagon and hit the road together with his loyal hunting dog, Huck. His vision? To find a place to settle down, put his skills to use and make his fortune. Silas and Huck travelled across the United States, navigating run-ins with wild beasts and wilder outlaws, but each time Silas' keen survival skills, combined with Huck's ferocious bark, saw them through. Their adventures, which unfolded over the better part of a year, eventually brought them to Oregon. Silas' wagon bumped and rattled through the forests until one day he came to a quiet, lush valley, at the bottom of which flowed a crystal-clear river; he imagined the gold that was hidden within. Trees were plentiful, trout jumped in the river and most importantly there were signs of beaver. *Plenty of beaver.*

So Silas set up camp. That summer he built himself a simple cabin and by the late autumn, although he hadn't found much gold in the river, he was trapping beaver, almost more beaver than he could process. Each month he would haul a cartload of pelts to town to sell and trade them for great profit. He earned himself the reputation as a hardworking and honest trader and within a year he married Sally, a good Irish wife who had an equally strong work ethic. Soon after that, they had a baby boy whom they named Jebediah. Jebediah grew, as did their small homestead. The number of settlers who passed by their little cabin also grew, many of whom were looking to stake their claim further up river. The quiet path to town became well-worn as other small-scale trapping and mining operations were set up. Soon though, these operations gave way to larger industrial endeavors and water got redirected from the river to hydraulic mining plants where massive cannons could blast away entire hillsides in a day, exposing their gold and other minerals for extraction. Not only had Beaver's environment been mostly destroyed but he had been so aggressively hunted that his population had dwindled close to extinction.

By this time Jebediah had grown into a strong young man and married a local woman called Rebecca, and within a few years the couple had a child whom they named Silas Jr. But times were challenging. A particularly cold winter had claimed the life of Silas Sr. and the income from beaver pelts was barely supporting the growing family. But the river was still healthy enough with fish, so later that year Jebediah decided to turn their property into a trout farm. He constructed a series of holding ponds that ascended up the muddy gulch, which became a breeding system for baby trout. Many years and many millions of trout later, Silas Jr. took over the family business, which they called "Grandma's Trout Farm" out of respect for Grandma Sally.

By the mid-1970s, Sally had long since passed on and since Silas Jr.'s children showed no signs of wanting to continue the family business he decided it was time to sell the operation. Almost one hundred years after his grandfather Silas Sr. had arrived in Muddy Gulch, as it came to be known, Silas Jr. would finally leave the wilderness and bring his family back into civilization. And at the exact same time as Silas Jr. was looking to sell the property and return to the city, a bunch of hippies from the city were looking to buy some property and return to the land.

The Summer of Love in 1967 had birthed a new wave of freedom and self-expression as hippies across the country protested the Vietnamese war while experimenting with drugs and practicing free love. The future looked hopeful as consumers of the cookie-cutter industrial era shrugged off restrictive social frameworks, smoked dope and dropped acid. During that fabled time of turning on, tuning in and dropping out, there was a conscious explosion that prompted the questioning of all that had come before.

The hippie movement might have been a little rough around the edges for the average American but to their credit the longhairs just wanted to explore what a more harmonious and liberated life could be like. So they got naked, danced around like loons, hollered at the sky and celebrated the dawn of the new human potential—*for a little while at least.* As is typical of human culture, a powerful swing in one direction inevitably gets countered by a powerful swing in the other. As exciting as the hippie movement was it was not very far-reaching and an increasingly conservative government began to put tighter restrictions on how people should behave. Our leaders believed it was crucial to, if only for the sake of morality itself, divert public attention away from the colorful hippies and instead focus it toward the more lucrative avenues of consumerism and war. But the seed had been planted and the new sprout, despite being somewhat wilted, was never able to be fully eradicated. Books like Rachel Carson's *Silent Spring* had brought attention to man's ravaging of the environment and people around the country became activists, tying themselves to trees and putting sugar in logging machines' gas tanks. Other pioneering groups decided to return to the land, sparking a movement back toward a deeper connection with nature and to man's place in the natural world.

The purchasers to the rights of Muddy Gulch were a group of twelve long-haired idealists who had found each other while travelling between Grateful Dead shows. These hippies, all in their early twenties, had come to southern Oregon, drawn by the dream of living in peace and harmony. It just so happened that along the way they met a local farmer who offered to introduce them to Silas Jr. over at Muddy Gulch. Some days later they all met at the property and were given a tour. Despite their looks, Silas Jr. enjoyed what these youngsters from the city were all about, something he'd hoped for in his kids, and in turn the hippies greatly appreciated Silas Jr.'s wisdom and his dedication to homesteading.

"You're the original, man!" one of them said as they shared a meal; they all laughed and the deal was soon struck. The twelve promised Silas Jr. that in addition to buying the deed to the property they would keep Grandma's Trout Farm running for as long as they could; after all, it was still a profitable business and the new hippie owners were smart enough to know that money, while *certainly* the root of all evil, didn't grow on trees and they still needed beer and pot. Silas Jr. packed up his truck, said goodbye to his home and the new homesteaders, and drove down the road, away from Muddy Gulch, never to return again.

As their first order of business, the twelve hippies created a crystal-studded medicine wheel at the highest point of the property and christened their new land "Manzanita" after the abundance of the pervasive, smooth and red-barked shrubbery. Times were good. And then, as was the case with most of the dreamers who returned to the land, the reality soon set in and was a little less romantic than the dream had been. Within the first year, three of the couples had broken up or reshuffled, one couple left the land when the reality of winter descended and one member, who had developed a heavy drinking problem, left after a bear got stuck in his cabin and destroyed the place while the guy was in town on a bender. *Can you imagine coming home to that?*

However, things eventually stabilized and over the next few years Manzanita became a workable example of what's possible when a community learns to live and work together. Bellies began to grow and one of the members, who had studied to be a midwife, opened up a natural birthing center on the land. It was so successful that other pregnant mothers from the surrounding area came to Manzanita to birth their little bundles of joy. In the years that followed, the birthing center evolved into a Montessori-style school. One community member drove a big painted bus to pick up the neighborhood children and bring them to Manzanita, where they would learn in a freeform way about their innate creativity and unique gifts. It was sheer hippie bliss.

Over the next couple of decades Manzanita flourished and became a thriving community hub. There were seasonal events and healing gatherings, and more often than not during the warm months naked people could be found racing each other around the ponds in inner tubes. After the trout business dried up, Manzanita produced a handful of profitable small businesses and led by a born-again former logger who'd named himself Song Manzanita, rallied the local community to successfully protect their surrounding forests from logging operations. In time, vast acreage behind Manzanita became protected land and cattle were banned from grazing in the meadows and forests further up the valley. Once again, the stream that ran down through the valley to the river became so clean that residents drank from it without even needing a filter.

But if we're seeing any pattern in these few short pages, it's that nothing lasts forever. The hippies' kids grew up and inevitably wanted to move away, more attracted to the buzz of the city than to the "Return to the Land" lifestyle that their parents had been so drawn to. For those members who remained, strong bones and strong ideals slowly gave way to a slower pace, and in the late 1990s when a flash flood ran through the valley, destroying structures and years of back-breaking work, many in the community had had enough; they had challenged the wilderness and given it a damn good run but most of them sold their stake in the property and soon left; *one guy even joined the Russian Ballet, which no one saw coming.* By selling a portion of Manzanita to buy out the departing members, Song and his wife figured out a way to keep the land and stayed on for another decade, while still supporting environmental campaigns and hosting the occasional event.

In many places the dream of the "Return to the Land" movement began to wane, due in part to poor social management, unrealistic ideals, inadequate financial understanding and a lack of knowledge that was crucial to survival in a rural community. Many tired idealists were lulled back into towns and cities by the new dream of an easy life *"Custom-built just for you!"* That's right, by this point companies had so successfully learned how to appeal to people's desires that the very people who had acted out in the 1970s were now inadvertently promoting the new self-expressive potential of the post-industrial, consumerist lifestyle: *"I'm an individual and I can finally express it with this [INSERT PRODUCT] so people know what I'm all about, man!"* But the dream wasn't completely dead, it was only in a coma. Volunteers at Manzanita came and went and helped keep it up and running. Eventually though, by his late 60s and after a particularly bad fall off a ladder while fixing a roof, Song and his wife decided to sell the property.

It was perfectly timed with yet another pendulum swing as the next generation aspired to transform their parents' conservative outlooks and consumerist behavior into a new and upgraded lifestyle of self-expression and environmental responsibility. While the pioneers of the 1970s will always be honored for their boldness to step into the unknown, times had changed and the new breed had more than just a bag of rusty tools and a half-baked plan. So, if you liked *Return to the Land* then you'll LOVE *Return to the Land: Part 2! Featuring solar power, satellite Internet and lithium-ion power tools!*

The advent of digitized information and global communication, a deeper understanding of the psychology of groups and individuals, better knowledge of financial and legal frameworks and a whole bunch of stories about how NOT to do it from elders like Song were just some of the assets that armed the next wave of homesteaders with the tools they needed to succeed. At the same time the sensory faculties of the digitally connected human population was under increasing attack from all types of beeps, buzzers, bings and dopamine-delivering digital distractions. There had never been a better time to get people off of their devices and back into nature, and business models for profitable land stewardship seemed like a real possibility. Festivals, retreat centers, endless workshops and ceremonies all promised that you'd emerge knowing yourself more deeply by disconnecting from the matrix. Ironically all of these offerings were promoted across social media and blasted through email channels to a frenzied public that was desperately searching for how to *not* feel like they were desperately searching. Well, shit, in a world in which no one knows who to trust, or what's even true anymore, maybe it's a good time to disconnect from all the insanity and reconnect with nature? Well, after a decade of endless emails, scrimping clients and shitty business partners, getting off the computer and heading into the wilderness sounded pretty damn good to me.

I know, I know. I still haven't explained *why* we were sitting at the dinner table arguing over a goddamn beaver. But just stay with me, it's kind of integral to this whole darn thing.

3. Path To Manzanita

About two years prior to the great beaver debate I was living in Los Angeles, flying high, making a ton of money and being a pretty fantastic example of what success looks like. But something wasn't quite right, I was moving too fast and soon the glaze began to crack. Finally the bottom of my life dropped out and within a couple of weeks I lost my job, my house and my girlfriend just before I was planning to propose. I lay on the bed of my bland, short-term apartment for a few days with the curtains closed as I stewed in my trifecta of misery. After a brief flirtation with suicidal thoughts, I pulled myself together, sold most of my belongings—this wasn't the first time—and decided to go travelling to gain some new perspective on life—also not the first time.

A friend of mine who was leading a one-month yoga teacher-training course in Thailand suggested I sign up, so I did, hoping to heal my serious case of creative and energetic burnout. On the beaches of Koh Phangan I practiced yoga, meditated and ate healthily every day, but at the end of the month I was even *more* anxious than I was when I started. So I told my yoga instructor about what I was going through.

"Congratulations," she smugly replied. "Now the work really begins." God. Dammit.

I soon began to see all sorts of areas of my life in which I needed to be more conscious, so I stayed for another month and one day while I was at a silent retreat I (silently) fired my financial adviser over email who, despite my requests, had continued dumping my savings into lucrative but ethically questionable investments. So I took control of my portfolio and sold any investments that represented pharmaceuticals, fossil fuels, shitty food, alcohol, cigarettes or morally corrupt mega-banks.

I got a tan, taught some yoga classes in straw huts and toyed with the idea of staying in Southeast Asia forever, but I felt like I wasn't quite fully ready to give up on my old life, and five months later I returned to Los Angeles with the plan to start a new business endeavor. But immediately everything felt different. The idea of event production, my old career, prompted a sinking feeling deep in my gut and the pace of the city felt like everyone was on amphetamines; barely anyone seemed to be able to have a conversation without checking their phones midway between sentences.

Meanwhile, and maybe it was because I was talking more about mindfulness and trauma than about technology and entrepreneurship, some friendships felt a little strained. Maybe it's that L.A. really only loves you when you're on a roll. After all, it's a powerful magnifier, a megaphone to the world through which you can amplify your dreams, and it can give it all to you just as happily as it can take it. I was still raw from my previous run-in with the city and decided that I had no intention of giving this seductive vampire any more of my heartfelt, fucking shine. What's more, my romantic life was officially dead in the water, and I was probably oversharing my feelings a little too much on social media. Yeah, I needed a whole new life direction.

So I started meandering around Southern California in "MoBo," my old, colorfully painted VW van, trying to catch a hint of what my next move might be. Yes, I was that guy living *down by the river* for a while, and I loved it, to be honest. I went from the desert to the mountains to the coast and then I'd circle back to L.A. and stay with friends until the next impulse struck. I was fortunate to be in the position, both financially and logistically, to be able to explore in this fashion. On one visit back through Los Angeles, I attended an event called *The Future of Storytelling*, during which a presenter talked about her vision, an evolution of the hero's journey as an individual, to the hero's journey as a collective. It all resonated so perfectly to what I had been feeling, yet not able to previously express. During the evening, I hit it off with a fellow attendee named Gabe, another event producer. We both agreed that we had become a little exhausted from event production and wanted to use our energy, time and money more responsibly, not just for these one-off events but by getting involved in more long-term projects that would be around for years to come. Gabe was a large, teddy bear of a fellow, easy to talk to and be around. The corners of his lips were turned upward and eyes relaxed in their sockets. I imagined that his was a largely jovial life. It was hard not to love the guy. He shared with me that the very next weekend he and some friends were going to visit a possible community property in Oregon. I was interested in how they were going to structure the financial and legal arrangements so I asked him to keep me posted.

A month later I met Gabe for lunch in Santa Barbara to get an update about how the project was developing. They'd made good progress so once again I told him that I was excited for them and to keep in touch. He had such an easygoing demeanor that it was hard not to love him. Just about anything he talked about brimmed with a magical quality of optimism and possibility. I was impressed by his team's dedication and he had a good track record for accomplishing big projects. *"Keep in touch?"* I said out loud to myself as I was driving away from lunch. What if this is the exact thing that I've been searching for? After all, we did meet at an event called *The Future of Storytelling* and share the same vision ... plus we have a bunch of mutual friends AND he's a big hugger, too? I'd never imagined myself going as far north as Oregon, but like Dave, a great mentor of mine always told me: *"Don't worry so much about what it looks like, focus on what it feels like."* And it felt good. I immediately called Gabe back, told him how I felt and he seemed excited to hear the news. He suggested I go up and visit as soon as I could, so with nothing else happening in my life I loaded up MoBo and left Los Angeles.

Manzanita was considerably farther north than my usual route, but even that felt exciting, forging new pathways in my van as well as in my mind. I remember passing Mt. Shasta and experiencing a powerful feeling of calm wash over me. An hour further north I stopped into the town of Ashland, best known for hosting the world-renowned Shakespeare Festival, where I stayed for the night before heading out to Manzanita the following day. As I drove through town I noted that pretty much everyone was white, which was a little strange coming up from Los Angeles, and that Ashland seemed to be a humorous blend of semi-conservative, old white people, counter-culture, neo-liberal white people, and a sprinkling of transient young white people who were just figuring their shit out.

From Ashland I drove an hour west, passing increasingly grand vistas of bucolic loveliness. Quaint homesteads, weathered barns and baby goats playing in meadows—that sort of delightful stuff. Eventually I turned onto a dirt road and after fifteen minutes of cliffside twists and turns I arrived at Manzanita, where I was met by Angela, one of Gabe's friends who had been involved since the start of the project. Angela was a real earth mama, short and stout with piercing blue eyes, the sort of eyes that looked me over like an outsider who had yet to win her trust. But a healthy skepticism can be a useful asset on a team and from what I could tell her dedication to the project was matched only by her dedication to the land itself. She gave me a tour of the property and the rickety old cabins, and I was soothed by the calm setting. Manzanita was literally buzzing with life. Bees hummed in the air, touching down only to make sweet love to the endless array of vibrant flowers in the garden. A stream flowed through the land from the upper valley and the sheer amount of green hues entering my eyeballs was a welcome change from the subdued SoCal desert tones that I was used to. The place seemed to descend from a dream realm, offering respite from the world, whispering promises of soul healing and creative projects. "It is also a great opportunity to develop new skills," Angela said, which was another way of saying that the whole place was pretty much falling apart. Regardless of its rustic nature, this place was offering me the chance to leave my old world and provide me with a fresh start as I rounded out my thirties.

"You know the thing about the rat race?" my mom had always asked me as I was growing up. "Even if you win, you're still a rat." I laughed at the memory as I drove away that day from Manzanita.

Was I ready to reclaim the endless days that I spent living on a computer, my bones and muscles slowly deteriorating from too much sitting? Was I ready to give up the constant arc of excitement and exhaustion that was event production? Was I ready to leave a racing world where I was a compulsive connector of ideas and people and projects? Was I ready to learn how to build stuff with my hands, physical stuff that would be around for years to come? Was I *really* ready to leave the bright lights of the city and uproot my life to the dark, starry nights of the wilderness? If you haven't already guessed, *you're damn right I was!*

For the next few months I worked with the new Manzanita members, most of whom I'd only just met, on forming a land-holding company. From there we began to lay out our collective vision for a revitalized wilderness community and retreat center, which already had a few structures on it in various states of habitability. We talked about our values and principles. We shared our hopes, concerns and dreams and by that autumn we began pooling our funds. In yet another sign that I was making the right move, the buy-in price for my rustic cabin was almost the exact amount of cash that I had from the shady investments that I'd sold earlier that year. We had talks with Song and his wife about purchasing the land, including an agreement in which they'd carry a portion of the purchase price as a loan, while we secured buy-in from some final members the following year. It should be an easy sell for the right people, we thought.

It was one of those really special moments in time, one in which everything was flowing and setting us up for success. While we certainly shared some of old Manzanita's values, this time we were armed with much more information than Song and the pioneers of the 1970s. Our group was experienced in finances, events and community theory, and was well-informed by various tales of challenges and successes from elders from other communities. In terms of knowledge, the Internet, which was beamed to our remote wilderness location via a series of orbiting satellites, would enable us to proceed with a deeper understanding of everything from building techniques to appropriate crop cycles. Manzanita had access to grid power although additional power could easily be generated from the numerous sunny days enjoyed by southern Oregon's temperate climate. Water was abundant, distributed via a gravity-fed water system with a backup well, plus a river that ran through the bottom of the property. We were equipped with all the latest tools and there was even a Home Depot under an hour away. We had everything we needed to make this work.

By late autumn, six months after I'd first visited Manzanita, we sealed the deal and while most of the other community members were waiting until spring to move up, like a child with a new Christmas toy, I just couldn't wait to play. So I gathered what few possessions I still owned, loaded them into MoBo and hit the road together with my loyal terrier, Tux. He seemed as excited as me as we pulled away from the city, paws on the dashboard and wet nose streaking the windshield as we left California, bound for a land of countless trees to pee on and squirrels to chase. And so my relationship with Oregon began, a seductive new lover that tempted me with her vitality, flowing waters and secluded delights.

It was the end of the harvest season by the time I arrived, and most of the outdoor activities were wrapping up. The days had grown shorter and the local farm store had hung a sign in the parking lot that read, "*Closed Until Spring.*" Frolicking in the parks, which I'd witnessed while visiting earlier in the year, had given way to people staying at home, cozy with their loved ones and wintertime hobbies. And here I was, an excitable fool from Southern California who'd arrived just in time to face Oregon's most brutal winter in a decade, huddled in a cabin full of cracked window panes and doors that didn't fully shut. During one particular stretch it got so cold that I had to staple a blanket across my door frame. For a while I was able to keep my spirits up, but I found it hard to make friends and soon began to feel incredibly isolated.

Worse still, I kept contracting blistering poison oak rashes but not having any idea how. At one point it got so bad that I took myself to the emergency room because one of my eyes had swollen shut from the oils of the toxic plant. Do you know what it looks like when a guy gets poison oak on his penis? Even with only one working eye I can tell you: *It's not pretty.*

I began to wonder what the hell I'd done to myself. Why had I left behind all those who loved me? Why had I abandoned a place where I had a good reputation and everything came so easily? I hadn't screwed anyone over, so why did I feel like such a pariah? Well, now here I was in the middle of nowhere; no women, no drugs, no pizza. With no distractions left there was nowhere left to hide from myself; I began to pick my life apart. Why did I need to subject myself to such struggle in order to feel worthy? Even the way Tux looked at me would plunge me into depression. Removing ticks and burrs from the poor pup became a daily chore and further showed how I'd made a terrible decision. Unable to cope with the added guilt I sent him back to L.A. to live with his aunt and uncle. And then I was totally alone ... *and persistently itchy from the poison oak.*

Some days I would just sit there, staring out into the forest, sobbing. I'd never witnessed such short hours of sunlight and by the winter solstice I was thinking about death on a regular basis. *Had I actually come out here to die?* The only thing that kept me from hanging a noose from the rafters was thinking of how terrible it would be for the other members of our new community to discover. On Christmas Eve, hoping to find some spiritual solace, I went into Ashland to enjoy some holiday poetry reading. However, after the gathering, I ended up in a bar again, drinking so much this time that I passed out in my van fully clothed. That Christmas Day I'd woken up alone and freezing. I'd vomited out the window in the middle of the night and was now extremely dehydrated. My water bottle had frozen solid. And that's when I saw it. The Best Western across the street, a beacon of warmth and cheap coffee and pancakes.

I walked over, approached the front desk and asked if they were still serving breakfast. The receptionist, who seemed somewhat startled, directed me to the cafeteria. A couple of motel guests glanced at me before quickly looking away. I poured myself an orange juice and downed it before heading into the bathroom to splash some water on my face. I looked in the mirror and that's when I saw the clumps of vomit on the side of my hoodie. That breakfast, smelling like puke and shamefully eating lousy pancakes, remains one of my more depressing holiday moments.

But then, shortly after the New Year, a curious thing happened. I had taken a little break from the snow and gone back to visit some friends in L.A. One day, I confided in a dear friend of mine that I thought I'd made a big mistake.

"I don't know, man. If I ever return to L.A. I'll probably be a totally irrelevant person," I lamented.

"Yeah, you could return like that," Eric had said. "Or you could return *as a legend*." A wave of his hand added the necessary gravitas. *And he was totally right.*

A little love and reassurance from my family was exactly what I needed and a week later I returned to Manzanita, dedicated to making it work. I began a daily health routine. I lunged back into my yoga practice, replaced alcohol with kombucha, and reestablished healthy eating habits. Each morning I meditated and journaled about my feelings and at night I read poems about gratitude and love. I began to sample all sorts of activities that I learned about on the community notice board, storytelling circles and open mics, acoustic music jams and group meditations, and I even got the chance to be rebirthed out of a giant earthen vulva at the Ashland Goddess Temple. Romance was still a distant memory, although I did get invited to a song circle by a woman who sold chocolate molds of her vagina. *Ah, Ashland!*

On Sundays I started dropping into an interdenominational church group called Unity, something I never would have imagined doing a couple of years earlier. It was a welcome weekly dose of spirituality that included insights into everything from the Kabbalah to Buddhism, to Celtic and Native American traditions, accompanied by music from all sorts of instruments. Afterwards I often helped rearrange the chairs or clean up coffee cups. It was a welcome break from thinking about my own problems. I began listening to uplifting podcasts and perusing the self-help book section. I busied myself with all the logistical life stuff that one needs to do to get settled in a new place. I got all my mailing addresses changed and my car registered. I joined a credit union, because you know, fuck Bank of America and the rest of those greedy assholes. I finally got health insurance and went for a checkup. While my body was decently healthy the doctor recommended that I seek therapy because some things had gotten flagged on my psychological tests.

The first counselor I saw said, "You might be bipolar and I think you should see our psychologist." So I went to the psychologist who said, "Well, you're probably bipolar and I think you should see our psychiatrist." So I went to the psychiatrist who said, "Yes, you're definitely bipolar, but I've seen worse." She was very nice and told me that individuals who suffer from my type of bipolarity are often responsive to treatment so I started attending weekly therapy sessions. Things were looking up!

Then, one day in late February, I was halfway through another self-help book, this one called, *Whatever Arises, Love That*, when I suddenly popped through a conscious doorway and just decided to accept this whole ridiculous situation. I had always thought of myself as some sort of benevolent trickster, poking people to get them out of their comfort zones.

"Well, you just pulled a big one over on yourself, old buddy! You knew full well what you were doing when you signed up for this!" I was laughing as I sat in the weathered, bluish-grey armchair in my cabin, hollering out loud to no one in particular. Yep, I'd already become the guy who lives in an off-the-grid cabin in the middle of the woods and hollers things at himself.

A couple of weeks later I was driving into town when I saw the sign at the local farm store: "Open for the Season. Happy Spring!" Tears came to my eyes.

"Sweet, baby Jesus, I fucking made it through the winter," I exclaimed.

Indeed, I had made it through the most challenging, dark-night-of-the-soul experience of my life. I'd touched such an edge, tasted such a deep despair that now, just a regular day just felt goddamn fantastic. If a person did something I didn't like, no big deal, no real expectations on my end. Someone let me down in some way? No worries, I'll just take myself elsewhere where I'm appreciated, nothing personal! Every little thing felt like a blessing and I was back to my old, but better-than-ever, version of myself. Gratitude poured from my heart into my writing and into my relationships with my friends and family. I stopped oversharing on social media and dove into restoring my old cabin with the help of a carpenter friend who had come up to visit. After long days of removing mouse crap and half-dead bats from its rotting walls, Davis and I would share dinners and stories by oil lamp, laughing about our tough times and strategies for how to best navigate through our shadows.

"Sometimes you've got the bear. And sometimes the bear's got you!" Davis would often say, pounding his chest and chuckling, a gold tooth glinting at the edge of his broad smile. Davis was a rock to me, and even when I got crotchety a few times during the cabin restoration, he'd say: "Oh, that's just the poison oak talking, buddy." And he was right. It felt good to have a brother at Manzanita and together we vowed to get healthy and strong for the times ahead. Slowly the other members began to arrive and everyone liked Davis so much that he was asked to stay, taking up residence in a tiny little cabin just through the woods from my place.

One day, I was walking by the gate that we would close to prevent cars from driving on our roads when the conditions were too wet. During the winter it had been my responsibility to open and close the gate when it rained. As I walked by, I noticed tiny buds were blooming in the tangle of vines next to the gate. Oily little red buds. Oh yes, when open the gate rested in a monster thicket of poison oak. I hadn't noticed before, as I didn't yet know what poison oak looked like in the winter, but the oils from the plant stay active for many months and over the seasons this gate had become saturated with the stuff. I had finally solved the riddle of my misery.

More people arrived on the land, bringing the numbers to around ten, and everything was great—for a few weeks, at least. There were some early disagreements but they didn't seem like too much of a big deal, probably just growing pains, I thought, and luckily I was still in my blissed-out state as a result of surviving my winter ordeal. I watched as some pretty antisocial behavior began to unfold as passive aggression became more overt. In retrospect it may not have been a good idea to get involved with a group of people I barely knew but I remained hopeful, certain that there *must* be a lesson in each uncomfortable and challenging interaction. I'd been sent to boarding school when I was eight years old and I liked to think that living around so many people for so long had made me a pretty easygoing and tolerant person. We are all adults and I we can work it out, right?

And then came the goddamn beaver.

At first it was just a joke. We'd begun to notice signs that a beaver had returned to our watershed. The environmentalists rejoiced, claiming this to be a wonderful sign of the health of our land and a powerful omen of good tidings. *Praise be! The beaver has returned to help us restore our waterways and bestow his animal spirit energy upon us all!* Well, we all went with that, at least for a little while. The previous owners, who we'd allowed to stay on the property in a tiny home on the corner of the land, gravely warned us about the beaver and told us of the challenges that they bring. Even so, at first there was a unified voice in favor of the beaver. We laughed about making T-shirts that said, "Respect The Beaver!" but the laughs didn't last long.

Over time, some of the members started to question the value of the beaver. While of course it was a nice *idea* to coexist, in reality the beaver had begun to chew down fruit trees and dam up our pond, early signs that his plan was to revert our property to its sodden former glory as a muddy gulch. While this may well be beneficial to the overall ecology of the land, we weren't all sure it would be beneficial to the day-to-day lives of the human residents. Research began into the pros and cons of beaver guests but the conclusion was that there was no definitive right or wrong approach. Some landowners chose to live with beavers while others claimed that beavers bring problems that aren't worth the hassle. So we began exploring ways to encourage the beaver to vacate the premises, which included caging trees, playing loud, heavy metal music near their dens and spraying other beavers' musk on their dams. How we got the musk, I never found out. We even consulted a beaver-relocation specialist. After all, this was the wilderness of Oregon and people need services like that.

Within a short period of time the whole community was up in arms over the beaver debacle. The community had fallen into two groups: *pro-beaver* and *beaver-hesitant*, and tensions were running high. By this point I didn't care as much about the beaver as I did about the time and stress that the burdensome beast was adding to our meetings. It felt like a skipping record of beaver facts and posturing over who cared more about the environment. And now here we were in yet another two-hour meeting around the dining room table, facing off over the little bastard.

"How can you *not* agree that the beaver isn't a natural part of this watershed? It's been here for millennia!" Gabe asked.

"Well, not for the last century it hasn't," Joel, a stoic member of the beaver-hesitant faction, accurately stated.

"Well, what a *blessing* that it's chosen to return and bring its wisdom to share with us," Angela retorted.

"Look, I love that idea, I really do," Joel continued, his clear blue eyes casting icicles across the table. "And I'm not saying that I'm not open to having a beaver here one day. Who knows, with the right plan, and the right people to oversee it, and maybe when we're a little less stretched just trying to get our basic living systems worked out, then yes, maybe that would be a good time to invite a beaver to live with us."

"I can't believe you say you care about the environment! We should have screened members of this community better from the start," Angela said, turning up the level of her trademark passive aggression.

"Well, there's something we can agree about!" Joel's girlfriend exclaimed.

And round and round it went. But soon an interesting thing happened; we realized that this wasn't really about the beaver at all. The beaver issue represented a larger, underlying rift in the community that had been simmering for a while; a misunderstanding that came down to the *very semantics* of the words that had called us all together in the first place. You see, even though we had done so much right in setting up our community, I don't think you can ever do it perfectly. After all, humans are unpredictable and if the core values of a group are out of alignment, bitterness and resentment are bound to emerge. So we fell back to our operating agreement, pouring over the words and putting our voting system to the test. But a vote is meaningless if the words are misinterpreted. Yes, we had all agreed to take part in restoring a "*Wilderness Community and Retreat Center,*" but apparently we all had different ideas as to what those words actually meant.

Each faction thought they were correctly following the guidelines that we'd all outlined at the beginning of the project. To the *pro-beaver* group "Wilderness Community and Retreat Center" meant living in harmony with all of life's creatures, of which humans were just one part. A totally noble and acceptable opinion. Meanwhile to the *beaver-hesitant* group, "Wilderness Community and Retreat Center" meant something a little more human-centric, in which we were carving out a homestead from the vast surrounding wilderness for ourselves and our visitors, prioritizing, respectfully *but definitively*, the quality of human lives. Losing old fruit trees and kids running the risk of getting giardia from beaver shit when they swim in the ponds just didn't feel good to the folks in the latter camp. Also a totally acceptable opinion.

As is usual for me, I found myself caught squarely in the middle. Personally I didn't really care about the beaver that much. If it wanted to live in our ponds, fine. If we trapped it and relocated it, fine. Surely there was enough space for everyone to live in peace? What I wanted was a quiet cabin where I could spend part of the year, to write and read and in general get away from it all. And if that meant having to beat a track to my door through trees that had been felled by beaver or dealing with the occasional challenging community member then it wasn't ideal but I'd deal with it.

What I wanted most of all was for people to stop arguing. Why couldn't we enjoy this beautiful place and all just be a little more tolerant toward each other? After all, realizing a shared vision means that there will always be give and take. And so I took the diplomatic path, having one-on-one talks with all sides. Just when things started feeling a little better, they would fall apart again. It felt like so many things were going well, but all people wanted to focus on were the few issues that weren't working. It felt like a microcosm of the world at large; in other words, a real bummer.

Meetings became increasingly tense as the beaver conversation prompted deeper misunderstandings. *"I don't feel heard"* and *"Well, I don't feel safe"* became phrases that were tossed around so liberally that they had lost all meaning. Soon other more pressing issues had begun to arise, in particular between Angela's somewhat antisocial boyfriend and the rest of the community. Despite continued efforts to integrate him he just did not seem able to mesh with the community. His communication style was a challenging combo of Aspergerian Narcissism and in his most abrasive moments, typically when he drank too much, he tended to mansplain over everybody and even become aggressive. Eventually he just stopped coming to meetings altogether, which was probably for the best because he seemed to get into altercations with everyone each time he did. But the biggest issue was that two of the female members, both highly assertive matriarchal types representing each side of the beaver debate, just could not learn to get along and damn, there's really nothing comparable to when two feisty women are at odds. By this point it didn't even matter what one was saying, you could immediately feel the other one bristling just at the sound of the first one's voice.

To make matters worse we still had a two hundred thousand dollar loan to pay off and only about eight months to do it in. It wasn't looking good. With an obvious tension in the air and without any clear, community-wide vision, the few prospective members that did come to check out the property never returned. The loan also created a challenging dynamic, because although we'd technically bought the property from the previous owners, they were the ones to carry the loan and we'd signed a document saying that we'd keep the place in the same shape as we got it until they were paid off. Even before they heard of trees being chewed down, they had made their stance perfectly clear: *they were NOT part of the pro-beaver group.* There was so much passive aggression and avoidance going on that it quickly became apparent that things would not clear up on their own. A disease had developed within the community and our social immune system was not strong enough to fight it off. As the summer months went by we enlisted outside help and asked a neighboring community leader to come in to mediate a special council. He came. *Twice.* Talking sticks were held, feelings were shared, misunderstandings talked through and intentions were set. But the peace treaties never lasted long before someone felt attacked or otherwise mistreated and the whole wound got torn open again. My angle, as the member who had arrived to the project somewhat in the middle of all the members, was to be as diplomatic as possible without being dragged too deeply into any particular drama.

By the end of the summer we were all growing weary of the whole affair, and my hypnotic optimism was beginning to wane; the cycles of unmet expectation and outspoken blame were beginning to drag me down. Besides, try as I might to act as a diplomat, my efforts seemed to be for naught. So while I knew that not much could be worse than the previous winter, I also knew that the coming winter might be the perfect time to take a little break from the project, so I began plotting a trip.

The plan was to leave Manzanita before Christmas and travel around Central America by motorcycle with the loose goal of exploring and researching local communities. I wanted to uncover which communities were succeeding, to see how they were managing themselves and to bring back some insights to share with Manzanita. I shared my plan with the community and they were supportive. At best any insights might help restore our faith in the project but at the very least I'd get a much-needed break, do some yoga and hopefully remember what it felt like to touch a woman.

The fall at Manzanita was stunning. The leaves exploded into more colors than I'd ever thought possible and the cool rains soothed the cracked land after the scorching summer. I hurled myself into projects, helping restore the old schoolhouse and taking care of chores around the property. We were all expected to do a few hours of tasks around the land each week as directed by a chore wheel in the office; except at Manzanita we didn't call it a *chore wheel* we called it the *"Wheel of Co-Creation*," which I had taken to saying with a magical wave of my hand. Well, my *chore of co-creation* was trash management and meadow mowing. I installed new double-glazed windows and doors at my cabin to keep the chill out as the long, dark nights of winter descended. As the day of my departure grew closer, I continued to spend time with both sides of the beaver debate as well as with the previous owners. I was determined to avoid being put in the middle and I tried to steer conversations away from gossip on to more productive topics. My best efforts were still only of limited success. It's amazing how stubborn people can be when their egos get in the way.

In my final days at Manzanita I got my cabin ready for the winter. I cleaned the chimney and chopped and stacked firewood so I'd have it when I returned. I turned off the water valves and drained the pipes so they wouldn't freeze during the cold nights ahead. I set some mousetraps and asked a neighbor to check on them once in a while. I packed up my backpack, loaded up my trusty van MoBo and said goodbye to everyone, pledging that I would still tune in for the regular weekly meetings. I shrugged off the feeling that I was bailing; after all, I'd certainly tried my best to help the situation and I was sure there'd still be plenty of problems for me to return to. And besides, what was the worst that could happen?

The bright greens of spring and summer and rich colors of fall had given way to the drab, dull hues of early winter. The fallen leaves had begun to disintegrate, leaving behind skeletal old oaks that faded into my rearview mirror as I drove south through Ashland and into California, leaving Oregon, Manzanita and most importantly the goddamn beaver situation behind me.

4. Where The Rainbow Gets Its Colors

If we pay attention, we begin to see the clues, recurring patterns of information that pop up on our radar. These clues might be in conversations with friends, in movies we watch, in posters we see, in magazine articles or in books we read. To the astute, these clues are telling us something. New Agers might call this feeling *synchronicity*, while scientists might call it *confirmation bias*. Either way, for months clues ranging from workshop posters at the co-op to offhand comments from my carpenter had been pointing me toward Lake Atitlán, a mystical volcanic lake in southwestern Guatemala.

At about ten miles long and five miles wide, Atitlán, a Nahuatl word that is best translated as "*the place where the rainbow gets its colors*," is ringed with small towns that each possess their own distinct character. There's a town where indigenous peoples sell arts and crafts, a town where young foreign students take part in homestay programs to learn Spanish, a town where expats and tourists enjoy cheap cocaine and cheaper booze, and a town where the locals really don't like to be bothered by *gringos*. As I continued to research Atitlán, it was an entirely different town that caught my attention. The town was called San Marcos La Laguna, a New Age vortex that promised yoga workshops, ecstatic dance parties and cacao ceremonies. My current mission was to heal myself, search out vibrant and healthy places and to share them with my community and the rest of the world, and a head-first dive into some heartfelt good vibes was just what I needed to start soothing my tattered soul.

Now upon quick glance I appear to be a pretty regular guy in his mid-thirties. I'm strong but not ripped, attractive but not strikingly so. My head is buzzed clean, less for style and more as a way to camouflage my male-pattern baldness, and I sport a shortly trimmed, dirty-blond beard that gets shorter as it travels up my sideburns, transitioning into stubble on the sides of my head. For apparel, I don't possess a lot of clothes so in an effort to match I generally wear mostly a range of faded charcoal tones, occasionally switching it up with some lighter gray and white in the summer months. Upon closer inspection one might see an agate crystal around my neck or catch a glimpse of my nails, which are often painted a light silver. My clothes are clean, I shower regularly and if I *do* apply essential oil, I steer clear of patchouli, opting for more cinnamon and woody notes. In other words, unless you look closely, I rarely trigger anyone's hippie alarm bells and usually pass as yet another, albeit slightly older, cleaner, and better-smelling backpacker. Don't let this fool you, however.

My undercover hippie ways may have started when I visited my older sister in San Francisco as a young boy, where she introduced me to crystal shops and to books such as *Siddhartha the Buddha* and the bibliography of Tom Robbins. I was young and impressionable and instantly intrigued by everything that was different from my conservative upbringing. After that first visit, when I was twelve, I returned to my English boarding school and during a public speaking assignment I declared to the entire room that I had officially converted to Buddhism. Shortly thereafter I was called to the headmaster's office where I stood behind his broad oak, leather-topped desk.

"Just what game do you think you're playing at, boy?" he inquired over the edge of his spectacles. So I made my case. He smiled and denied my declaration. However, to his surprise I had arrived at his office armed with a letter from my dear mother that stated that she was supportive of my spiritual evolution, and the headmaster was forced to relent. Never again did I get out of bed early to dress up for morning chapel only to learn about the wickedness of my very existence. Instead I slept late in my bed of spiritual independence, even if that wasn't the most typical of Buddhist practices.

In time I began to read more about the metaphysical world and became curious about other realities, which in my imaginative young mind simply *must* lie hidden beyond my limited perception. At first this mostly meant pressing my eyeballs to watch the geometric patterns appear, or spinning around on the lawn until I fell to the ground laughing. But as I read more I learned terms like *astral travel* and *lucid dreaming* and wondered what mysterious realms might be tucked beyond this veil that the crotchety adults called "reality." These were my first small steps into the realm of the mystical.

Some years later, after my first visit to California, I returned from more than a decade of boarding school in England and enrolled into college at the Rhode Island School of Design. If all-boys English boarding school had been all that was soul-crushingly conformist, my experience at RISD was the antithesis. It was like all the weird art kids from around the country gathered to out-compete each other's creative talent and eccentricity. During my four-year total immersion with these wonderful oddballs, I was encouraged to express myself by all means possible; with my art, with how I dressed, with my sexuality, and with illicit substances as I sloughed off the shackles of my inhibited youth.

After college I moved to California, where I surrounded myself with other weirdos and dreamers, many of whom had been called out to the West Coast for the same reasons that lured Silas Brown almost two centuries earlier. Back in Silas' time it had been all about gold and animal pelts. Decades later it would become the place for Hollywood stars, and later still Silicon Valley would give birth to the world's uber wealthy. California's legacy was a place where dreams could become a reality, where judgment was cast aside and replaced with an exuberant, if at times maniacal, celebration of what's possible.

My first experience of living in Los Angeles was a rocky one. I was unemployed and while I was away for a few days visiting family on the East Coast, my roommates, a money-hungry stripper and a devastatingly handsome failed actor, robbed me to pay for their rent and growing cocaine habit, and both had vanished by the time I returned home. After a brief escape to nurse my wounds I once again returned to L.A. and this time everything was aligned. My first year back I volunteered at the TED conference and attended Burning Man for the first time; my mind was doubly blown. I'd felt like an outsider for my entire life, and suddenly I was living in a golden land where no one really cared where I came from, but they loved my weird history and weirder ideas. L.A. was a place where: *"Oh, you want to dress up in a tuxedo and tour the world for charity?"* would barely register as strange and instead more probably prompt something like:

"Actually I have a friend who runs a production company, you two should meet!" I had finally found my home.

I moved into a spacious warehouse where I began hosting eclectic, intellectual soirées that gathered creative entrepreneurs, scientists and artists. These became my friends, many of whom also enjoyed experimenting with different substances and peeling back the edges of their own awareness at late-night parties or on camping trips. I began going to music and art festivals like Lightning in a Bottle and Lucidity, attending esoteric workshops and meditation retreats, and bam! Before you knew it, I was asking for kombuchas at bars and disappointed when they couldn't provide. Yes, this was my slippery slope into undercover hippiedom. I might not have dreadlocks or smoke much pot anymore but underneath this clean exterior the transformation was in motion.

And you know the rest. A decade later, after my previously mentioned mini early-midlife crisis I'd left Los Angeles and moved to Manzanita until a beaver argument prompted me to follow a series of clues that pointed me toward the town of San Marcos La Laguna along the edges of Lake Atitlán and the strange and mystical activities that happened there. My undercover hippie was intrigued and it became the obvious place to begin my trip.

It was late December when I arrived at LAX with nothing but a backpack, a yoga mat and a one-way ticket to Guatemala. The plan was to fly into the capital, immediately take a bus to the old colonial town of Antigua, chill out for a few days and then head northwest to Lake Atitlán, where I'd decided to spend the holidays at an Airbnb that I'd found in San Marcos. This seemed like a relaxed way to ease into my winter sabbatical.

After a thoroughly unenjoyable eleven-hour layover in the Mexico City airport, I landed in bustling Guatemala City and immediately caught a shuttle bus to Antigua, a couple of hours away. Antigua is a colorful and quaint town, if slightly unexciting, but has good restaurants and a fairly well-preserved Spanish colonial aesthetic. Many of the buildings, which range across the spectrum from yellows to violets as if children's drawings had been brought to life, contained spacious courtyards just beyond their large wooden and wrought-iron doors. There are some notable nearby volcanoes to climb and other outdoor excursions for the adventurous, but overall I imagine Antigua is best suited for older folks, maybe the kind of place your mom would really enjoy. I mainly used my time in Antigua to sleep, eat, practice some Spanish and read up on the country's history.

A couple of days later, I was on a janky shuttle bus, along with eight other tourists, on a three-hour roller-coaster ride to Panajachel, the entrance town to Lake Atitlán. From the shuttle stop I hiked over to the ferry launch and boarded a small boat, along with some other tourists and a slew of local villagers who were carrying baskets of all sorts of fruits, vegetables and chickens. The diversity of Lake Atitlán became quickly apparent as the boat made stops at small impoverished villages as well as more opulent-looking hotels. After thirty minutes or so we arrived at San Marcos on the northwestern shore of the lake.

The town of San Marcos sits nestled between clear, blue volcanic water and steep cliffs that rise up to meet the rim of the crater behind it. As I disembarked, I noticed that the locals paid significantly less for their fare. Fair enough, I thought, as I paid the boat man a couple of bucks and thanked him in Spanish.

Immediately I could tell that I'd made the right choice. Everyone was smiling and seemed friendly, and there was no one hassling me for money on the pier. The narrow pedestrian road that led from the dock through the town was lined with murals, small shops and restaurants, people selling artwork, crystals and handmade jewelry, and numerous signs for yoga and organic food. Further along I passed a large community notice board that boasted a dazzling array of workshops, healing modalities and cacao ceremonies. I would soon find that the compounds in cacao permeated through much of San Marcos and the neurochemistry of its blissed-out residents. All the while, almost everyone I passed made eye contact, sharing pleasantries or at least a smile or nod of the head.

Humans acknowledging the presence of other humans on the street is one of those things that gives me great pleasure, yet seems to be so rare in large cities. I've actually heard that in some countries, even saying hello to a stranger indicates that you may well suffer from mental problems. Maybe it's a coping mechanism for people when they feel threatened or overstimulated, but it still made me want to grab the person by the shoulders and shake them just to elicit some reaction. Anyway, I didn't have that impulse here and I immediately felt welcomed by the bright-eyed people of San Marcos.

At the end of the narrow pedestrian street I took a right and walked past a basketball court where some local kids were playing a pickup game. I walked by a market stall that had a ridiculous amount of eggs for sale and passed a skinny, stray dog that was sniffing around for any morsel it could find. I left the center of town, passed a hostel called Del Lago, rounded a corner and arrived at the Airbnb that I'd rented for the holidays. Sunflower House, as it was called, even though there were no sunflowers anywhere in sight, was right off the main road and surrounded on three sides by jungle. I rang the bell and a man came to the door.

"Hello, you must be Dougie!" the man said.

"Yes, hello! Nice to meet you! This place is amazing!" I replied.

"I'm Erik, let me show you around." Erik was the Airbnb caretaker and an extremely kind Norwegian man, probably around thirty-five, who took his sweet time giving me the grand tour of the two-floor cottage. There was a porch that overlooked both volcanoes on the other side of the lake and a backyard patio with a firepit. The kitchen was simple but had a cappuccino machine and I even had a guest room in case I found a roommate that wanted to share the cost of the place. But if not, the whole cottage was only about forty dollars per night, pricey for Guatemala but a welcome splurge for a two-week holiday home.

"This is perfect!" I said. "And this town seems so charming. I could see how people want to stay here for a while."

"Oh yes," said Erik. "My brother and I came here as we were travelling through Central America, and San Marcos was as far as I got."

"Ha! That's funny! And what about your brother?"

"He got tired of waiting for me so he kept heading south."

"How long ago was that?"

"Let's see." He looked out the window for a moment, making the calculation in his head. "About thirteen years ago now."

Apparently that was the kind of vortex San Marcos was; I would have to be careful.

After lying down for a little while I got into some more comfortable clothes, my summery white outfit, in fact, and headed back across town for an event that I'd heard about days earlier, and for which I had made a significant effort to arrive on time for. It was called the Sunset Cacao Dance at a place called the Eagle's Nest.

I left Sunflower House and made my way back past the market, the eggs, the dog and the basketball court before continuing up the hill. I was a little lost until a pretty, young Austrian girl gave me directions.

"Look for the small, painted eagle signs," she said, pointing up a side street. "Have fun! Maybe I'll see you there later." I certainly hoped so.

The hill became steeper until I finally saw one of the little signs she'd been talking about, attached to an electricity pole and pointing down an alley. Each hand-painted eagle symbol I followed led me down an increasingly narrow walkway until I finally emerged through a door to the most radiant and lovely woman. "Welcome to the Eagle's Nest," she smiled. I expressed my gratitude for finding the place, paid her the entrance fee and walked into the majestic scene.

Colorful fabric was draped over a large, wooden dance floor that protruded from the cliff's edge and was supported by thick bamboo posts. Beyond the platform, while being careful not to fall over the side to the terrace below, one could observe a spectacular view of the two volcanoes on the far side of the lake.

A group of around thirty people sat on the dance floor, facing a facade of intricate stonework that had been built directly into the cliff and included framed alcoves in which candles had been lit. Above the dance floor, facing the lake, was a DJ booth, or more accurately a DJ *altar*, the front of which was emblazoned with the Eagle's Nest sigil. A hush fell over the group as a tall, slim man began to talk; I had made it just in time for the start of the proceedings.

By chance I saw a friend who I knew from LA, a tantra teacher called Sharon, so I walked over and sat next to her and we both exchanged big smiles as the cups of cacao were passed around.

"Now one thing to know about real cacao, cacao like you have in front of you," the man began, "is that it contains a variety of chemical compounds, including one called anandamide. These compounds can create an extremely euphoric sensation. It's especially powerful for people that don't use many other stimulants such as coffee, alcohol, sugar or other things that spike our brain chemistry." He continued, his voice sing songy in nature: "Movement helps to activate the compounds and hence the enjoyable combination of cacao and dancing. Of course the sunset makes it that much more *delightful*." Everyone giggled as the rest of the cups were passed out.

By this point, a petite young woman had sat down on the other side of me. She had a few ornate feathers woven into her blonde hair and we smiled at each other. I was quickly becoming aware of the sheer amount of well-toned, attractive people in this town. She looked at me again, this time for a moment longer.

"Hey, I recognize you!" the woman, who was apparently Russian, whispered as she jabbed me in the arm. At first I didn't recognize her but then a glimmer of recollection entered my mind. "I'm Nadia!" she said as she swept her hair away from her face. Her skin was impossibly smooth and her broad smile gleamed, a poster girl for good exfoliation and healthy dental hygiene.

"I'm Dougie!" I whispered back, but we were apparently both still unsure of how we knew each other.

"Hmmm ..." She examined my face with her sharp brown eyes. "Well, cheers!" We clinked our cups of cacao and I downed the rest of the sweet, thick, and slightly spicy mixture. By this point the tall, slim man had wrapped up his soliloquy and the music had begun. People were getting up, stretching and beginning to express their somatic impulses to the ambient, electronic melodies. "To be continued!" she said as she got up, smiling and twirling off into the mix.

Often called Ecstatic Dance, although technically that term is trademarked, these types of dance "parties" have started popping up all over the place. These dance gatherings, which usually happen during the daytime and last a few hours, are *mostly* sober events that take place in dance or yoga studios, and sometimes even those banquet halls where old guys in funny hats still sometimes hang out and talk about the good old days. The experience starts with some light yoga or stretching and the music matches the chill mood before slowly increasing in tempo. Talking is discouraged and while it's okay to dance with others, if they're receptive, it's typically more of a solo experience; some people even keep their eyes closed completely. If the occasional creep invades your space, then you may employ the international signal for *"Please go away,"* which is expressed by putting your hands in a prayer position at your heart with the optional head bow to break eye contact if necessary. Anyway, once you get over yourself and really let go it can be a surprisingly cathartic experience. Usually after thirty minutes or so, I experience a rush of endorphins, resulting in a blissful mood; hence *ecstatic* dance. At times the movement can even trigger emotional responses as our bodies release tension, perhaps even stored memories of pain or trauma that become dislodged by the motion. Some people whoop with delight but it's also not unusual to witness others quietly sob as they dance. There are sensual dancers, body-contact dancers and usually at least one joker that runs around the place like a loon to stir things up. But most people just do their own thing.

An hour into it about fifty people, all high on cacao, were getting ecstatic as the sun set over the larger volcano on the other side of the lake. As if on cue, two eagles swooped down from the cliffs above to ride the wind a few hundred yards out over the lake. I danced like a carefree fool for another hour or more, eventually weaving my way silently through the crowd and taking a break near the edge of the platform. I stretched and gazed out across the water. My heart felt so full with love and appreciation for this moment that my eyes welled up. The fact that moments like this exist, in places like this, make me feel like the world might just be alright. I told you, people get emotional during these things.

A while later the music faded out and most people had stopped dancing and were lying down on the platform, some in savasana, others in fetal position. The tall, slim man requested that we gather into a closing circle. Nadia sat down next to me and smiled blissfully. We went around the circle and each shared a word, "liberated" … "grateful" … "cosmic" … "blissed-out"—that kind of thing, which was followed by some community announcements. Open mics and jam bands, yoga classes, new moon dances, cacao-making workshops and a myriad of activities with New Age catchwords like "galactivation" were all on offer. Finally, the whole affair ended with a big collective "ohm."

"I remember!" Nadia turned to me and said, excitedly, "FACEBOOK!"

At that exact moment, I realized the same thing. She was even sporting the same feathers that she'd had in her profile picture.

"You contacted me on the San Marcos group. You were thinking about renting my extra room!"

"Yes!" She exclaimed.

"What a coincidence! So I guess you found another place?"

"Well, I decided to take this course at The Pyramids of Ka. I don't know how long I'll be there so I'm taking it day by day."

"The Pyramids of Ka? That sounds like an interesting place!" I replied.

"It is! You must visit!"

"Well, the room is still open so let me know if you're still interested."

"Okay, let's stay in touch! So fun to meet you here!"

"So fun!" I agreed. What a great way to arrive in San Marcos.

She hopped to her feet. I followed suit and she gave me a big hug.

"Welcome, brother! See you soon," she said before twirling away once again.

As I was leaving, the Austrian girl, the one who had helped me find the Eagle's Nest, approached me.

"Hey, you! A bunch of us are going to Del Lago for dinner," she said. "Want to come?"

"Sure, I'd love to, that's actually right next to my house." So I joined her and her friends and together we left the dance floor on the cliff. We walked through the narrow alleys and down the steep hill, laughing and speaking different languages. It was my first evening in San Marcos and I already felt at home, surrounded by a bunch of smiling people and enjoying the sweet, lingering effects of the cacao's heart-opening compounds spiraling around my brain.

5. A Poco Strange Place

I made peace with the spiders that came out at night; for the most part they stayed on the walls, content to catch mosquitoes. Even the scorpion, which I almost grabbed when I reached for the dish sponge, seemed mostly happy to remain behind the sink. Besides these uninvited guests, Sunflower House was perfect. I woke up with the light from the jungle streaming through the window and felt completely rejuvenated. It was away from the buzz of the town center and it turned out that Del Lago, right next door, was a cool spot to hang out. Del Lago was a hostel as well as a restaurant, and every night they would have music or drums or a movie that people from the town would gather for.

San Marcos was a blissed-out little town that seemed largely comprised of radiant Westerners. Passersby held each other's gaze long before they were close enough to exchange verbal greetings which, when given were often expressed as New Age niceties such as "Blessings, friend" or "Aloha, brother." When people hugged it was the sort of long hug that someone who's not used to long hugs might find uncomfortable. I was loving it and soon I was feeling more positive, healthy and excited about life again. I imagined this as a regular winter location to return to; maybe rallying some friends to find some property down here and to create a community! Maybe a retreat center, organic restaurant, with yoga and all other healthy things! Or maybe start a high-vibe, adventure tour company! Activism, volunteering and a center dedicated to the healing arts! There were a lot of exclamation marks going on in my head so I decided against the second cappuccino and did a little meditation, reminding myself that my involvement in one community experiment might be more than enough for right now.

This familiar manic sensation reared its head whenever things started feeling good and I would wonder if *more* would feel *better*. I laughed at myself as I identified that old energy loop. *Just settle down and enjoy the moment*, I told myself. All of our work must start with ourselves and I know I am my most creative and effective when I am feeling grounded and centered. From that foundation I can move outward, thus avoiding any feelings of burnout or resentment. For now, I didn't have to make any big decisions.

After bringing myself back down to earth I walked briskly into town and made my way through the narrow streets, toward The Pyramids of Ka. I was running a little late so grabbed a bottle of jun, a type of fermented honey tea, and a superfood, cacao treat; these delightful morsels, also known as bliss balls, seemed to be for sale just about everywhere I went. After making my way through some back alleys near the dock, I arrived at The Pyramids of Ka just in time to meet a few people who I'd met the previous night at Del Lago. One of the smiling young ladies, a flowy blonde Canadian named Masha, had told me that this was the last day of the seven-day Moon Course, led by a mystical woman who had founded The Pyramids of Ka many years earlier, when San Marcos was a new community. It sounded intriguing so Masha had invited me to come along.

As we waited to enter the largest of the pyramids, we were told to remove any metal objects such as sunglasses and cell phones from our pockets. We then descended into a stone tunnel and up some steps into the structure. The inside of the wooden pyramid was spacious and sunlight streamed through the glass apex, twenty-five feet above our heads. There was a small, thigh-high pyramid on the floor in the center of the room that was surrounded by candles. Small alcoves in the walls contained effigies of various deities and other holy figures. People sat on cushions along the perimeter of the wall, facing the teacher. I saw Nadia on the other side of the room and she smiled and waved at me. I waved back and found a spare cushion just as the trap door to the tunnel was closed, sealing the room.

The teacher, a striking-looking woman with silver hair who was dressed in flowing white robes, began to look around the room. Her gaze stopped at me.

"And what are YOU doing here?" she asked me in a thick, Spanish accent.

"Oh, hi! I heard there was a wonderful workshop going on today," I said innocently, but suddenly getting the distinct feeling that I was crashing the party.

"And who invited you?" She looked around. Masha guiltily raised her hand.

"Well, we don't usually invite guests on *l'último* day of the Moon Course." She was silent for a moment as her gaze returned to me. "So *por que* did you come?"

"Well, I heard there was a metaphysical talk led by a powerful and wise teacher," I said, hoping that a little charm might soften her up a little bit.

"Well, you are *muy* correct." She seemed receptive and smiled. "And you are *afortunado, por que* you get to skip the six days of preparation and jump right to the topic of astral projection!"

And so, over the next couple of hours, as my lower extremities cramped up from sitting cross-legged, the teacher, whose name was Chaty, outlined the seven stages of existence that were represented by the seven inner tiers inside the pyramid itself. Chaty's language was an expressive blend of English and Spanish and she often combined languages creating a *"poco strange"* effect. Together we discussed how a disciplined initiate might ascend from the material world and our physical bodies, up the ladder toward the dream realm, eventually into a fully actualized dimension, to a state of egoic transcendence. Now, this was all just theoretical discussion but still fascinating. What I found most illuminating about the discourse was that Chaty was not suggesting that we were expected to *live* in any of these elevated states but instead to develop the ability to gracefully move between them, gleaning wisdom from the other realms to inform our day-to-day human experience. This resonated with me. I liked the idea of living in different settings as a way to inform how we act and behave as we move between them.

Chaty also spent a good deal of time talking about lucid dreaming. In my limited experience with lucid dreaming I'd already witnessed some profound benefits by being able to play out challenging situations in my dreams as a means to practice my reactions. Of the few times I was able to do this, when the real-world situation subsequently arose my reaction had been more manageable.

For example, I used to argue with my mother a lot. And then one night in a dream I was able to practice some breathing exercises as she railed on me for some aspect of my lifestyle and ever since my ability to handle those situations has improved. After Chaty's talk there was an extended period of Q&A:

"How can you tell the difference between intuition and a choice made out of fear?" someone asked.

"How do you ask for permission before exploring someone's past, present and future from a remote location?" asked another.

"How do we practice these things without getting ourselves or others into trouble from things we don't understand?"

Chaty entertained each question with respect and mystical insight. It might be a little *too poco strange* for some but I've always prided myself in being able to glean something useful from even the most bizarre of experiences. Sometimes they could be life-changing or at the very least I might gain the realization that something is definitely not for me. An excessively strong aversion might even prompt me to wonder why I'm being so defensive about my own beliefs in the first place. Besides, I'd been around more outlandish teachings than Chaty's. This one time a friend of mine roped me into an intergalactic communication circle in a parking lot in Venice, California. Well, before I knew it, I was dancing and chanting with a bunch of oddballs, summoning aliens from a hidden nearby planet. Apparently these aliens were our masters and we were just their holographic projections.

"We don't always do that," my friend had said afterward, seemingly a little embarrassed.

So in the grand scheme of things, this was just another morning in the magical little town of San Marcos La Laguna.

After we exited the pyramid, Nadia came up to me.

"Good to see you again, Dougie!" she exclaimed.

"You too. What a *poco strange* and interesting experience!" I laughed and she laughed, too.

"I know! I'm thinking about doing the Sun Course. It's a month long, at the top of a mountain with barely any water," she said.

"Well, that sounds terrible," I replied. "I don't think I'll be dropping in on that workshop. Speaking of workshops, are you going to the new moon ceremony after this?"

"YES! A few of us are. Let's all go together." She took my arm, which made me feel like the luckiest guy in town, and we set out, walking away from the pyramids and back toward the dock. We walked past a sprawling ceiba tree, its roots twisting all around its base as if it wanted to escape the confines of the earth. "So, I've been thinking," Nadia continued, "we have to be back here by 10 p.m. every night because they close the gates so I decided that I want to move to a new place. And I said to myself, 'If Dougie shows up at the pyramids today, then it's a sign.'" She smiled and in her powerful Russian accent stated: "We should be roommates."

"I think that sounds like a great idea." I really did. She was so lively and bubbly and I was aware that I was developing a crush on her. I wondered if the feeling was mutual. We discussed details and made plans for her to arrive with her things the following day at noon. So my new roommate was going to be a sexy Russian tantrika named Nadia. Oh, I didn't mention that part? Yep, Nadia was also a tantra teacher.

Our posse continued on, stopping for some vegetarian empanadas along the way. The little doughy pockets of deliciousness were served with some rice, beans and hot chilies, and all for about USD$1.25. We said goodbye to the smiling empanada lady and headed back to the main street to grab a tuk tuk. A tuk tuk is a glorified three-wheeled, motorized taxi that can fit three people in the back and another two in the front, one on either side of the driver, if you really needed to pack them in; ideally the weight was balanced well enough to prevent the contraption from tipping over on the potholed roads. We all fit into a couple of tuk tuks and were soon bumping our way over to our afternoon destination, a new moon ceremony at a place called the Tribal Village. The tuk tuks clunked and sputtered west over some dusty hills and about ten minutes later dropped us off at a nondescript structure upon which a small hand-drawn sign read, "Tribal Village," with an arrow that pointed down some stairs. The tuk tuk journey cost about USD$0.75 cents each.

We walked past the building and down a long, straight concrete staircase that descended a steep, grassy hill, past some cliffside stone structures and down a few more hundred steps. Finally, we reached a welcoming bunch of folks; the members of the Tribal Village were finishing their preparations for the ceremony so we all jumped into the lake and shared a bag of nuts. There were macadamias, almonds, peanuts and a strange thing that I thought was a nut but wasn't. I think it was actually some sort of bean and not very delicious at all. These were the snacks that every local kid in town seemed to be selling.

Eventually we got called to gather into a circle for the new moon ceremony.

"The cycles of the Moon offer us a great opportunity to set intentions and to release fears, stories and expectations that are no longer serving us," one of the hosts explained. After the introduction we were led through a water-blessing ceremony in which another member told us that he'd employed a special technique to create a "hyper-structured" water that he called "diamond water," which we'd soon be pouring into the lake.

"Within a few weeks," he continued, "the entire lake will become diamond water and be so clean we can drink right from it." He paused. "Although I'll still probably pass it through a filter," he added, without any sign of humor. We each poured a ceremonial cup into the lake. After the water blessing, we planted an avocado tree and someone blessed it, putting the bow on an all-around pleasant hippie afternoon.

After a short break, a small, elfin-looking girl began serving large portions of cacao from a bubbling cauldron. She talked about where the cacao was sourced and its health benefits: "... although there's a few reasons that you shouldn't take cacao." She explained, "The first is if you're on antidepressants, as it can cause unintended drug interactions; also if you have heart problems, it's not recommended as it can speed up your heart. And lastly you shouldn't consume cacao if you're a horse, a parrot or a dog, as it can be deadly." She was in her late twenties and looked Spanish but sounded Swedish and had a very dry, humorous delivery in how she spoke.

After she'd served everyone, I approached the petite Cacao Fairy to ask some more about her cacao. And also maybe to flirt with her a little, which we will blame on the cacao's heart-opening effects. She had just arrived at the lake and we both agreed that it would be fun to meet up sometime. In a hilarious moment, as I pulled her Facebook page up, I realized that we were already friends. She'd messaged me a few weeks ago about possibly renting the spare room at Sunflower House. This lake seemed full of strange coincidences.

After drinking the cacao, we all moved into a room that was constructed out of intricate stone masonry with windows that overlooked the lake and volcanoes in the distance. We were told to get comfortable and to give ourselves enough space to lie down, as we'd soon be taking part in a breathwork ceremony. As you can tell, there are lots of opportunities for ceremonies out here on Lake Atitlán, apparently even ceremonies *within* ceremonies.

Anyway, breathwork. Have you ever had one of those experiences that unexpectedly blows your mind, the kind of experience that makes you see everything differently? Sure, this can happen if you're super high but it's even more impressive when no illicit substances are involved and even *more* impressive when you're not moving and your eyes are closed. I'd first heard of "breathwork" a couple of years earlier. It was described as a healing technique that promised some deep catharsis by employing a style of highly controlled breathing. I was dating a woman at the time who was also curious about personal growth. Sometimes our fascination with transformational work got a little far out but it was a mostly healthy obsession, although we definitely lost a few of our more skeptical friends along the way. One summer evening we found ourselves in a mansion near Venice Beach, blindfolded, breathing heavily and howling from the depths of our souls. At least, I was howling because after receiving instructions from the facilitator, triumphant music had been turned up so loud that I couldn't hear anyone else. Like the music, the use of a blindfold was employed to give each of us more of a private experience despite being in a large group. I was amazed at the emotional release that I'd witnessed in just that introductory class so I had decided to sign up for a weekend intensive at a retreat center in Joshua Tree the following month.

If the introductory course was the appetizer, then the full-weekend "Holotropic Breathwork" workshop was the main course. I already knew that I had some repressed trauma to process. I *also* knew that I'm pretty sensitive to the energy of the people around me. Those things combined with this breathwork thing, man, that was one memorable weekend. By lying on my back for hours and employing a certain style of breath, I found myself traveling through my childhood memories of physical and verbal abuse. Tears and groans burst forth from the deepest parts of my very soul, finally freed from their years of containment. By the end of the weekend I left Joshua Tree feeling like a giant weight had been lifted from me.

So when I saw "breathwork" listed as part of the Tribal Village's new moon ceremony I was both excited and a little nervous. After the cacao we gathered in the stone room, which they called the temple, and I was once again lying on my back and practicing the same style of deep breathing that I recognized from the holotropic breathwork sessions. Rather quickly my brain and body began to hyper oxygenate. My head and face began buzzing and my lips began to cramp up. The rush of oxygen, combined with the cacao, seemed to have a magnified effect. I felt the buzzing descending down into my chest, and from my feet upward. Both of my hands cramped up into crablike claws, but I persevered through the discomfort, encouraged by the facilitator's instructions to keep breathing. As my heart began beating faster I felt the buzzing expand, but for some reason I couldn't feel any sensations between my chest and my knees.

I pushed beyond until suddenly I felt an amazing rush of compassion explode through my entire being. I felt it for myself and everyone else in the room. The blockage in my torso vanished and I felt connective vibration flood to my core from both directions. My body felt both alive and extremely heavy. I felt like a thousand-pound ball of light, immobile on the floor. The emotions continued to amplify and I soon felt tears well up in my eyes. At first, I cried for myself, but as the breathwork continued my focus turned outward toward those who had caused me suffering, crying for them and the misery and pain that they must have been feeling in order to inflict abuse on me. I felt the blame begin to release and a sense of compassion move into its place.

Around the room, other people were experiencing all varieties of emotion. Some laughed, some cried. I could feel my ego pulling me back, attempting to rationalize the experience. "Keep breathing," the facilitator said, urging us on. I once again resumed the deep-breathing style, and as I moved away from my thoughts and reconnected with my body, I felt the energy of the room supporting me. This time I almost immediately fell back into the holotropic state, tears once again streaming down my cheeks. My arms and legs were outstretched, back arched and head on the ground. I continued to release whatever I needed to until I felt another shift, this time away from my own story and toward a deeper sense of sorrow for what our world was going through, a deep soulful sorrow for the pain and suffering that my ancestors had gone through, sorrow for the pain they inflicted on others. My sorrow extended beyond my own lineage and ethnicity as I wept for Native Americans, Aborigines and Africans. I felt the suffering of people everywhere who had been subjugated, abused and displaced. It felt like my heart was connected to so many hearts before mine, like an ethereal string, spread across space and time, all beating in unison.

By this point, the facilitators of the ceremony had started drumming as a way to bring us back into the room and into the present moment. I don't know how long it had been but it had grown darker outside. We were instructed to get up with our time, light a candle and bring it out to the fire pit. Experiences like this have the power to dissolve blockages of the mind, body and spirit and it took me a moment to collect myself. Each time I allow myself to go this deep I am able to connect more with myself, and hence connect more with the rest of the world. Each time I release old layers of emotion or tension, I feel my capacity for forgiveness and compassion increase.

"In healing ourselves we heal the world!" was the phrase that jumped to mind so I sat up and I made a pledge to keep that notion alive. What better life path than to heal our suffering and to live in service to this world, to give back for all of those who came before us, whose shoulders we stand on today? I got up and smiled, reminding myself of how many times I'd made a similar pledge, and how many times I'd forgotten it. I found it fascinating that I could feel something so deeply, only to forget it so quickly, content to replace a divine experience with an abstract story. But such is the power of experiences like this; they alter our perception and by doing so help bring us closer to ourselves, to remind us of something we might have otherwise forgotten.

As I knelt down and lit my candle, I promised I'd try my best to keep remembering. *Re-membering*, kind of like becoming whole again. Hmmm, I liked that. I walked out to the firepit and joined the circle. Together we lit the fire with our candles and played songs, laughing and telling stories by the side of the lake until the stars pierced the descending darkness of the new moon sky.

6. Meet My Grandma

When I woke up, I had no idea that the day would involve getting intimate with a butch, hairy-chested, bald man as that just wasn't typically my sort of thing. But let me back up a little bit before getting into that whole situation. Since my earliest memories I'd always been a seeker; of what exactly I wasn't sure but immersing myself into different experiences was one of my best skills. In my boarding school years I was equally likely to romp with members of the drama society as I was to geek out with the chess club or get drunk with the rugby team. I liked the diversity of characters. In my mid-twenties I flowed between the worlds of art and design into science and entrepreneurship, always with a passion for promoting the bright people and ideas that I found along the way, and then in my late twenties I began producing events that combined TED-styled talks with Burning Man's expressive flair.

After my mini early-midlife crisis I started exploring self-help/wellness/New Age communities as a way to uncover some personal healing. Many appreciated the vulnerability, although for some of my more skeptical friends, this softer inquiry through meditation, fasting, workshops and conversations about emotions was a little much. So if any of what follows seems strange, I'll offer that we don't necessarily need to fully understand or even believe something in order to benefit from it or gain new insight. I don't know if distant planets influence our physiology, or whether the coins of the I Ching can know our fate, but I do know that reading horoscopes or philosophical musings can inspire and influence our thoughts and behavior.

As I walked toward town to find some breakfast, I met a friendly older guy with an impressive beard, whose daughter had wanted to visit Guatemala. Concerned for her safety and looking for an adventure, he had decided to drive her down from Texas on his motorcycle. As I talked with him, listening to tales of his travels through dusty Mexican towns and negotiating with crooked border officials, my desire for a two-wheeled adventure was reawakened.

After parting ways with the bearded adventurer, I found a cafe, run by a lean, blond man who also taught Pilates above the cafe. He had a slightly unsavory vibe, but he ran a tight ship and the *tipico* that I ordered was superb. The meal consisted of bright yellow scrambled eggs, sliced avocado, two strips of fried plantain, a slice of local fresh cheese and a generous portion of warm, blue corn tortillas. This breakfast was found almost anywhere throughout Central America and became a regular way to start my day.

I struck up a conversation with the girl next to me and proceeded with the typical backpacker volley of information: *Where are you from? How long have you been travelling? How much longer will you travel for?* It was all a little bit repetitive but she was friendly and we soon found that we had a bunch of things in common. We both enjoyed being solo travelers, getting dropped into strange new cultures, and having to make new friends and learn how to get by. There was something thrilling about it. As a young boy I had been moved around a lot so I learned to embrace the challenge and to enjoy novel experiences, or at least tolerate them when they were less than ideal.

In my earlier days on the road I'd gravitate toward the party crowd, often the loudest and hence easiest crowd to find; new friendships forged through blurry nights of drinking games, bar-hopping and hungover sightseeing during the day. Now, in my late thirties, my trick is to find the yoga studios, look at their notice boards, take a class or two, talk with some bright-eyed, healthy folk, and find out what's going on in the neighborhood. Worst case, say if there's no local yoga studio, you can still usually find the health-conscious folks congregating at vegetarian restaurants or upscale coffee shops that serve the alternative, wide array of nondairy milks. Here in San Marcos it wasn't hard to find these people *at all* because the entire town felt like a living, breathing transformational workshop. After breakfast, I strolled down the muralled alleys to the large noticeboard that I'd seen upon my arrival and began perusing the town's offerings. A tapestry of overlapping flyers promised every sort of esoteric and consciousness-prodding workshop.

On a whim I decided to head to a "Conscious Touch Workshop," led by my friend Sharon, an L.A. tantra teacher whom I'd run into at the cacao dance a few days earlier, and I weaved my way through some flowery paths and into the garden of the Ananda Wellness Center. The center was a beacon of New Age chill, right on the water, gentle waves lapping at the shore with reeds swaying in the breeze as the sun glittered on the surface of the crystal-blue lake.

About eight people had shown up for the workshop, and to my surprise, and slight dismay, almost all of them were men. That's okay, most of the guys who would show up at a conscious-touch workshop are probably the pretty heart-open, easygoing type, so it shouldn't be too awkward. Sharon, an excitable and vivacious blonde, projected full embodiment of her sensuality as teachers of workshops like this often do. As we sat down, she launched into her introduction.

"Welcome everybody!! I'm SO excited to have you all here. YAY!!" she clapped. "This is actually my first workshop that I've ever taught in San Marcos, so DOUBLE YAY!" To call her bubbly would be an understatement, the woman was effervescent to a fault. "I know I called it *conscious touch*, but what we're *really* going to be doing today is *tantra*." She giggled as some of the men in the group exchanged nervous smiles. "However, they wouldn't let me *call* it tantra. So, shush! Don't tell anyone that you went to a tantra massage workshop!" Apparently San Marcos, for all its openness, possessed a strict judgment toward the word tantra. Some years back, as a hoard of New Age healers and gurus had flooded the sleepy lakeside town, there'd been some rather dubious teachers that had established reputations for being a little *too* involved in their students' progress. I hadn't heard the full story but I was already well aware that teaching tantra was historically a very rocky affair, especially for male teachers. In our culture there is certainly a lot of healing that needs to be done and a huge, and often unspoken part of it surrounds our sexuality. Many people, often due to trauma of one form or another, suffer from a restricted or even completely blocked connection to their sexuality. And while there are certainly techniques for healing this trauma, some might appear to the uninitiated public as inappropriate or downright immoral, occasionally prompting them to start rumors.

Sometimes the student, exposed to a sudden and unfamiliar rush of sexual response, can become very shocked and even recoil from the experience, directing accusations toward the workshop or the teacher. Some students, newly liberated from their repressed sexuality, might become romantically attached to their well-intentioned teachers, only to later report them when their love went unreciprocated. *And then of course* there are CERTAINLY the blatantly inappropriate teachers who abuse their position of power and who rightfully get exposed and labeled as sexual predators. Regardless of whatever happened in this case, it left most of San Marcos reluctant to use the term "tantra" ever again. So here we were, a group of mostly men, at a *conscious-touch and definitely not tantra* workshop.

"And how exciting that we're mostly men!" Sharon quipped gleefully. "I love teaching men. I find women are a lot more open to many of these practices already so it's great for guys to be putting in the extra effort to get in touch with their sensitive sides!" The smile on her face seemed to know no bounds as she talked in all caps. "And don't worry guys, we'll ALL get turns with different partners!"

We broke the circle into pairs and sat cross-legged, facing each other as the exercises began. The first exercise was deep eye-gazing for minutes on end. The initial awkwardness quickly subsided and besides the occasional loop of smirks, my partner, a lanky Dutch fellow named Niels, remained calm and connected. At times his face seemed to vanish completely and all that was left was a narrow tunnel into his left eye, upon which my focus was directed. After that we switched partners and this time we were instructed to extend one hand onto the other's heart, while still eye-gazing, as a way to deepen the connection. The next round, in which I was partnered up with a tanned Spanish man, was all about asking for consent and handling rejection. We each got to ask the other if we could touch certain parts of their body, to which the other person would say, "No." The rejected person would then respond by saying, "Thank you for expressing your boundaries."

"Consent is SUPER SEXY, everybody!" Sharon clapped and squealed.

We moved on to our next partner and I found myself sitting across from a very pretty German girl. Once again we were instructed to practice asking for consent, and this time the other person got to choose whether or not to give it. She was strikingly beautiful and I felt a rush of excitement as we began. Almost immediately, however, I could tell she was a little uncomfortable. Her voice was so soft it wasn't much more than breath with a little sound, like she'd been wounded somehow, and her eyes contained a melancholy far heavier than her young years should have bestowed. While she was bold enough to both give and receive openly during the exercise, even this basic level of intimacy was obviously challenging for her. I immediately tempered my initial excitement, calming my instinctual desires and turning the focus of my energy toward more of a soothing, fraternal expression of love.

"Okay, everyone! Are you having fun?! You're all doing SOOO GREAT!! It's time to meet your next partner!"

The German girl moved along and now facing me was a burly, hairy-chested, bald man named Steve who I recognized from the new moon ceremony a few days earlier at the Tribal Village.

"Okay! GREAT! Now that we're all warmed up and feeling *yummy*"—important side note that tantra teachers like to use the word *yummy* almost as much as they like to use the word *juicy*—"it's time to move on to the juicy main course of the workshop! *The Five Elements Tantra Massage!*"

I smiled. Steve smiled back. The two of us, our bald heads, broad furry chests and all, were going to be partners for an activity called The Five Elements Tantra Massage.

I was first to lie on my back and receive the massage, which was intended to take the recipient on a journey through different styles of touch, as related to the five elements. I closed my eyes as Steve started with the *earth element*, which was expressed as a powerful, deep-tissue massage. Steve wasn't shy and made sure to get *really* into it, massaging my entire body, while narrowly avoiding my nipples and genitals. *He had large, strong hands.* The next element was *water* and Steve's hands washed over me, still forceful but more flowy this time. *Fire,* the next element, was more choppy and sharp, pokey and slappy and Steve shook and rattled me, which I especially enjoyed as it seemed to wake up and activate parts of my body that had felt a little sleepy. The fourth element was *air*, which moved over the surface of my body like a gentle breeze, and Steve amplified the sensation by lightly blowing on my skin. I had lost myself in the moment; it felt so good that I felt my sexuality begin to wake up and all of a sudden I was thinking, *"Please don't get an erection in the conscious-touch workshop with Steve!"* Don't get me wrong, he seemed pretty cool and may not even have minded, but still, I had just met him and getting an erection in a class of strangers still seemed a little bit inappropriate. I moved my attention to things that dulled my sexual excitement, in this case scrambled eggs and wrinkly old men. Not that I don't like either of those things, just not usually in a sexual context. I took some deep breaths and felt relieved as my erection began to subside. It must have been quite a scene for any onlooker to watch these two large, hairy bears share such an intimate and tender moment with each other. Luckily the last element, *ether*, was more hands-off and Steve passed his hands above my body, hovering a few inches from its surface, while being instructed to project loving intentions toward me, but try as I might I didn't feel much. Maybe I'm not sensitive enough to feel that level of subtlety, I wondered. Or maybe I'm a little suspicious about energy work in general. Are people really feeling anything or just imagining it? On the other hand, does successfully imagining a feeling make that feeling any less real? I decided to remain open to a continued exploration of the energetic realm. We switched roles and I attempted to treat my new intimate man friend Steve as lovingly as he'd just treated me.

After the workshop I went to dinner with Sharon and Steve. It turned out that he was a film producer and had recently returned from Nepal to bring awareness to human trafficking. From there the conversation veered toward some of the more shadowy aspects of humanity. We talked about the unfortunate statistics of abuse that many people, most often women and children, face at the hands of sexual predators. Sharon shared some tales from the darker side of the tantra community, and how certain styles of tantra can be used for manipulation. We wondered what could possess people to perpetuate such violence. Sharon also shared a story about one of her tantra teachers who'd recently killed herself after struggling with depression that stemmed from her own childhood sexual abuse. Despite being a world-renowned teacher, she'd never been able to fully face and deal with the shame she still felt, which she'd hidden behind her role as a teacher. The dark reality of the conversation was a stark shift from the light and sensual nature of the afternoon's activities, but I appreciated it. Places like San Marcos can be bubbles of brightness, at times feeling completely cut off from reality. It was a welcome reminder that life isn't all abundance and sunshine and that it's good to practice being able to face and discuss the more challenging stuff. While it's not helpful to dwell too deeply on our shadows, it's important to acknowledge them and not to just want to drown it out with our light.

The following days were a blur of transformational workshops, longer-than-typical hugs, bliss balls and good dose of unmet sexual desire. Despite some early fantasies of tantric romance with Nadia it quickly became apparent that our relationship was to be more of a sister-brother dynamic. At first I was okay with this; she was a great roommate and we made excellent partners-in-crime on the social scene of San Marcos—in fact, I could barely keep up with her. We'd hit the town nightly, jumping on every opportunity to dance, flirt and connect with new people, all the while consuming a copious amount of cacao. Yet while Nadia soon developed an array of beautiful and adoring suitors, I was finding romance elusive. I liked to think that I was beyond the age when personal satisfaction depended on victorious sexual conquest, and high vibes and interpersonal connections were the jam, but in reality I was feeling thoroughly sober and in need of some affection. It was strange since I was feeling more confident than ever, but something just wasn't gelling in my game. I tried to stay upbeat and not let it affect my mood. When I felt a longing for something I didn't have I thought back to self-help books that I had read and turned my attention to what I was needing within myself. What was I trying to fill through whatever form of external validation I was desiring? And could I give that to myself instead? If I could, then the neediness would surely pass and I would be left feeling lighter and more complete as a human. Recently this meant a lot of masturbating in the shower.

One evening, I saw the Austrian girl who I'd been flirting with at Del Lago after the Sunset Cacao Dance, and she was in the arms of a local guy that everyone called Panther. I'd missed her message the previous night and now apparently I'd missed my chance. I immediately felt my ego bristle for a moment but then, instead of sitting there simmering in self-sorrow, I walked right up behind them and gave them a hug. "You two are adorable!" I said and was happy to find I really *meant it*. They smiled back and it felt good. These days I know that the more I let love and affection flow freely around me, the more frequently they seem to appear.

And now the inevitable rub. Sometimes when things get too positive and heart-centric I can become a little cynical and begin to withdraw. My shadows tell me that all this bright, high-vibe crap is just a facade and that behind the *ohms* and *namastes* these people are just as inauthentic as everyone else. People might *say* the words but are they really *feeling* it? Are they actually doing the work? Or do they just want to avoid anything that's going to harsh their vibe. Some people call this behavior *spiritual bypassing,* and be aware, because it runs rampant in the New Age, hippie circuit.

Sure, I was feeling a little bummed about my unmet desires, but there seemed to be something else to this marked dip in mood I was experiencing. I didn't feel worthy of all this brightness, so instead of leaning in further I just wanted to self-eject from the love train and begin dismantling this whole uplifting, positive story. I knew that if I didn't interrupt this thought pattern the isolation and darkness would continue their descent. So I gathered up the reins. Since starting bipolar therapy back in Oregon, I could see that my judgment of the world was more often a judgment of myself. *Who's the spiritual fraud now?* I laughed. All this was another good reason to have Nadia as a friend and roommate. I shared some of my frustrations and she reminded me to not withdraw, but to stay open and optimistic and just hop back on the train when I fell off. And I offered the same reminder to her when she inevitably came home and shared her own insecurities. We provided a sweet balance for each other.

We had developed a fun group of friends and the next day we all decided to go on an adventure to Santiago, a town on the other side of the lake. After a thirty-minute boat ride we arrived at a bustling dock that led to a series of small stalls and restaurants. We walked up the road from the dock, bright fabrics and locally made crafts bursting forth from the countless stalls of hopeful merchants. We had the afternoon to explore so Nadia and I hopped in a tuk tuk and took a tour around the town. Mario, our driver, took us to see some picturesque views of the nearby San Pedro volcano, which watched over the town like an overprotective father. He then took us to meet local craftspeople with whom we practiced our slowly improving Spanish.

The highlight of the tour was a fascinating visit to the temple of the Mayan deity Maximón, the patron saint of the small lakeside town of Santiago. Each year, a shaman chooses a new location for Maximón's temple, which usually ends up being in someone's living room. For an entire year the chosen family doesn't have to work and is responsible for hosting the deity. In return people come and offer donations. This year's temple was a small room filled with candles and hanging fabrics, certainly not the most flame-resistant environment, but you know, *Guatemala.* A fascinating mixture of Mayan and Catholic symbolism filled the room, there was even an empty crèche for the soon-to-arrive baby Jesus, who'd also be taking up residence at the mysterious deity's temple for Christmas. In the center of the room stood the torso of a man set on a stand, wearing a hat and at least a half-dozen colorful scarves. Besides tourists and locals paying homage, a dozen or so "patients" came by each day in order to don a ceremonial hat and scarf while the shaman communicated with Maximón on their behalf. All the while the shaman's assistant lit cigarettes and filled shot glasses with whiskey, putting both in the mouth of the deity. It was the responsibility of the shaman to then inform the patient about the sickness that they were suffering from and how to deal with it. As we left I asked Mario what he thought about it all. *"Maximón is both the dark and the light. He is Grandfather, Wise Man, and Patron of the people. But he doesn't always tell you what you want to hear, or make things easy for you. But through that, we grow."* Maximón the trickster. My kind of guy.

Speaking of guys, on the way back to our water taxi a radiant, young man down by the dock had passed me a flyer. It was for a men's circle the following day. "It's going to be the first one of the series and we'd love for you to be there. Guys need to connect more with each other!"

"That sounds wonderful! Dougie, you should go to that," Nadia said.

"Sounds great, thanks buddy," I replied to the young man.

"See you tomorrow, I hope!" He waved and went on his way.

I was no stranger to men's work and in general it was a good practice to connect with the brothers, so the following day I decided to head back up to Eagle's Nest for the circle. About fifteen guys had gathered on the cliffside platform and, after a physical warm-up, we launched into more eye-gazing, group-singing exercises, dancing around to tribal rhythms until the big climax, during which we shouted off the edge of the platform, over the cliffs and across the lake, as loud as we could. I can only imagine what the people in the village below must have thought. But strange things happen in this town and they're probably used to it.

Toward the end we sat in a circle, shared our experiences and discussed things such as: *What does it mean to be a man? How can we embrace both our masculine and feminine energies? Where does our anger come from and how may we channel it, such that it doesn't get blocked, but also such that it doesn't hurt others as it is processed?* You know, all that new paradigm, man stuff. I shared about how I'd been working over the last couple of years on my own masculinity.

"I like to think of myself as a mast in the storm. As the winds and rains beat down and the ship is tossed about, the mast remains standing. Like that we bob and weave through our challenges." I shared with the group that this was how I dealt with the chaotic, the uncertain, the ever-changing. Not to feed the storm, but to witness it, to give it space and let it pass on by. "By following this metaphor, my relationships with everyone have improved, not just with women, but with this wild feminine aspect within all of us, myself included." It felt good not to be swept up in anyone else's story, but to listen, to observe and to allow. It was a good lesson from my first year at Manzanita.

We talked about the important role that women had played in our lives and many of us found that our mothers all shared a common intensity, elevated levels of stress and anxiety. We wondered if that because of absentee, or even abusive, fathers they had been exhausted by trying to fill both parental roles. There was a deep acknowledgement for how challenging this must have been and for all that they'd had to deal with. Appreciation and love flowed from this circle outward to our mothers, and mothers everywhere.

"You know, I used to have a tough relationship with my mom. And then one day I had a funeral for the mom that I wished I'd had and just decided to love my mom exactly as she is," I said. "It instantly took the pressure off the relationship. Now whenever I need to, I just conjure my own internal mom, who can talk to me whenever I need, however I like. These days when my actual mom is going on a rant about something, I don't get so affected. I just love her for the wonderful, creative force of nature that she is, stay calm, read through the emotions until we figure out what's at the root of things, and before long we're talking about how great our relationship is."

"And that's a useful practice not just for our mothers but for everyone!" one guy across from me said. "When our own well-being is not reliant on the actions or behavior of others, that's when we can show up as full human beings. We avoid cycles of disappointment and codependency."

Everyone "Aho'd" in agreement. Final announcements and comments were being made as the circle began to wind down. It felt good to share in this strong, yet vulnerable fraternal environment.

As we were gathering up our belongings I pointed across the lake at San Pedro, the larger of the two volcanoes. "I want to climb that thing before I leave town. Who's with me?"

"I've been wanting to climb it, too!" said a strong, German guy.

"Alright, let's talk afterwards!" I said. The circle wrapped up with a couple of shared breaths and thanks for the facilitator, the handsome young man who I'd met at the dock the day before.

Afterwards the German guy, Max was his name, came up to me along with a couple of others who were interested in conquering the volcano, so we traded contact info and made a tentative plan for later that week. It was late afternoon and I needed a snack, a bliss ball or something. I was just about to leave the Eagle's Nest when another fellow from the men's circle, whose name was Yello, came up to me to say hello. He was a curly haired, wild-eyed British fellow that I'd learned during the workshop had taken a full year to go around the world for a honeymoon with his new wife, during which they had partaken in all sorts of bizarre activities along the way.

"I'm especially excited about this New Year's Eve," Yello said as we walked away from the Eagle's Nest, heading back toward town.

"Are you going to the Cosmic Convergence festival?" I asked, referring to a New Year's gathering that was to take place on the other side of the lake.

"Actually, Yoshi and I are going to a sensory-immersion retreat."

"Like those floating tanks in which you're in complete darkness? I experienced one of those before in Venice Beach and it was really memorable. My mind played all sorts of tricks on me!"

"No, not in tanks, we'll be in a totally dark room."

"How crazy! So that's how you'll ring in the new year? In total darkness?"

"Yeah, we'll be there for Christmas, too."

"Wow, so like six days in total darkness?!"

"Two weeks, actually!" Yello and his new wife Yoshi were going to spend two weeks in total darkness, with just each other for company. The retreat even passed food through a special trap door through which no light could pass.

"Apparently if you stay in the darkness for long enough people lose and regrow their hair," he said.

"Amazing. And weird." I said, unsure of the benefit exactly. "I can't wait to hear about how that goes." We talked a while longer about other things we'd done in San Marcos and I told him about the breathwork at the new moon ceremony.

"Oh yes, I'm very familiar with that technique. Actually, Yoshi is a rebirthing practitioner."

"What's *rebirthing*?" I asked.

"Oh, it's another type of breathwork. It's like what you did, but can be a little more ... intense."

"*More* intense? Wow! I'd love to give that a try," I said, half-seriously.

"Well, Yoshi is offering it while she's here. I'll connect you if you like?"

I took Yello up on his offer and gave him my number to give to his wife. Yoshi messaged me later that day and we made a one-hour rebirthing appointment for the following morning. Our meeting spot was a place called the Blind Lemon, owned by a highly opinionated American guy named Carlos.

"I haven't paid American taxes in years. People probably wondered what happened to me but I live like a king down here! If I was back there I'd probably be a Walmart greeter! *Fuck that!* I'll hang out here with my guitar in the sunshine, thank you very much." Carlos made a good point. It was always so fascinating to me how people choose to spend their lives. How they use their assets and knowledge to live in ways that deviated from the norm. Carlos continued ranting for a while on a variety of topics so I was happy when Yoshi eventually showed up. I followed her up a small path to a quaint cottage that she and Yello were renting while they were in San Marcos. He was outside working on his laptop and after a brief hello Yoshi invited me inside.

"First let's just talk for a bit," she said, gesturing for me to take a seat on the bed. She asked about my previous breathwork experience. I told her about Venice, Joshua Tree and the experience during the new moon ceremony. "Well, rebirthing is always a surprise. It might be a bit more subtle, or could be more intense. We just never know so I find it's a good idea not to expect too much."

To be honest I already wasn't expecting too much; after all, I'd already blasted through time and space just a few days earlier on the floor of the temple at the Tribal Village and wasn't sure how we were going to top that.

"No problem, I'm open to whatever happens."

"Great, that's the spirit! And I'll be close to you the whole time."

I laid down and Yoshi sat next to me. She told me to follow her breath and I did. It wasn't too fast or slow, just even, maybe about eighty percent of capacity and with no pause between the inhalation and exhalation. It began through my nose and then a while later, after I'd settled down, through my mouth. Fifteen minutes went by until I began to feel the familiar tingling sensations in my hands and face. I wondered if I was going to have any real release this time, if maybe I was fresh out of emotional buildup, but she just kept reminding me to stay with the breathing. Sensing that I was still in my head Yoshi touched my arm at one point and it seemed to bring me back into my body. I continued the breaths when all of a sudden that sweet, melancholy German girl from the conscious-touch workshop entered my mind. I'd seen her around town a couple of times since the workshop and I'd gotten to know her a little more. Her name was Nina. During that time I had continued to witness her brightness as well as her shadows. Nina's life had been filled with trauma of various sorts and she now lived in a world of physical and emotional suffering. She had come to this lake to find healing. She was a bright soul, burdened by a harsh world, yet through it all was still reaching for the light. In a way, although we were so different, I felt a connection to that same duality within myself. As my focus turned toward Nina something happened. I rode a wave of feelings, sweetness and compassion until I suddenly felt my heart crack open. It was like I'd moved through a portal, and any remaining numbness was gone; I felt sensations flow into the rest of my body. My feelings moved to my own history of pain and abuse. My thoughts moved between characters from my past but they didn't linger there for too long. Instead the focus turned toward my sweet dad and the challenges that he'd experienced as a boy. He'd told me about how strict his father had been on him. I could feel how beaten down he'd been and felt deeply for him. Tears welled up, tears for him and how he must have shut down and locked up his emotions as a young child. And then my feelings moved to my grandfather. I could only imagine what sort of childhood he had experienced that had resulted in him being so quick to take his belt off to discipline my father. I wondered about my great-grandfather, who I didn't even know anything about, and sent all three of them my love. How long it had been since I'd even given this side of my family so much thought? As usual it was the thinking too much that brought me out of the experience and suddenly I was very aware that I was lying on the bed.

"You're doing great. Just keep the breaths going …" Yoshi said. So I continued the breaths and once again I conjured the sweet face of the melancholy German girl to help me unlock the blockage I felt around my heart. Once again, more quickly this time, the wave of emotions rushed over me. My feelings moved toward my two older sisters, who had been so good to me when I was little. I went deeper and thought about them and their childhoods, their unique lives that were so different from mine, despite our shared parents and genetics. I felt a flood of love and compassion begin flowing toward them. How we all react differently to the challenges we face! I began to think about my mom, such a source of both ferocity and creativity in my world. How she'd both inspired me and scared the hell out of me when I was a boy. It was only recently I'd figured out how to really understand her, by learning to understand the reflection of her within myself. My tears returned and I cried for the little girl she had been, remembering a small black and white picture of herself that she used to keep on a dresser. The tears continued, a mixture of joy and sorrow as I thought about that sweet young child, with such big dreams and relentless energy. How had the challenges of her life made her who she was? What a special experience to feel so deeply, possibly more deeply than I ever had, for my family.

I settled down once again, aware that at some point Yoshi had put her hand on my chest. "How are you feeling?" she asked.

"So ... powerful!" I managed to stammer.

"You've done some good work. I'll make some tea; you just relax and take it easy." I kept my eyes closed and nodded.

Yoshi's hand was still on my chest when I began to hear sounds coming from the kitchen. For a moment I was confused until I realized that the hand that I was feeling on my chest wasn't her hand at all, but the hands of my grandmothers, two women whom I'd never met. I'd always longed to have grandmothers and since I didn't know much about my own, I romanticized the sweet energy that my imaginary ones possessed. I felt them in the room with me as they spoke through their hands:

"Settle down, dear boy. Don't take this all too seriously. Life is a long, long journey, there's no need to race through it like a crazy person." I imagined their wrinkly hands extended over my heart, their smiling faces and sweet eyes gazing down upon me as they continued, "Just make sure to take care of yourself along the way." It was so beautiful that any remaining tears that had not already exited my tear ducts now streamed down my cheeks and all I could say was: "Thank you. Thank you."

Yoshi came back with the tea and we meditated together. I felt the vibrations in my body begin to settle back down.

"Well, it seems like that was powerful for you," she said after a while. I told her about the wave of experiences I'd felt, culminating with the feeling of connecting with my grandmothers.

"I felt you put your hand on my chest, but then you left to make tea and realized it was their touch I felt."

"Oh, Dougie, I never touched you at all," Yoshi said. And so went the story about how I met my grandmothers, in the space between my breaths and tears.

7. Of Cacao And Dictators

The days continued to tick by. Just before Christmas, Nadia and I decided to go to a winter solstice ceremony at a place called the Yoga Forest. We walked for twenty minutes or so up some narrow dirt paths, through an increasingly jungle environment. The walkways got steeper and we were soon climbing well above the town. Eventually we arrived at the Yoga Forest and found ourselves in yet another spectacular location.

The Yoga Forest is comprised of a series of structures, gardens and walkways, all nestled into the cliffs above San Marcos, and many people had gathered to celebrate the day with yoga, music and dancing. The Yoga Forest also serves some of the most delicious food that I'd experienced in this succulent little town. The day started out in a cave at the top of the property where, unsurprisingly, the ceremony began by drinking a large cup of cacao. The few dozen who'd gathered sang songs, led by a wrinkled and colorful indigenous woman, to honor the medicinal properties of cacao and the sacredness of this place.

The winter solstice marks the shortest day of the year and while its effect is considerably less distinct the closer you get to the equator, it still represents an important metaphor. With patience even the darkest times give way to light, just as the brightest times can never fully fend off the shadows, and this glowing little town of San Marcos was no exception. Besides reports of the occasional robbery or petty crime; besides the fact that recently there had been a fatal shootout between locals; besides the occasional sleazy teacher looking to score with the waves of naive, young women on their spiritual quests; besides all of those things, today I began to learn that something far darker simmered just beneath the surface of this little town.

"A few decades ago, this very cave in which we've gathered was a hiding place for many indigenous people and anyone else following Mayan traditions," one of the Mayan elders explained to us. "Many tried to escape persecution during the civil war, a war during which a cultural genocide had ravaged our country." A shadow exists under the brightness of San Marcos, a shadow that I'd begun to feel as I spent more time here. "Besides any of the healing work that we are doing here as individuals," she continued, "we are also taking part in a collective healing of this land and its history. With each shadow that is brought to the surface, there comes the opportunity to shine light on it, to witness it, to heal it, to transmute it back to light."

After she'd finished and some music and dancing had begun, I decided to take a stroll around. The mystical retreat center was built right into the cliffs overlooking the lake. Apparently they had started construction only six years earlier by hosting simple workshops that funded the first basic gathering spaces. Over the following years the Yoga Forest developed into a full-blown venue for healing gatherings, ceremonies and yoga workshops. A network of paths spread out from the kitchen, meandering to various workshop spaces and naturally built structures. Lush green plants sprouted from every crack and streams of water flowed down from the cliffs above. The sheer hours of manpower that it must have taken to move rock and haul construction materials up the uneven path from the road was mind-boggling. Yet it was apparent within each carefully tended nook that this place had been conscientiously and lovingly created, with deep intention and patience.

I was sitting on a rock, totally lost in thought, when Nadia stumbled on to the scene. "I think someone gave me magic mushrooms!" she blurted, pupils the size of saucers.

"Oh no! How did this happen?" I asked.

"This guy put some powder in my drink, I thought he said it was *reishi mushroom* powder. *But this is not reishi!*"

I laughed, and immediately shifted into tripper-guide mode.

"Well, in that case, you need to check out these flowers." I took her hand and led her down the path to an array of the most spectacular tropical flowers.

"Behold, the ridiculous beauty of the Passion Flower," I said. Nadia's eyes were wide, her mouth agape. The passion flower, even when totally sober, was a sight to behold. Slim blue, white and purple spines radiated out from the center, from which an array of green petals and other shapes and colors sprung.

"Is this real?" she gasped. We both laughed until tears formed in our eyes.

We spent some time exploring the flora of the Yoga Forest and after a while Nadia had settled down so we went back to the cave where music was playing and where some of our friends had gathered, also apparently high as kites. The rest of the day was a blend of yoga, meditation, sound-healing and smiling faces. Very *white* faces for the most part, I noted. I wondered about the influence that foreigners were having down here. Lots of foreign investment was flowing into the country, creating jobs and supporting local families. However, a lot of foreigners were also buying property down here, which often priced the locals out, pushing them further away from where they had previously lived. I wondered about the impact of this international gentrification. *Who owned the Yoga Forest?* Whoever it was I had the distinct feeling that it wasn't a Guatemalan family, but again it seemed like they were employing plenty of locals and in general doing good work. That seemed like a fair trade, right? Or was this just a more personal version of neo-colonialism? Maybe it was my white guilt talking but there was still a piece of it all that didn't sit quite right with me.

After the final activities and a big organic vegan feast, I set off down the dark pathways, back into town. As I walked back to Sunflower House, I thought about what we'd heard at the cave. I was interested in finding out more about what had happened in Guatemala's past, so the next day I took some time off from any further transformative temptations to research Guatemala's history. I read a Lonely Planet book that someone had left at the cottage, watched some YouTube documentaries and poured over Wikipedia. By the evening I had begun to learn that what these sweet people had endured was truly heart-wrenching. For example, who would have thought the repercussions of a U.S. entity called the United Fruit Company would have resulted in civil war, genocide and military dictatorship? *Well, they did.*

In the 1950s, the liberal Guatemalan President Jacobo Árbenz initiated a movement of agrarian reform that planned to buy back unused, fallow land from foreign entities and redistribute it to over half a million peasants and indigenous people who had been dispossessed, centuries earlier, after the Spanish invasion. Much of the land Árbenz targeted was owned by the United Fruit Company, a U.S. corporation that owned vast swaths of land and also happened to control much of the local transportation infrastructure. Unhappy with Árbenz, the United Fruit Company, a wholesome-sounding yet powerfully influential company, immediately began lobbying politicians in Washington, D.C., to support a U.S. intervention in Guatemala. Within short order, President Eisenhower branded President Árbenz a Socialist and an American coup d'état against his government began. The CIA spread propaganda through the streets and empowered local rebels to rise up against Árbenz's supporters, spurring civil unrest. Soon Árbenz was overthrown, which directly led to the subsequent downward spiral of Guatemalan civil rights under a string of military dictators, all of whom benefited greatly from the cresting wave of Capitalism. One of the methods employed by these dictators to achieve their nefarious ends was to spark cultural reform, and by the 1980s this had taken on the form of genocide. No towns, not even the small towns around Lake Atitlán, were spared as government forces swept through and massacred indigenous people and anyone displaying signs of their customs. It became a witch hunt in which neighbors reported on neighbors and people were taken from their houses, never to be seen again. Healers, shamans and anyone else that was labeled as the enemy were rounded up and shot, but the lucky ones managed to flee into the mountains and neighboring towns.

"In total, it is estimated that 200,000 civilians were killed or 'disappeared' during the conflict, most at the hands of the military, police and intelligence services. Victims of the repression included indigenous activists, suspected government opponents, returning refugees, critical academics, students, left-leaning politicians, trade unionists, religious workers, journalists, and street children." -- Wikipedia.

As for Árbenz, branded a Communist, he lived out his melodramatic life as a pariah and his exile spread across several countries as his family gradually disintegrated. After his daughter committed suicide, Árbenz descended further into alcoholism, dying in Mexico in 1971. The Guatemalan civil war eventually ended in 1996 and since then it has become safe enough for indigenous rituals, practices and ceremonies to remerge. In October 2011, forty years after his death, the Guatemalan government issued a formal apology to Árbenz's family and his legacy.

And just like that the depression train had pulled into the station. I was lying on my bed, watching yet another documentary on how Guatemalans had been mistreated over the years, witnessing the recurring story of power being used to manipulate, control and ultimately extract value from citizens. *How much can humans extract from the earth and each other before there's nothing left?* The best produce flowed out of the region and many local people, who'd long forgotten how to grow their own food, lived off imported processed foreign food. Coca-Cola was available in even the most rural places and Betty Crocker herself would be proud that the American Dream was fluffy, moist and freshly baked in Central America. I wondered why locals were even friendly to us after all we'd done, after how we'd intervened so heavy-handedly in their culture? Were they just super friendly and forgiving? Or more likely were most people down here, *especially most foreigners,* just totally oblivious to this murky history?

When moods like this descend, I start seeing everything in black and white. People are selfish. There's no such thing as altruism and anonymity breeds sociopathic behavior. Want to save the planet? People can't even seem to sort their goddamn recycling, let alone take responsibility for their behavior toward their fellow man. It was the kind of moment during which you could feed me anything and I'll give you back shit. Laughing children? Well, their naiveté will soon be shattered by the stark, cruel world. Blossoming romance? We all know how those invariably end! The wealth gap is growing, tolerance is shrinking while we choke on filthy air and the planet shakes.

I grabbed my phone and pulled up Instagram, navigating to my emergency "Feel Better" folder. The first photo is a baby owl getting a bath and looking pretty grumpy about it. I scroll to the next, a piglet in a bow tie. Puppies of all types tumbling around. I feel the emotions begin to move within me and my heart begins to soften. Yes, the world can be rough and we might all be going to hell in a handbasket, but there's also baby giraffes learning to walk and bear cubs licking peanut butter off their noses. And suddenly, the world didn't feel like it was completely falling apart.

I was feeling a little bit more hopeful by the time a message popped up on my phone. The Cacao Fairy had messaged me to invite me over for dinner at the Tribal Village.

"Maybe you can learn a little bit about the cacao business," the message read.

Before leaving Sunflower House I pulled myself together by writing a journal entry, doing some yoga and a short meditation, and within a couple of hours I had shaken off a good amount of my shadowy feelings. I walked through town and picked up a few ingredients before grabbing a tuk tuk the rest of the way. Within an hour I was in her sweet company and drinking some fantastic wine. After we'd finished eating a delicious meal of veggies and rice, I watched her make her handcrafted artisanal chocolates.

"You know, I don't share the secrets of my trade with just anyone; you're a *very* privileged man," she said as she melted down the ground cacao, infusing it with coconut oil and a witchy blend of medicinal herbs and spices, and pouring the final concoction into small, paper cups. After the first batch had set she gave me one to taste. The flavor was rich and complex. As we let the chemical compounds swirl around our neurochemistry, we began to open up to each other. She'd recently been through a difficult breakup during which her trust had been shattered by a cheating boyfriend.

"But you still believe in monogamy?" I asked her.

"You don't?"

"I don't think so. I mean, the whole idea of one person filling all your intimate needs for the rest of your life? Seems like a little too much pressure for everybody. These days I'm more of a *monogamish* sort of guy."

"Is that just another word for *polyamorous*?" She grinned inquisitively.

"Well, it's a *little* different. First of all, polyamory is done very differently by different people." She seemed curious enough so I continued. "Some choose the *'don't ask don't tell'* policy as a way to reap the sexually promiscuous benefits while avoiding the challenging conversations, while others share everything. Some have no real primary partner, kind of like dating a bunch of people openly, while my last girlfriend and I chose to be openly *monogamish*."

"So how is that any different?" she asked, now genuinely intrigued.

"Well, it was mostly just the two of us, but once in a while other people got involved."

"So monogamish means *mostly* monogamous?"

"Yep. We were each other's primary partners, and we communicated this fact clearly with any other non-primary partners that we had. Everyone knew everyone else and respect and communication remained paramount," I explained. "I mean, a big benefit of polyamory is the development of clear communication skills. You don't have to discuss *all* the intimate details, but sometimes I'd ask anyway, just to see how my jealousy meter was doing. I don't know, I've always found it to be a good way to practice emotional intelligence."

"That sounds awful," she said.

"Well, jealousy *feels* awful. It shoots tension through my entire body. So I thought, wouldn't it be nice to not feel that so sharply? And you know what is on the other side of all that jealousy?" I asked.

"What?"

"Openness." I smiled. "I don't want to limit anyone's experience in this short life, including my own. And now I like to practice compersion instead."

"What's that?"

"Compersion is feeling pleasure and joy for someone else's pleasure and joy."

"So your girlfriend felt joy when you boned another girl?"

"Well, I'm not saying it was always easy. I don't know, any rigid structure usually makes most people want to do the exact opposite thing anyway, so it's only a matter of time until something has to give. *And you want to know something funny?* I didn't even have to take advantage of the arrangement most of the time. Just knowing that I had the *freedom* to was usually more than enough."

"So how did that work out? I mean, it sounds like she's your ex-girlfriend now."

"Yes, that's true. After some years we just felt like we'd started to go down different paths."

"And it wasn't because she had another boyfriend?"

"No, in fact I really liked her other boyfriend. He helped us through some tough times. And talk about unique experiences, I even got to console her when they broke up because he wanted to experiment with monogamy."

She laughed at this.

"*Experiment with monogamy!* That's funny. You live in a strange world, Dougie. But monogamish or not it still didn't work out between you two."

"What didn't work out? That we weren't together forever?" I asked. "Most relationships end and most marriages end in divorce. The odds aren't great so why not try something new? Our relationship didn't end in a big drama or accusation of cheating. We ended our relationship by employing the same open communication that we'd been developing throughout. We even called it *'intentional decoupling.'*" Even I had to laugh at that memory. "And we're still great friends. In fact, she recently invited me over to dinner to meet her new boyfriend and I think they make a great couple."

"Americans are so strange," she said. "I wish I could do it but I think I'm too jealous. I just wish it hadn't ended the way it did."

"You know, people come together for reasons, seasons or lifetimes," I said, remembering a quote I'd heard somewhere. "It takes a wise person to know when the reason has shown itself or the season is over, and it takes a strong person not to linger beyond that."

"That's true. Well, to be continued, I guess!" she laughed. "So changing the subject from my misery, have you been enjoying San Marcos? What have you been up to since the new moon ceremony?"

I shared my past ten days with her; the various workshops, the manly tantric massage, the rebirth breathwork and my recent historical detour.

"Yes, I'm familiar with that history. This land certainly carries a lot of suffering that needs to be healed. Trauma remains locked in the mind and body of people and of a culture. Trauma weaves itself into our DNA itself so we are all responsible for helping heal the wounds of the past."

I explained how I'd begun feeling guilty about the whole damn thing, even things I had in no way been involved in, long before my time.

"Well, you know, guilt isn't very helpful," she consoled me. "It's far better for us to learn from the past and move on swiftly to the solution."

"Just like moving on from cheating boyfriends!"

"Touché! You know," she said, handing me another chocolate, "I find it so inspiring to watch as the local population perseveres, keeping their traditions alive. It's a testament to the deep reserves of their strength. While on the surface there might seem to be a separation between the local and foreign cultures here, I think it's largely just a language barrier. Even if you don't speak perfect Spanish, as soon as you make an effort to communicate it's immediately well-received."

"And what do you think about the number of foreigners here, the tourists, the business owners, the people buying property?" I asked.

"Well, it's not all bad and it's not all good, of course. A lot of it is truly helping the economy, that's just how it works. I have a great respect for those foreigners that are working to build bridges between the cultures, many are even helping reinstitute old ways of living, like organic farming methods, while also exposing locals to new knowledge and technologies."

"I agree," I said. "As we heal the scars of our old cultural behaviors, we're witnessing the unfolding of a new culture, a nexus point that combines the best of the old with the best of the new. Not a monoculture, but a rich polyculture, tolerant of each other's differences, being innovative with creative solutions, healing the planet …"

"... and paving the way for the liberation of all beings from the shackles of lingering oppression!" she concluded.

"Well, I don't know if we solved it all tonight, but we certainly made good progress," I joked.

It was late by the time she'd finished her chocolate making and I didn't really want to walk back along the dark, hilly road to town.

"It's pretty late, do you mind if I sleep here?" She eyed me suspiciously.

"Well," she paused, "you can share my bed, if you can behave yourself."

"I was more worried about YOU behaving yourself!" I laughed. "The only thing is it's laundry day today and I'm not wearing any underwear."

"No problem, I sleep naked anyway," she smirked.

After borrowing her toothbrush, we took off our clothes and got into her bed. Our bodies were warm and naked against each other and I think the intimate human connection was appreciated by both of us. I knew she was still processing her breakup and general distrust of all things masculine so I offered my sweetest, no expectation cuddling while doing my best not to inadvertently jab her with my cacao-fueled erection.

8. The Volcano And The Gift

It was Christmas Eve. Nadia and I got dressed up and strolled arm-in-arm through town on the way to a cozy lakeside restaurant where I'd booked us a table. She told me about the challenges she was having juggling so many fantastic lovers and how she didn't have enough time to herself. I told her of the challenges that I was having, having too much time by myself and not juggling nearly enough fantastic lovers.

Even in tropical places, far from any snow, there was something about Christmas that seemed to put me in an extra jolly mood. We smiled and greeted people as we passed them by. Guatemalans celebrate Las Posadas, the nine nights representing Mother Mary's nine months of pregnancy. Smells of traditional holiday food wafted into our nostrils from a local restaurant. Chicken and pork tamales in banana leaves and sweet, black rice tamales with mole sauce were being served up, accompanied by plenty of *ponche,* a holiday punch of fresh pineapple and dried fruits.

"Feliz Navidad!" Nadia said to the lady at the giant fruit stand down by the dock. She returned the greeting with "Feliz Noche Buena!" flashing a smile that included at least a couple of silver teeth.

"Tonight is more important than tomorrow to Guatemalans because it's the night Jesus was born," Nadia told me.

At the restaurant, as we enjoyed local wine and organic food with a view of the volcanoes in the distance, Nadia told me her story in which she'd escaped from her rich and controlling Russian fiancé some years earlier.

"He just couldn't understand why I wasn't happy. He treated me like I was just another one of his possessions and inside I was nauseous from all the fancy meals and champagne," she admitted. "So one day, while his yacht was docked in the South of France, I took my passport and cash from his safe, put it all in a plastic bag and took a floatie over to another boat which happened to be heading to the island of Ibiza, so they gave me a lift. I left everything behind and began traveling, eventually figuring out how to support myself along the way." It turned out that Nadia was quite the businesswoman. In the last couple of years since fleeing the yacht she had launched an exotic feather company that funded her living costs and her ongoing itinerary to exotic locations like Goa, Koh Phangan and Ibiza. Now she was exploring Central America as yet another possible stop along her yearly circuit. Besides funding her travels, she used the money to participate in all sorts of workshops.

"I *just* finished my Tantric Yoga teacher training in Thailand," she said. "And now I'm studying to be a facilitator of sex magic through ISTA, the International School of Temple Arts."

"Okay, wait, stop right there," I said, holding up another glass of sweet Guatemalan wine. "So what exactly is *sex magic*?"

"So we all love to orgasm, right?" she said, not waiting for a response. "Well, with sex magic you harness your sexual energy and put it toward manifesting whatever you want."

"Isn't that how the Gnostics rolled?" I asked, remembering a documentary that I'd seen about gnostic practices of channeling sexual energy into creative endeavors.

"Yep, and like so many other traditions that have been suppressed. The power that we hold, both as individuals and even more so in partnership, is extremely strong, one of the most powerful forces in nature, in fact." She took a sip of her wine. "We can harness this power, as long as we don't waste it in the endless pursuit of pleasure. Now I'm not saying there's anything *wrong* with pleasure, at least not until we lose our balance and the quest for pleasure becomes, well, the quest itself."

"So how do you discern that balance?" I asked. "I mean, who doesn't like pleasure …?"

"Pleasure," she began before letting me finish, "should not be an end unto itself, but a welcome addition to our experience along the way toward becoming embodied, self-actualized humans."

"Well, I'm definitely still a work in progress," I admitted, grateful for having met this tiny, wild tantrika.

"Of course! That's what life is for! How fortunate we are to have this time to practice being human!"

"Well, with that, what better day is there than Christmas to consider all that we have to be grateful for?" I raised my glass. "To our continued health, our freedom of expression, our vibrant and resourceful communities, and the brief time that we occupy these physical bodies."

Nadia raised her glass and continued the toast:

"What a privilege to exist in these bodies through which we can experience all that it means to be human, a divine gift that we receive not just on Christmas but in every moment that we are breathing." She was a good match for my flowery verbosity. "May we increasingly embody this wisdom and share it outward with all of our energy and actions! Together we can work through struggles and mend any fray in the fabric of our fields. When we spend time counting our blessings, we inevitably watch them expand."

"Aho, sister!" I said, clinking her glass.

"Merry Cosmos and Happy No Fear," she grinned tipsily.

The stroke of midnight was marked by a cacophony of ringing bells as a barrage of fireworks erupted from all around Lake Atitlán. It was a spectacular vista as we walked home from the restaurant. The streets were filled with kids shooting fireworks at each other and adults who didn't seem overly concerned about it.

"I appreciate your friendship so much, brother," Nadia said. "I'm looking forward to more adventures together in the future." I agreed.

When we returned home, I gave her a hug and wished her good night. Any part of me that still lamented our lack of romantic chemistry had by now mostly dissolved.

The following morning was a beautifully sunny Christmas Day. Nadia and I made a celebratory breakfast of scrambled eggs with sautéed veggies, fresh-toasted bread spread thick with local cheese, and a dollop of delicious sauerkraut from a fermenter in town. As we ate I nodded at the view behind her, toward San Pedro volcano, the larger of the two.

"That volcano has been staring me in the face every morning since I arrived!" I said. "Well, it's my last few days and I have got to climb that damn thing."

"Well, I won't be joining you on that adventure," Nadia replied. "By the way, I'm going to this thing called Hare Krishmas later. It's a day of singing, meditation and a big, vegetarian potluck. Want to come?"

"I'm a little over-peopled so I'm gonna hang back." I replied.

After Nadia left, I lounged on the porch, lazily looking at the volcano while catching up with some friends and family back home. All the while I was well aware that the Manzanita email thread had been refreshingly quiet, which was a welcome, if only temporary, respite from the struggles and tense meetings that would surely begin again after the holidays.

I sent my sisters some photos from the trip and dutifully called my parents to wish them Merry Christmas. It was only lunchtime in Dallas but even still my dad had already gone to *two* church services. He's a quirky character, a bit of a loner and an avid botanist. His apartment resembles a plant nursery in which one could barely move around for all the plants laid in rows on the floor. Saplings and starts even sat in the racks of the open dishwasher. His favorite hobby, besides sitting in his inoperable Cadillac, drinking beer and listening to old 8-tracks, is to renegade transplant his leafy children all around town. Sometimes, during the service at his Presbyterian church, he would sneak out to his car, take a plant out of his blossoming trunk and smuggle it into the church. The mystery that played out over coffee and cookies was one of his greatest weekly pleasures:

*"They simply have no idea where all the poinsettias came from," h*e told me. By early afternoon he was well into his daily routine of conservative talk show radio programs and college football games. He'd already accepted that I didn't know, and probably never would learn, the rules of football, but despite all of our differences we'd found some decent common ground in the spiritual realm.

"Well, some of those things you do sound like some good Christian activities," he told me as I explained what I was up to in my life. "Working together, building community and volunteering. Treating others as you want to be treated. Praise the Lord, Jesus Christ," he said.

"Absolutely right, Dad." He listens to sermons, quotes the Bible and sings hymns to get spiritual and I just happen to like drinking cacao, quoting Rumi and dancing around like a nut. Not that different at all, really.

Meanwhile, my mom and I talked about art shows and her current creative projects in between her lamenting the recent behavior of my mischievous and increasingly senile step-dad. Last year, just before his 100th birthday, he'd been relocated to the veteran's hospital to live out his days, which were spent flirting with his female caregivers and attempting to escape the ward. Decades earlier he had been quite a society man around San Francisco so now, in his dreamlike world ruled by Alzheimer's, he was constantly starting new businesses and planning fictitious corporate meetings.

"You've got to check the accounts," he'd tell my mom, who played along. "I seem to have misplaced the information. And I think the maid stole my wallet again." He said this last part under his breath, jabbing a finger toward his caregiver. "Do you think I can borrow some money?" he'd ask my mom. So she photocopied a $100 bill and taped it up on the wall next to his bed. It seemed to pacify him. When I visited, he would regale us with stories that he and his friends had just come back from swimming under the Golden Gate Bridge, and that he didn't like this country club very much because they had a terrible wine selection. Still, some days weren't so fun and it couldn't be easy for my mom to watch his slow decline.

Conversations with my mother were as entertaining as they were good practice for patient communication. When she was in a good mood the conversation was easy enough but if she wasn't, she'd turn toward her own darker outlook, ranting about how the world had become a superficial and violent place, robots replacing people and AI threatening to take us all down. I used to get all wrapped up in her tirades but these days I would lovingly acknowledge all humanity's challenges—I mean AI *might* actually take us all down—while gently pointing out all the things that were going right and that we had to be grateful for. Inevitably that approach seemed to make us both feel better.

After enjoying a quiet day of journaling, I decided to spend Christmas evening as anyone might—anyone in San Marcos, at least—by attending a Tantric Puja ceremony at a nearby ashram. Forty or so people sat in a circle, facing a rather mysterious teacher who, dressed all in red and kneeling in front of us, chanted and gyrated for more than an hour while encouraging us to do the same. By about halfway through the ceremony, some people in the room, including my conscious-touch teacher Sharon, seemed to be experiencing full-body orgasms. Meanwhile I just felt frustrated and uncomfortable from sitting cross-legged for that long.

As I stumbled out of the ashram the Cacao Fairy sent me a message inviting me to hear her sing with her band, the Raga Funk Spaceship, at a local chocolate factory, so I hopped in a tuk tuk and headed over. The band was a trippy ensemble of colorful characters whose ongoing mission was to take the audience on a journey through mysterious soundscapes with a sprinkling of humorous dialogue. The lead guitarist sported a faux-hawk, wore an iridescent rainbow robe and one of those vintage pilot hats with the furry earflaps.

"So where do you trippy travelers want to travel to tonight?" he asked over the microphone.

"Take us to outer space!" one guy in fluorescent leggings shouted with glee.

"To OUTER, outer space, man!" another chimed in.

"To OUTER, outer space it is," the front man replied as he strummed a cosmic chord on his guitar. Meanwhile, a fellow on the synth who was apparently the spaceship's copilot, would maniacally laugh in a high-pitched tone at every chance he got, twirling knobs, pressing buttons and producing a wild array of sounds. There was another guitarist, a drummer and a guy who seemed to pull a never-ending selection of strange instruments from behind him. The Cacao Fairy stood stage right with another singer, occasionally adding their vocals into the mix. She had a delicate and ethereal voice that provided an organic backdrop to the unrehearsed performance. Since the event was taking place at a cacao factory, it was of no surprise that everybody was hopped-up on it. I had a hot cacao drink, spicy and sweet, which helped wash down a basket of cacao bites that I shared with people as I twirled around the room. Even the basket itself was made of cacao. Everyone was pretty blissed-out. I was going to miss this trippy, delicious vortex of a town.

A while later I realized that I'd finally overdosed on cacao. My head was aching from the vasodilating properties of the substance so I decided to take my cacao-junkie ass home. I was walking by a group of women when I heard one of them talking about hiking the volcano.

I had never heard back from Max and plans with the other guys hadn't panned out but tomorrow was my last day in town and my final chance to make the climb.

"Did I happen to hear you ladies talking about hiking a volcano?" I inquired, pointing across the moonlit lake.

"Yes! Have you done it?" one of them asked.

"Not yet. But I took part in a very powerful men's circle the other day ..." I let the manliness of the statement hang in the air for a moment. "And a few of us were interested in hiking it."

"I think my boyfriend was at that men's circle!" one of the women said in a German accent.

"Is your boyfriend Max?"

"Yes!" she exclaimed. "He said he'd met a guy who'd told him about the hike!"

"Well, it seems destined that we're meant to hike that volcano! What are you up to tomorrow?" I asked. They weren't doing anything and all liked the idea, so we planned to meet the following morning at the dock. When I got home, I messaged the guys from the men's circle again and told them about the plan in case they were still interested. I also told them that I'd found a bunch of lovely ladies to join, including Max's girlfriend, in case that swayed their decisions.

For more than a couple of weeks I'd been lustily staring at the San Pedro volcano from my porch. Little did I know that something *even more powerful* than man's love of scaling things much larger than himself was calling me to this place, and I would soon discover that my trip was about to become an *entirely different* trip altogether. What can I say? Sometimes you're just in the right place at the right time. And *sometimes* the right place is on top of a volcano and the right time is about 2 p.m. on a Thursday.

I'd woken up barely able to contain my excitement for the day's adventure. I packed up a small daypack with a couple of liters of water and headed down to the dock to meet the others. On the way I grabbed some fruit, a bag of nuts from an appreciative young nut merchant, and of course a couple of bliss balls, just in case. A group of eight intrepid adventurers had assembled for the expedition, four women and four men, and everyone was excitable. We boarded a water taxi over to the neighboring town of San Pedro, where after some minimally successful haggling, we crammed into two tuk tuks that brought us to the trailhead of Vulcán San Pedro around 10 a.m.

We paid a small entrance fee which included a guide, less for showing us the route and more just to make sure no *banditos* messed with us gringos; it happened rarely, but it happened, so better to be safe, they insisted. It was a three-and-a-half-hour hike straight up through the jungle, including a run-in with a questionable rope swing along the way, before finally reaching the top of the volcano.

To be honest, after all the foreplay it was a little anticlimactic. The view out onto the lake was pretty with the clouds seeming to scrape by just above our heads, but it wasn't the 360-degree view I'd expected and we couldn't see any sign of the crater for the sheer amount of jungle foliage that stood in the way. There were some trash cans and some kids had sprayed graffiti on the rocks. I laughed at how sometimes reality is less impressive than fantasy. But getting to the top had still been an athletic undertaking and we were all hungry so we began to set up a potluck picnic. Max and his girlfriend Julia kept pulling more things out of their backpack, creating an impressive spread of fresh bread, avocados, refried beans, cheese and hot sauce. *Goddamn, Germans know how to picnic!* I thought as I shared my meager selection of fruit and nuts with the group. I was saving my bliss balls.

At around 2 p.m., satiated by our picnic feast, everyone set about relaxing and taking in the view, and I walked over to the far side of the summit to take some panorama photos. After successfully not capturing the full glory of the moment I sat down on a rocky outcrop and was trying to make out San Marcos when someone approached me from behind.

"Well, hello there, good sir," a voice said and I turned my head. It was a smiling fellow, my age with an American accent.

"Hi there!" I didn't recognize him but mirrored his friendliness. "Well, we made it to the top!"

"Indeed, we did," he replied. He was clean-cut and there was a certain something about him I found instantly intriguing. We looked at each other for a moment before he continued. "I couldn't be sure from a distance but now ..." he paused, "yep, you look like the kind of guy who likes a good adventure." It was a refreshing change of script from the usual volley of backpacker chitchat.

"How can you tell?" I laughed.

"Oh, I have a keen sense for these things." He took a seat next to me.

"Oh really?"

"Yep." He turned his gaze out toward the lake. "Plus, your fingernails are painted silver and you're wearing a large agate around your neck. I can tell an undercover hippie from a mile away."

"Impressive," I replied. "I'm just wrapping up two weeks of getting blissed out in the vortex of San Marcos. So, yes, busted, I guess."

"You gotta get out of there before it's too late. I only narrowly escaped." He smirked. "It's something in those damn bliss balls."

"The whole place is full of cacao addicts," I replied.

"*Cacrack* addicts," he said, and I laughed. "No, I'm serious. Cacao is literally more addictive than crack. You gotta watch out for that shit." I followed his gaze down the sides of the volcano, which were blanketed in think jungle. Beyond the shores of the lake, large clouds cast slowly morphing shadows onto its otherwise glittery surface.

"Are you going to the Cosmic Convergence festival?" I asked, gesturing across a narrow stretch of water toward the small town of Santiago where the festival was being held.

"No, I gotta get home. Back to work."

"Too bad, I hear it's going to be pretty fun."

"Yeah, festivals aren't really my thing these days. I'm trying a new tactic."

"Tactic for what?"

"For promoting conscious expansion, my friend." He smiled. "Festivals are great but dreadlocks, smoking pot and ogling crystals isn't the only way to achieve that mission."

"Oh really?" I said, mockingly.

"Yeah, no. To *really* create change you gotta clip those things, take off the glad rags, have a shower and maybe put on a button-down shirt if you really mean business."

"So you're in the corporate world?"

"No, not really. Although it's all pretty blurry these days."

"Politics?"

"No. Now THAT'S a tough audience for conscious expansion!"

"Ok, what then?"

"I work for an organization that is involved, or has been involved in some pretty awful activities. Both at home *and* abroad."

"That sounds like a terrible job."

"Absolutely terrible. You can't even imagine."

"Well, why are you working for them?" I laughed. "And how is that promoting conscious expansion?"

"By slowly infiltrating, my friend." His voice fell quiet. "It's far easier to do battle from inside the gates of Troy. You'd be amazed at some of the tight asses who soften up when given just a little glimpse into a different way of being." He grinned. "People are pretty easy. Give them a taste of an experience that opens their mind even slightly and let the magic take hold. All you gotta do is crack the door open a little bit and curiosity does the rest. It might take some time, but that's how these things work. Before you know it, policies are changing, legislation is happening and the world gets transformed."

"Before you know it, huh? It all seems like a pretty complex, gnarly mess right now, if you ask me."

"Ok, maybe not *'before you know it'* on a human scale but you gotta think bigger, my man! In the grand scheme of things, on an intergenerational scale, *certainly on the scale of cosmic time*, this is all the blink of an eye." He paused. "If you have a big enough eye, that is." This guy was a trip.

"So what are you doing down here? Vacation?" I asked.

"It might look like I'm on vacation. But there are different fronts of conscious expansion. Some are in the office; some are out here in the field. You know about the history of U.S. involvement in Central America?"

"Actually, I've just been researching it."

"Then you know it's a pretty fucked-up bag of worms, right?"

"Yeah, totally fucked-up."

"Well, for my vacations I like to go to places that we fucked up and spread the good message that us Yanks aren't all that bad. Spark a little benevolent mischief. Maybe shake up a few travelers, a few locals, take 'em out, you know, blow their minds a little. Give them a new perspective. An experience they will never forget."

"Sounds like a *great* business trip," I replied.

"Indeed." He smiled. "Or maybe I'm totally fucking with you and I'm just a guy from California with a desk job, on a two-week vacation in Guatemala to climb some volcanoes." I looked up at him and he looked back at me with a mischievous look on his face.

"Well, now I honestly don't know what to believe!" I laughed. A long moment passed before he spoke again.

"Yep, you're the one. I have something for you." He put his hand up to my ear and then brought his fist down in front of me. He slowly rotated it, uncurled his fingers and in his palm was a small object. One of those little minty breath droppers.

"Breath freshener. How considerate," I said.

"Yep. But a drop of this particular breath freshener will do more than just freshen your breath. *It'll freshen your mind.*" He paused and lowered his voice. "This is about seventy-five doses of some of the finest LSD known to man. I can't tell you how I got it but I can tell you that it's research-grade quality."

"Well ..." I began. "I was definitely not expecting you to say that. And while it's a very nice offer I don't think I should be buying acid from some crazy dude that I just met on the top of a volcano."

"Oh, it's not for sale," he replied. "*It's a gift.*" The tiny bottle sat in his hand, barely bigger than the tip of a pinky finger. I didn't know what to say so he spoke first. "You see, I don't need it anymore and I think you should have it." He was obviously enjoying this entire exchange. I thought about it for a moment and looked around.

"Well, I wouldn't want you traveling back home with it so, what can I say?"

"How about just *'Thank you?'*"

"Thank you!"

"Don't mention it." I looked around again to make sure nobody was watching, took the tiny bottle out of his hand and pocketed it quickly. He smiled. I glanced over to the rest of my expedition party who were beginning to load up their backpacks.

"It looks like we're heading out. Want to join us for the descent?" I asked as I got up to go.

"Oh, no thanks, I think I'll stick around here for a while more. I have some thinking to do and I find I do my best thinking from the top of volcanoes."

"Yeah. they're powerful places." I smiled as I stood up to go. "What's your name, by the way?" I asked.

"It's Loki," he replied as he stood.

"I'm Dougie. Nice to meet you, Loki." We shook hands. I pulled my other hand from my pocket, bringing it up to his ear and back down in front of him, slowly rotating my fist and uncurling my fingers.

"Perhaps I can interest you in a bliss ball?" I offered. He grinned, reaching out to take the crunchy sphere of deliciousness.

"A sweet gift, indeed. Thank you, Dougie." He took a small bite. "Ah, San Marcos ... What a wonderful place! Now don't do anything I wouldn't do out there, Dougie Fresh." From the little I knew about Loki, that left things wide, wide open. I grinned and walked away. We packed up our things as brooding afternoon clouds swirled around the top of the volcano. As we began the two-hour descent, I looked back one more time to where Loki and I had been sitting but he was already gone.

That night, mostly intact besides some achy joints and shaky knees, I hosted a final potluck dinner with Nadia at Sunflower House for our new group of friends. Sharon, Yello and Yoshi, Steve, Max and Julia all came. The Cacao Fairy couldn't make it but we had planned to meet up at the Cosmic Convergence Festival, which I'd decided to attend after coming down the volcano. We shared fruit smoothies, homemade hummus with plantain chips, and a gigantic salad. I'd discovered a hidden trove of firewood so when the overloaded bamboo porch threatened to detach from the side of the house, we moved down to the patio to have a bonfire and had a sweet final evening together.

The following morning I would travel to Santiago before heading on to the festival a day or two later. After that I had no real plans except to end up in Costa Rica a month or two later. This was my favorite way to travel; no strict itinerary, no return flight, just an openness spread out ahead of me, an invitation to go wherever I felt called. This style of travel offers one the opportunity to let go of control and remain open to how things want to unfold. I'd found some bright highs and shadowy lows in San Marcos, new moons and winter solstices offering inspiration from the natural world about balance and cycles of change. Finally I'd been called across a magical lake, ascending a volcano to receive a powerful gift from a stranger called Loki. Ah, the mysterious Loki, representing both the light and the dark, a trickster and human embodiment of the Mayan deity Maximón himself.

9. Just Say *Maybe*?

Okay, let's all just slow down for a moment and rewind. Let's go back to lying in a bathtub, high as a kite. Candles were lit and Beres Hammond was singing a sweet, if perhaps morally questionable reggae song about an underage girl. I was nineteen years old and a completely tormented soul. I had emerged from a decade of institutional living in an all-boys English boarding school, a blur of grey, stone halls, bullies, Latin textbooks and malevolent teachers who wore capes and carried canes; luckily for me, corporal punishment had been banned a few years before I arrived, but some teachers still kept their canes on display in their classrooms as reminders.

From the bathtub, I reflected on the previous year, when my college roommate, both a fantastic teacher and complete asshole, had opened my mind to a variety of illicit substances. Thanks to him, much of my first year at the Rhode Island School of Design was spent in a haze of pot smoke and existential dissolution. He'd borrow my stuff and return drunkenly in the middle of the night to pick fights with the couch and other furniture. One time I returned late from studio to find him having sex on my bed. The following year I moved into my own place. So here I was, in a candlelit bathtub, smoking a large spliff and appreciating my newfound love of reggae. *And who could blame me?* It had been a challenging decade.

During my first year at college I began sloughing off a lot of my restrictive youthful behaviors, but I was still a control freak and overly concerned about cleanliness. I had big round glasses and my wardrobe consisted mainly of polo shirts and corduroys. Fashion issues aside I was also in a cultural identity crisis. I had always been seen as a Yank in the UK but now here I was, apparently back home, and everyone thought I was British. I was still *mostly* a virgin, after an inaugural sexual experience that had put me off the whole concept a few years earlier. On top of all that I felt anxious, and despite having become adept at cheery facades, I was struggling. Here I was, stepping into manhood, wondering who the hell I was and how and when I'd ever get laid. At first, through secondhand smoke, and then by sheer perseverance from my roommate, I began to embrace marijuana. Bong rips immediately relaxed my nerves, calmed my mind down and helped me not to fret so much about everything. My earliest relationship with this little, illegal plant was finally helping me chill the fuck out.

During my summer vacations I traveled from Providence to Los Angeles, where there was much better pot, and of course an abundance of cocaine and ecstasy. I soon obtained a fake ID, trading money under a table at a Chick-fil-A in a shady part of town, and began going to nightclubs. But despite plenty of psychedelics being on offer at RISD, it wasn't until *after* college that my real experimentation with these illicit substances began. Soon after graduating, I realized that I was just using pot to numb out so decided to ditch it. I fell into a circuit of cocaine parties in Los Angeles but they quickly became cliché and boring for me. Ecstasy was an occasional indulgence, but it was hard to find good quality and besides, it didn't usually leave me feeling so great in the days afterward.

I'd never tried any psychedelics until a business partner surprised me on my birthday with a Play-Doh container full of magic mushrooms. So one night, when no one was at home, I gobbled some down and soon my entire world was melting. With no idea what to expect I started off in my room but soon began roaming around the loft, delighted by the shifting textures of the wooden floor. To calm my increasingly racing thoughts, I moved my attention toward my palm and spent a good long while attempting to levitate a leaf, soon forgetting about the leaf and just staring at my hand's translucent skin. Inspired, I went into the bathroom where I stared at my face in the mirror, admiring my saucer-like pupils and eyeballs morphing around in their eye sockets, until I finally spooked myself out and had to get the hell out of there. From there I meandered onto the balcony, and spent the rest of the trip watching the buildings of downtown Los Angeles smear across the skyline as trains in the adjacent train yard melted right off their tracks. As I came down I laughed out loud at the ridiculousness of it all. I was never quite the same again and much to my mother's dismay was soon regularly attending Burning Man.

I became fascinated by psychedelics but they were hard to come by at first, at least until I started producing events and I soon met a scientist from Caltech who gave me my first LSD. It was Halloween and I was dressed in an old tuxedo, a top hat and ruffled shirt. A bunch of us, artists, entrepreneurs and scientists, hiked to the top of Echo Mountain, high above Pasadena, and lay out some blankets, watching as the stars and the lights of the city below gave way to the pastel palette of dawn. Tripping with scientists was definitely a whole new experience. We talked about our neurochemistry and the scale of cosmic time and space, laughing at the sheer number of unpredictable events that led to sharing this moment together.

Over the next few years our band of mischief-makers hosted regular trippy soirées and psychedelic camping trips. I began dating a scientist who was especially interested in the medicinal benefits of psychedelics and other illicit compounds. Thanks to her, I attended all sorts of bizarre ceremonies from Ayahuasca to 5-MEO-DMT, which opened me up to a deeper sense of understanding for myself and others. It was all totally different than anything I had expected. Besides a few challenging trips here and there, my psychedelic experience was hugely positive, my compassion grew. My tendency for control continued to loosen, and my openness to try novel experiences increased. I felt productive, creative and surrounded by individuals who were achieving great things in their lives, not at all like the burnt-out, drug-addict image that I'd imagined came with the territory. *And I was always told drug use led to a wasted life!*

So why is it that some drugs were legal, and others weren't, especially when they seemed to have the possibility for such profound impact? *Oh, you wonder why, too?* Well, since a large quantity of LSD has just appeared as a new character in my story here's a quick primer on the history of illegal drugs:

In 1971 the pre-scandalous president of the United States, Richard Nixon, declared an all-out War on Drugs. He realized that people on drugs didn't really like him or want to fight his wars and so this was a great way to disrupt the hippies and "colored folks." In addition, many servicemen returning from Vietnam were testing positive for heroin use. Drugs were, Nixon claimed, *"public enemy number one."* In the decades that followed, the War on Drugs would become the longest-running and most costly war ever. At first the federal budget allocation for the initiative was around USD$100 million and for a few short years this was the only time in history that the majority of funding went toward treatment rather than enforcement. Five decades later the budget had ballooned to over USD$50 billion *and yet*, even with all that money spent on the war, the DEA has said illegal drugs are more prevalent and affordable than ever.

If you don't know about the DEA's scheduling of drugs, it basically goes like this: Schedule 1 is claimed to be the most dangerous, with high potential for abuse, while Schedule 5 is the least. Schedule 1, which also claims to have no medical value, includes PCP, crystal meth and heroin. Fair enough. This same category, however, also contains marijuana, magic mushrooms, ecstasy, peyote and LSD. Schedule 2, meanwhile, which claims to be less dangerous, includes cocaine, crack, crank and opiates. Does it seem strange to you that marijuana should be listed as more dangerous and less medicinal than crack? Yeah, it seemed strange to me, too.

It should come as no surprise then that money is at the root of this logical discrepancy. For example, who are the main funders of the *Partnership for a Drug Free America*? You guessed it! The pharmaceutical, tobacco and alcohol industries lobbied for rules and restrictions to give them the most profitable opportunities. Cigarettes, booze and many prescription drugs are just as dangerous, mind-altering and addictive as smoking a joint, if not more. Nixon's War on Drugs also happened to be the perfect cover for the carnage that was being waged throughout Southeast Asia. Many claim that rather than benefiting the public, drug prohibition was really spurred by racism and empire building. Unsurprisingly, the War on Drugs fared no better abroad than it did at home. When Nixon gave USD$50 million to the Nepalese government to criminalize marijuana and hashish, the subsequent increase in heroin production devastated Nepalese culture. The once-peaceful country of Nepal was hit with a wave of opiate addiction and violence from a burgeoning black market and the surplus soon reached the U.S. anyway.

The next two presidents after Nixon continued with more of the same, but it wasn't until the mid-1980s when the War on Drugs took an especially devilish turn. Ronald Reagan's 1986 "Anti-Drug Abuse Act" transformed any hopes for a rehabilitative system into a largely punitive one. The act created a slew of new, mandatory-minimum sentences for drugs, including marijuana, and made the punishment for the possession of crack, a smokable form of cocaine, one hundred times stricter than its powdery white sibling. Most people hadn't even heard about crack but soon its coverage in the media hit a fever pitch and whether intentional or not, did a fantastic job promoting this new, cheap and powerful substance. Suddenly it was everywhere and people began trying it, despite Nancy Reagan's advice to *"Just Say No."*

So where did all this crack come from and how did it get so popular? After all, it wasn't just *appearing* in South Central Los Angeles out of thin air. Or was it? Well, in the 1980s Reagan and the CIA needed money to fight the Soviets and it's now public knowledge that they came up with an ingenious idea. The clandestine plan, now known as the Iran-Contra Affair, took money that the U.S. made from selling arms to Iran and funneled it to a Central American militia called the Contras. The Contras, whom a proud Ronald Reagan referred to publicly as his *"Freedom Fighters,"* were fighting the Soviet-funded Sandinistas for control of Nicaragua. And so, the stage for tragedy was set. While Reagan and Bush Sr. waged the War on Drugs back home, fleets of planes were flying to Central America, filled with guns, and coming back filled with cocaine. *Just to clarify:* these were CIA operations, run by the White House, during which huge amounts of cocaine were dumped, via CIA sources, *into the inner cities of the United States. This was the same cocaine* that was being turned into the crack that was putting so many young, black men behind the bars of the newly privatized prison system.

Los Angeles was a particularly lucrative market with one of the most notorious dealers, known as "Freeway Ricky Ross," bringing in as much as two to three million dollars a day thanks to the cocaine from his CIA supplier. A good amount of the profits were funneled directly back into the Contra Revolution against the Sandinistas. Years later, even the former head of the DEA, Judge Rob Bonners, would admit on public television that the CIA was involved with importing illegal cocaine from Central America. Yet even after the whole Iran-Contra Affair was brought to light, who was the only person that was actually punished? Yep, you guessed it, Freeway Ricky Ross, a young, black drug dealer from the hood. All of the rich, well-connected white men, including National Security Council staff member Oliver North, had their convictions overturned.

As the drug hysteria of the 1980s continued and mandatory sentences for drug offenses began to be handed out with impunity, the prison industry became big business. As many towns went through hard economic times it became a great opportunity for a privatized prison to pop up, employing out-of-work locals to run the show. The streamlined business practices of these for-profit companies led to cheaper inmate costs, higher profits and the added bonus that inmates could be put to work for next to nothing. Just like any company, there were corporate meetings, investors, and business was booming *as long as prisons remained full*. And that was one of the problems. Like all purely capitalistic models, continual growth is required and continual growth in this case meant creating a continual supply of prisoners. When the War on Drugs began, the U.S. prison population was two hundred thousand. Five decades later it stands at over two million. That's more than any other country on earth by far, with a quarter of those people still behind bars for nothing more than a drug law violation. *Want to talk about a socially destructive feedback loop?*

We might not hear about the War on Drugs as much these days and for good reason: it's a smooth, well-oiled machine. The drug money is flowing, people are going to jail, investors are happy and everyone is looking the other way. Some even believe that the entire U.S. empire would never be able to sustain itself without the money generated by the drug war. And over the years, whether by chance or by design, it has proven to be the perfect way for the ruling class to stay in power while creating the easy felonization of entire sectors of society. How much is still fueled by racism, empire building and the almighty dollar? It might be easy to label people as addicts but addiction of any kind should not be seen so much as a criminal problem but as a medical, social and individual one. Addiction is a call out for help, not punishment. Whichever side you're on, it's a very sad reality for a lot of people.

But enough history lessons for now and back to my story, because despite all the positive progress up into my early thirties, life was about to take a challenging twist. After producing events in Los

Angeles for five years, I wasn't feeling as productive as I thought I *could* be and I became convinced that I had ADD. After all, I'd tried Adderall while cramming for Art History exams at RISD and it felt just *fantastic, so* within a short amount of time I got prescribed a high dose of the drug. In retrospect, my psychiatrist was undeniably zonked out on whatever meds he was on, and the only question he would ask me was whether I needed a higher dose.

Over the next three years my productivity, as well as my dosage, just kept going up. If bipolar disorder swings between mania and depression, then what I was experiencing was a type of *unipolar* disorder, an almost continual state of amphetamine-fueled mania. I was moving so fast and spinning so many plates but felt totally detached from my body; it was like I was cut off below the head. To balance it all out I was smoking too many cigarettes and drinking heavily. My life, which appeared highly successful to onlookers, was coming unglued at the seams. Even with all the good things happening, of which there were many, it was just never enough. Eventually, exhausted and unable to sustain it, I finally admitted that I'd had enough. I stopped going to the psychiatrist and cold turkey'd the ADD meds, but without them I just couldn't maintain the endless energy that I'd crafted my life upon and soon the plates began to fall. My energy and mood slumped to an all-time low and I piled on the pounds. Before long, I lost my girlfriend, my job and finally, my house. I became resentful and fell further into a pit of my own remorse. For a week I lay in bed and fantasized about the end. This was my mini early-midlife crisis. Luckily I had the clarity of mind and support of some amazing friends to turn things around. I stopped smoking, began eating more healthily and started going to the gym. A few months later I attended that life changing yoga retreat, you remember, the one in which I realized that I was basically an anxious mess.

Well, around that time, psychedelics reappeared in my life, this time helping me go deeper into my psyche to unearth what lay hidden. Over the next two years I lost the weight, created a healthy lifestyle and my relationships with my friends and family blossomed once again. So by the time I left Manzanita for Central America I was mostly sober besides a glass of wine now and then and the occasional dose of mushrooms or LSD. Okay, and maybe a little MDMA on special occasions. But besides the wine, psychedelics and MDMA, *mostly* sober.

Wait, I hear some of you say. Mushrooms? LSD? MDMA? That's all still pretty dangerous, right? Well, I'm not going to go too deep into this now but just for some scientific reference here's a snippet taken from an article in The Economist: *"In 2010 Lancet, a British peer-reviewed journal, published a study titled 'Drug Harms in the UK: A Multicriteria Decision Analysis' which ranked a list of 20 drugs giving them a score out of 100 that combined both their harm to self and others ..."*

Alcohol	72
Heroin	55
Methamphetamine	33
Cocaine	27
Tobacco	26
Cannabis	20
Ecstasy / MDMA	9
LSD	7
Magic Mushrooms	6

Even if we believe this study, which indicates that LSD and magic mushrooms are ten times less harmful than alcohol, *is there really any benefit one gets from tripping out?* Historically, hallucinogenic compounds have a long record for being an integral part of many ancient and indigenous cultures. Shamanism is the oldest form of spirituality that we know of, and the use of substances that prompt a devotee to think from other perspectives is prevalent among most cultures. Long before modern synthetic drugs, shamans made use of plants that contained psychoactive compounds to conduct ritualistic and therapeutic ceremonies. *A few examples:*

- The Mazatec people of Mexico referred to their magic mushrooms as "tiny gods." Today the Multidisciplinary Association for Psychedelic Sciences (MAPS) has found that psilocybin, the active compound in magic mushrooms, can effectively be used to treat mental illness, especially when administered by a trained therapist.

- The Huichol culture, also in Mexico, consider peyote to be a life-bestowing deity and once a year many still make a pilgrimage that includes the consumption of the plant.
- The Bwiti tribe of Gabon use the root of a plant called Iboga as a rite of passage through which they believe they can travel through worlds. And now ibogaine, the primary psychoactive compound found in iboga, is being studied as a treatment for addictions to such substances as heroin and alcohol, in addition to other mental illnesses.
- Ayahuasca, which is becoming increasingly popular in the U.S., is native to the Amazon River Basin and made by brewing a combination of plants. The resulting dark liquid contains a powerful dose of the active chemical DMT. After drinking the liquid and getting through the powerful, if at times unpleasant, experience, the recipient often claims to feel a greater sense of acceptance, awareness and other positive effects. And yes, despite centuries of reported benefits, it's still classed by the United States as a Schedule 1 substance—in other words, having "no currently accepted medical use."

Now, in the age of modern chemistry, we have access to an ever-growing list of synthetic drugs, both legal and illegal. What's interesting to note is that scientific studies, previously not permitted for Schedule 1 substances, are now showing that they may well have powerful effects on prevalent, and even currently incurable, illnesses. And the reports are coming in. Psilocybin, the active compound in magic mushrooms, can cure migraines, treat depression and even help soften the fear of dying in those who don't have long to live. While some of the most profound findings show that MDMA, the active compound in Ecstasy, when administered in the proper *"set and setting,"* can even effectively cure a veteran's PTSD in as little as two MDMA-assisted therapy sessions. Not a lifelong dependency on questionably effective prescription drugs, *but actually cure it.* That's a pretty important thing when you consider that more than twenty veterans commit suicide daily in the U.S., largely in part due to untreated PTSD.

Even in 2018 marijuana, despite its undeniable medicinal benefits, remains classified as Schedule 1 by the DEA. Why are these substances still illegal? Certainly some of them do carry the potential for addiction but making them illegal doesn't stop them from being used. Time and again prohibition has proven to be a poor strategy to regulate and control anything, instead often backfiring by fueling black markets, organized crime, poor quality and general abuse. As soon as we prohibit something, we give up control, not to mention making it more exciting. Education and regulation are far more effective solutions in terms of reducing addiction and increasing public well-being. *So why still illegal?* Well, you guessed it, it's the money again! It's not about addiction or public well-being at all. And this time I'm not even talking about profitable prisons. If the average person is smoking pot, they're usually not drinking or smoking cigarettes as much. And it certainly doesn't help pharmaceutical companies for people to have access to unpatentable, unprofitable medicinal compounds that are often even more effective than their own products, or even worse *cure* the illnesses. Did you know that traditional Chinese medicine doctors only get paid as long as you stay healthy? *Now THAT seems like a way better feedback loop!*

It's truly the age of the personal experience and there's a million ways to get your mind blown. And in my opinion, that's a good thing; however, there's not always as much credence given to the *integration* side of things. How are we changed on the other side of the experience? How do we return to our old lives, to our day-to-day existence, after we've witnessed alternate realities, or come face to face with the divine itself? Whether we go on trips using airplanes or psychedelics, we have the opportunity to return transformed. It's so easy to jump from experience to experience without giving ourselves the time to absorb what we've learned, to see how we've evolved, and to intentionally proceed from that new place.

As I close out this slight tangent of a chapter, and regardless of where you stand on the issue, how about this for a takeaway: *we're all on drugs, all the time.* Our brains, reacting to stimulation and pulsing billions of signals, are suspended in a sea of neurochemicals. Anything can affect this balance, so why not consider people, places or really any external experience as a drug, perhaps not ones that we have to inject, snort or swallow, but ones that affect us nonetheless. Does the presence of someone you love give you a rush of sensations that feels good? If you've taken Ecstasy, you'd probably note its similar effect. DMT, the most powerful hallucinogen currently known to man, is created *endogenously.* Yep, that means you don't necessarily even need to smoke DMT to tap into its power; it's created right inside your own skull! So when it comes down to it, whether it's sugar, cacao, psychedelics or spending time with your buddy who loves to drink, it's all about understanding where your addictive tendencies are *and learning to dose yourself, whether with substances, people or anything else, accordingly.*

Thank you for tuning in to this PSA, which hopefully gave some context to the rather large amount of LSD which I now had in my possession. And now back to the show …

10. To The Moon And Back

"Sounds like a bunch of hippies doing drugs and running around naked in the desert," my mom said when I told her I was going to the Burning Man festival for the first time. She'd been in her late twenties during 1967's Summer of Love but was far more inclined to support Richard Nixon than Ken Kesey.

"It's a lot more than just that, Mom! There's art, music and all sorts of self-expression!" I'd replied, somewhat defensively, before admitting, "And there's probably a few naked people on drugs, too." But forget Burning Man for a moment. What do *you* think of when I say the word *festival*?

You might think of a weekend full of movie screenings or stage performances. You may conjure visions of a pagan springtime gathering and dancing around a maypole. Or you might imagine people dressing up like Renaissance characters, reciting poetry, playing games, gorging on roast meat and swilling mead served up by busty wenches. But if you're a child of the late 20th and early 21st centuries then it's more likely the huge array of dance-centric events that come to mind. They take place all around the globe and range from the beat-thumping, consumer-friendly variety to *transformational* festivals, as they're sometimes referred to, which highlight art, talks and workshops *in addition* to music.

Let's jump back to the 1980s once again as Margaret Thatcher-and-Ronald Reagan-inspired conservatives on both sides of the Atlantic declared war on the party-inclined nature of youth. Humorously enough, their aversion inadvertently paved the way for the dance-centric rave culture by prompting event producers to move their events from cities into the forests, deserts and other distant lands. In the mid-1980s on the West Coast of the United States, the oft-celebrated bellwether of social expression, something was born on a beach near San Francisco. It started as a gathering of eightyish friends and the burning of a wooden effigy which was intended to help one of the attendees process a recent romantic breakup. The attendee was Larry Harvey and this was the first Burning Man. The event's yearly attendance quickly grew, until like other gatherings of their type, they were forced out of the city and into the wilderness.

The next phase of Burning Man would become richer and more interactive as yearly revelers transitioned from mere spectators into active participants. Everyone was encouraged to get involved by making their own art projects and to create experiences to share with others. In time, Burning Man became a values-driven party scene and soon the organization released its own version of the Ten Commandments, a list of ten core principles that include things such as radical expression, acceptance and self-reliance, as well as introducing the environmental concept of *"leaving no trace."* The event, known to participants as the *Burn*, became so integral to people's lives that social activities during the other fifty-one weeks of the year often revolved around fundraising for, planning for, or otherwise just getting excited for, the following Burn.

"You know what would be awesome for the Burn this year ...?" That was a phrase that became part of the usual at-home conversation. Just as *"You know what would be awesome at next year's Burn ...?"* was regularly overheard at the event itself. All shapes and sizes of camps and offerings grew up out of the Black Rock Desert, from small rag-tag camps that served tea to giant music camps whose lasers and sound waves blasted into the night sky. Around 2007, I started a camp with some friends that still continues to run to this day, independently of my involvement, many years after my last Burn, such is the spirit of the Burner community.

Soon, and largely inspired by Burning Man, this new style of festival multiplied across the globe, growing larger and more accessible. Music still remained a huge focus but soon became interwoven with other types of artistic expression. Performance, interactive art and games, and giant, beautifully lit sculptures created a rich visual feast for attendees. The event producers pushed the boundaries of cutting-edge audiovisual equipment and experience design. Huge, custom stages attracted the world's top creative, spiritual and intellectual talent. Knowledge-sharing became a big part of the offerings, as discussions, presentations and workshops filled the schedule in addition to the DJs and bands. Healthy food options began to be served up as yoga classes appeared on the program. The clandestine raves of the 80s and 90s had officially graduated into *transformational* festivals, full-on epicenters of human expression.

As any attuned transformation geek can tell you, transformation is not always a cakewalk. Transformational festivals not only offer us the opportunity to experience all of the beauty and joy that we are capable of feeling but they also offer us the opportunity to have a *miserable fucking time*. The combined intensity of extreme conditions and incessant overstimulation can bring up all of the emotions, especially for the uninitiated. Furthermore, the added effects of dehydration, lack of sleep and mind-altering drugs all wreak havoc on relationships and can leave a grown man sobbing in his tent. *Yet it's precisely that range of experience that makes them so powerful.*

"This is why we come out here," my ex-girlfriend said to me as I babbled about some existential crisis one year. And she was right. We don't grow as individuals, nor as a species, by mollycoddling ourselves into cookie-cut citizens that follow all the rules, keep up with the latest trends and long for television time while we sit at jobs that bore the shit out of us. We transform when our comfort levels get peeled back, when our edges become exposed and everything we thought to be real is suddenly exposed as just as fleeting and indefinite as everything else. *Those are the times that define us.* And more often than not, as we nurse our wounds, we realize that we survived and have become stronger and more resilient versions of ourselves. Yes, I admit, my mom's initial reaction wasn't completely far off: sometimes transformation takes the form of hippies, doing drugs and running around naked in the desert. But a few years later after reading that the founders of Google had their own Burning Man camp, my mother's reaction took a surprising turn: "Honey, I think you should submit your résumé to Burning Man." *Behold, the power of the transformational festival!*

In recent years, I decided to stop attending so many festivals. I was appreciative for all that they'd opened me up to, and remain very grateful that they exist, especially as a place for newbies to have their minds blown for the first time. However, after a decade or more they'd begun to feel a little repetitive and whenever something feels overly repetitive, I begin to lose interest. Even Burning Man, the mother of them all, had become predictably awesome, and to keep attending felt like a form of *experiential masturbation.* Besides that, festivals demanded a huge amount of time and money only to have all your hard work vanish into the dust soon after the event ended. I was in my late-thirties, right after my mini early-midlife crisis, and I was ready to reclaim the huge amount of energy I put into festivals and funnel it toward more long-term projects. *All of that said, how could I miss out on a New Year's festival on a magical lake in southern Guatemala?*

So on the morning after the bonfire at Sunflower House I left San Marcos and headed across the lake to the quiet town of Santiago. The Cosmic Convergence Festival—*Cosmic* as it was known—was taking place just outside the town, nestled in a quiet—for now—inlet on the south side of the lake. Some of my friends had decided to get hotel rooms in Santiago, including the Cacao Fairy. Without having received an explicit invitation to bunk with her—something about an ex-boyfriend attending the festival and wanting to keep her options open or something—I opted to bring my tent and sleeping bag to the festival; she kindly let me store some of extra belongings in her room.

Cosmic, as compared to the festivals that I was used to in California, was raw and intimate in nature, which I guess was to be expected from a festival taking place in a developing country. As we approached the gates, we passed a large array of local vendors selling fruit and tamales. The first thing I noticed as I entered the festival was the striking disparity between the local people and festival-goers. What we had paid for a weekend ticket, a couple of hundred U.S. dollars, was likely the sort of money that some of them made in a month. Things inside the gates were hilariously disorganized and still under construction but overall the vibe was friendly. I soon found some friends and set up my tent near their camp, down by the edge of the lake.

The first night was relaxed; the scheduled activities started the following day, so after a dinner of local tamales I decided to take it easy and get an early night. My tent, which was really primarily a hammock that doubled as a tent, was laughably small, far smaller than I had expected from the picture, and as I squeezed into it and lay down, I realized that the top surface was suspended just a few inches above my face. I soon realized, now finding myself on the *south side* of the lake, that the nights were far colder and more damp than anything I had experienced in San Marcos. When I woke up the following morning my sleeping bag, which had been rubbing up against the sides of my tiny tent all night, was covered in dew so I was grateful when the sun finally emerged above the southern mountains. Those hotel rooms began to seem *a lot* more attractive. It was New Year's Eve and I hoped I could find a nice snuggle buddy to celebrate the occasion. "As long as it's at her place," I thought as I extracted myself from my damp tent.

I walked away from the lake toward the food vendors and I soon stumbled upon a place that was serving Guatemalan coffee and my entire world started to feel a little bit better. Before long I had run into some more friends from San Marcos and we spent the rest of the day attending all sorts of workshops, including how to run successful communities, how to have difficult conversations and how to grow mushrooms. There was also a workshop on natural building techniques that incorporated bamboo, a material that was lauded as an attractive building component because it grew so quickly. The example bamboo structure, in which the workshop took place, had been built in the week preceding the festival and was going to be disassembled afterward and reassembled at a local school as a demonstration structure for others in the community to learn from. My penchant for white guilt was somewhat assuaged when I learned that Cosmic was using ticket funds to help the local community in numerous other ways, too. This should be exactly the sort of direction that more festivals begin to follow, I thought. Indeed, it's a natural evolution that what comes after having your mind blown, after all the talks and presentations, and after the hands-on workshops, is to actually help the world by applying those skills in real ways, outside the events. It was the kind of thing that filled me with hope for humanity: amid all of the challenges going on we are also seeing slow but positive cultural transformation take place. Wouldn't it be nice to party your face off all while knowing that you'd made a difference?

Cosmic was billed as a three-day festival themed around *Tribal Technologies*, the intersection where old and new knowledge combine to create useful and balanced solutions. *At least that was the idea,* although I'm not sure that the toilets near the camping area fit the theme very well. The toilets, rather than the typical blue porta-potties found at most events that I was used to, were an *experimental* type of composting toilet. In reality they were rickety structures built above large pits in the ground. Some of the doors had already fallen off and the pits seemed large enough to swallow the structure, and anyone unlucky enough to be using it at the time.

Whether it was the tent or the toilets that had prompted it, I began to wonder if I really wanted to be here. But I was determined to have a fun New Year's Eve so I actively put on my cheeriest of vibes, intent on coaxing myself back toward a less bitchy mood. I took my yoga mat and caught the last part of a class, which immediately made me feel better. I then went over to the healing tent to book myself a massage. To my delight, a strong Dutch woman said she was available to give me a Thai massage, so I booked a slot that evening before the festivities.

San Marcos had left me a little workshopped out but even so, later that afternoon, I decided to go to a workshop hosted by teachers from the International School of Temple Arts, the same organization that Nadia had told me about. ISTA prides itself on opening up people to their sexuality by removing any blockages that they may be experiencing. The women and men who'd gathered for the workshop stood in two concentric circles, facing each other. Each gender got to share with the other how they were feeling about the expectations and pressures they felt had been imposed on them by the outside world. Some people laughed, some people cried, some people looked like, *"Wait, what the fuck did I get myself into?"* and I did all those things but in reverse order. It felt good to be comfortable enough to not even care anymore, to just let the emotions come out, free of shame.

After getting some snacks—thankfully bliss balls were available in abundance—I went to get changed for the evening and night was falling as I walked back to the festival grounds. In my pocket I fiddled with a small object. The mint dropper of LSD, destined for its inaugural unveiling. I'd told Nadia about it on the boat ride over and since then we'd rallied a small, psychedelic adventure posse for the experience. But first it was time to treat myself to a massage. I smiled; I was already feeling like things were looking up.

My masseuse had prepared a comfortable space for me inside the healing tent and began to give me an expert massage as the music began on the stage outside. And then, suddenly, I began to sneeze. It began as just a small tickle in the back of my nose but I must have sneezed twenty times while I was getting the massage. I hoped that it was just a small thing that would go away soon, maybe just a lingering effect of the damp sleeping conditions. I thanked the masseuse and headed out of the tent and into the night.

The Red Tent was the chosen meeting spot for our psychedelic posse and by the time I arrived I found Nadia and a few others had already gathered. The tent was an intricate, stretched-fabric structure that was dedicated to women, with a special emphasis given to those who were menstruating. And this being a full moon, it was apparently an especially auspicious—and busy—time to honor the feminine, by offering your menses back to the earth via the altar. If so desired, a menstruating woman could enter a smaller tent off to the side of the altar, where they could deposit some of their blood into a receptacle. They would then mix the blood with water, funneling it down a series of tubes onto an altar which diverted it back down the earth as an offering. While that might make some people uncomfortable, proponents say part of the intention of this practice is to transform any shame around this very natural human process. I was more or less fine with it but know plenty of others, women included, who wouldn't be. And I get it, shame can be a funny thing. Often as people strive to free themselves from it, they also feel the need to overtly share their new liberation with everyone else around them. Regardless of where anyone stood, Nadia had chosen this to be our psychedelic launching womb, right here in front of the Red Tent's blood altar.

By 8 p.m., ten of us had gathered: Nadia, Nina, the sweet and melancholy German girl from the conscious-touch workshop, my bromantic massage partner Steve, a fun Slovakian girlfriend of Steve's, a woman from New York, an older, cool guy named Angel who'd also been at the Eagle's Nest men's circle a few days earlier and his equally awesome girlfriend, also a tantra teacher, as well as a few others who Nadia had roped in. It was a fun bunch and it was apparent that everyone, many of whom were new friends, was sharing a giddy excitement for what the night might bring. No better way to get to know people that by taking psychedelics together, I thought to myself, immediately questioning the validity of that statement. Personally, I felt that familiar, pre-psychedelic sense of nervous apprehension growing inside me. I was experienced enough with LSD to know that it's often one of those things that's often more intense than you remember it being. Since I was the person sharing the "sacrament," as Nadia called it, and since it was some people's first time, and since I'd never even tried this particular batch, I decided it was best to stick to a low dose. One by one, shrouded by the womb-like red tent, each person came and sat in front of me and each time I asked what their intention was, which they then spoke out loud for all to hear:

"I am letting go of fear."

"I am no longer affected by the judgment of others."

"I am open to what the experience wants to teach me."

That kind of thing.

After each person spoke, I asked them for their hand and held out the dropper. Without letting the drop fully form, I passed it close to their skin, breaking the drop and effectively giving them something smaller than a full dose. Each person then licked the tiny patch of liquid off the top of their hand.

"And so it is! May your inner light guide you!" I exclaimed each time, summoning my best bodhisattva nature. Steve asked for a full drop so I joined him on the same dosage; after all, what kind of psychedelic buddy would I be if I didn't? After the last person had gone, we all got up, left the Red Tent and set off on our New Year's Eve adventures.

"Just remember the plan in case we lose each other!" I said as we drifted into a sea of sparkling lights. "And if you get lost, just chill out and remember that everything is going to be alright!" What a responsible trip leader I was.

We roamed around together and within an hour everybody seemed to be feeling fantastic. Lights were beginning to twinkle with just a little more magic and any former sleepiness gave way to an increasing sense of levity. By this time most of us were exhibiting the typical onset high, a tendency toward perma-smiles and sudden bouts of laughter. Now, one thing to understand about trippers is that once the acid kicks in they can be very similar to cats, in that they become easily distracted by shiny things and extremely difficult to herd. Our amorphous blob of psychonauts stuck together for a while, roaming between stages and art installations, but soon we'd separated into a few sub-groups. At some festivals this might be the last time you would see your friends until the next day, but Cosmic was small enough that we were likely to run into each other again. Just in case, and as long as the curious cats could keep at least some track of time, we'd made a plan to meet at the main stage at 10:30 p.m. for the headline act, none other than San Marcos' very own, the one and only, *Raga Funk Spaceship!*

We lost one group to the cozy interior of the tea lounge and another to the crowded bass stage, so the rest of us wandered up the hill to the art gallery. We lingered around the gallery for a while, eventually moving to an adjacent building, an old corn-drying facility that Cosmic had turned into a chill lounge. It was my kind of vibe. Lights were dim, shoes were off, cushions and blankets were laid all over the place and the music was deep and groovy. The tunes emanated from a small stage, a three-dimensional, multicolor structure in which the DJ stood in the center. The music was downtempo bass, peppered with higher-frequency accents, all combining into a delicious auditory experience. It was an intimate scene and there were a bunch of people dancing just beyond the cushions, a few feet in front of the DJ. My senses were already heightened and the sensuality that was exuding from the room created powerful ripples throughout my body. I felt energized and had all but forgotten about my sneezing attack and tickly sinuses. We decided to flank the edge of the room to see what else we could discover when, like a beacon of sweet, dark bliss, we stumbled upon a cacao table that had been set up by the same San Marcos chocolate factory where I'd been just a few days earlier.

"I think we've found our place," I said to Steve, like an opioid addict in a poppy field.

"Agreed." he replied, his eyes wide, and smile even more so.

"Let's get some cacao and chill."

"Good idea. Wait ..." He paused and looked around the room, his smile growing even larger. "Dougie, this is awesome." And it really was. We got some hot cacao and brought our small earthenware cups over to the cushions and sat and watched the scene around us. Lights matched the music, in bursts of blues and reds, fading only to explode once again with the rhythm. People danced together, energies intertwining to create an entirely new frequency. My thoughts were moving increasingly quickly, jumping between the past, present and future, from the profound to the shallow, loose fragments strung together by the hilarity of it all. What a reality we live in, to be able to travel to these places with pockets full of magic molecules that can alter our thoughts and seem to bend time and space itself.

"One drop on that hand, what a tiny yet inconceivable thing!" I exclaimed suddenly, out loud. "Dude, no matter how many times I take it, *it's always a surprise!*"

Steve looked at me and started laughing.

We'd finished our drinks and the DJ had changed. It was less my vibe and I was a little antsy for adventure so I decided to make a move.

"Hey, you guys want to go for a walk?" I asked. Steve was intertwined with a pretty, short-haired brunette, so I was pretty sure what his answer would be. He consulted her for a moment.

"I think we're going to stay here for a while," he replied.

"Right on. But don't forget, get your asses over to the main stage for Raga Funk Spaceship," I said as I got up to leave.

He made two circles with his thumbs and forefingers and held them up to his eyes like glasses. "See you there, Cap'n Dougie!"

I managed to locate both shoes and put them on the right feet before stumbling back out into the night. It had gotten significantly colder so I beelined over to the bass stage, intent to warm up with some dancing. I was standing at the back, trying to make out if I could see any friends when the Cacao Fairy appeared. We'd tried to find each other earlier in the weekend but had just kept missing each other.

"Hey!" she said.

"Hey! How's things?" I asked.

"A little weird, but otherwise good, I guess."

"Oh yeah? What's up?"

"My ex-boyfriend showed up. I don't know, whatever, it's just weird."

I was in no position to delve too deeply into that topic.

"Well, sorry about that. Hey," I said, deflecting to another topic. "Isn't Raga Funk on soon?"

"Yeah, I'm actually just grabbing my tea, and then heading over. My throat is feeling a little sore."

"Yeah, mine too. I wasn't expecting this cold weather. And my tent situation is a sad story," I said, part of me hoping that if I played my cards right, she might take pity on me and invite me over.

"Oh, too bad for you!" Not too much pity in her response, so I didn't push it. "How's your night going?" she asked.

"Great. I gave a bunch of people acid and we are planning to meet over at your set."

"Are you serious?"

"Well, as serious as I can be with your face doing the sorts of things it's doing right now." Indeed, the bone structure of her face seemed to have taken on a freeform fluidity, barely containable by her skin.

"Haha! Come on, you tripper!" She grabbed my hand and led me to the side of the bass stage. "I don't want you getting lost in the dark and falling in the lake before my big performance!"

She grabbed her tea from behind a speaker and we were off, skipping across the grass toward the mainstage. When we got there the rest of the band was setting up and she led me to the side. She put her tea down. "Well, this is my stop."

"Good luck out there!" I said as I took her hand. "You're going to do awesomely."

"Aww, thanks! Happy New Year!"

"Hey, so I imagine that you're going to be on stage at the stroke of midnight with no one to kiss, soooo …"

"Sooo?" She smiled back.

"So, this!" I pulled her toward me and I looked at her for a moment. "May I kiss you?"

"Oh, how nice of you to ask," she replied.

"You know, all this radical consent stuff the kids are talking about these days ..." I didn't finish before she pulled me toward her. I closed my eyes as our lips touched, thousands of fireworks exploding behind my closed eyelids. Rainbow-woven flower petals bloomed out of thorny tentacles, morphing into crystalline mandalas set in a dazzling fractal backdrop. Her scent mixed with the sounds and flavor of her lips as the visuals fell into alignment … Time stopped and melted into the rest of the synesthetic soup. And then the moment was over.

"Okay, tripper," she laughed. "*Go have fun!*" I wanted to ask her if she might need some company later that night but my verbal faculty was unresponsive as she jumped on to the stage. Besides, there'd been some solid progress and I'd catch up with her after the show; no need to rush anything.

I walked around to the front of the main stage and a large crowd had already gathered as the lead guitarist, still in his rainbow robe and pilot's hat, began to hype up the crowd.

"How's it going out there, Cosmic?" he asked dreamily.

"Yaaaay! Woohee!!" the sea of excitable fans replied.

"Fantastic, that's what I like to hear." He was so relaxed up there, it was awesome to behold. His slow gaze drifted over the crowd and then he struck a chord. A couple of drum beats from the back. The guy on the synth laughed like a lunatic.

"So where are we going tonight, Captain?" the synth navigator cackled.

"I don't know," said the group's rainbow-clad front man. "Let's see, where do the *passengers* all want to go tonight?" He waved his arm toward the crowd. People began yelping and one girl, shrill above all others, yelled and pointed at the full moon that was just beginning to crest the stage. "To the moon!!" she shrieked.

"Oh, we'll be going to the moon; in fact, that's our first stop!" And so the music began.

If Raga Funk Spaceship had been a trippy experience while high on just cacao than the LSD brought everything to the next level. Their seemingly disorganized and slightly chaotic medley of sound waxed and waned organically, the jam session meandering until suddenly becoming aligned in an apex of improvisation. The music itself felt alive as the band created things that had never been practiced or played before. I drifted around to the back of the crowd, eyes scanning for my friends. I soon realized that trying to make out anyone in this mass of morphing faces was a futile endeavor, so instead I decided to head directly into the fray. I worked my way toward the front, bobbing my head, and probably smiling like a nutcase. I was almost at the front when I spotted a familiar blonde and feather-adorned head. "Nadia!" I said, as I hugged her from the back.

She turned. "YES! We were wondering where you were!" My eyes scanned around. The whole posse was present, accounted for and seemingly having an awesome time. It was a beautiful sight to behold, everyone was smiling and dancing and laughing. Even melancholy Nina seemed to have just let go of all her concerns and was smiling and swaying to the tunes as Raga Funk Spaceship brought us to different planets. The Cacao Fairy had her own solo performance, where she was the focus of attention, leading the audience down an eerie vocal soundscape. We all clapped and whooped as she smiled bashfully.

As the stroke of midnight approached, the rainbow-robed captain counted down. "10, 9, 8 …" The crowd was getting ecstatic.

"7, 6, 5 …" He was bending his guitar chords to create an endless array of cosmic sounds. "4, 3, 2 …" The synth guy twiddled his knobs, releasing more interstellar effects. There was a funny moment in my mind just before the last seconds of the old year expired. "Wait a second," I thought, "who is going to kiss who at midnight?" I laughed to myself at the hilarity of it all. "1 ... 0! The spaceship has landed, my friends!"

And with that our entire posse formed into a group hug, everyone laughing and kissing each other. Our captain continued. "Oh my goodness, what strange planet is this? Wait a minute, it's our very own planet Earth!! We've made it all the way home!" As we hugged I felt more people joining in, and more people, and more until almost the entire audience had congealed into a massive sea of bodies in the largest group hug that I'd ever been a part of. I looked around and all I could see was more people running toward us from every direction. And just like that, as our captain struck a final chord the entire human blob collapsed, arms and legs in every direction as hundreds of people fell to the earth into what can only be described as an *epic cuddle puddle.*

Reality set in a few moments later. How do you even extract yourself from something like that? Everyone's arms and legs were so intertwined that no one even knew where to begin. The pile of humans may well have stayed there for a long time had Raga Funk Spaceship not come to the rescue, pulling one more rousing tune from their colorful sleeves. Slowly, as the band strummed people began pulling themselves free, a leg here, and arm there, and helping each other back up. Afterwards I tried to find the Cacao Fairy but I couldn't see her anywhere so a few of us went to the nearby fire pit instead, where there was an indigenous man tending the fire and people singing sweet songs. I was sitting next to Nina and told her about my recent breathwork experience in which she'd played a role in opening up my heart. She was so happy to hear that.

"Never forget how much power that you have, that you can have that sort of effect on people," I said to her.

"I could say the same thing about you. It's been really good to connect with you, Dougie." Her lips spread into a smile that shined brighter than the fire and filled my heart with warmth.

Sometime later the next band came on; they were not very enjoyable at all, so I decided to break off on my own for a while and head back up to the chill lounge. I was just getting to the hill when I saw the Cacao Fairy. She was looking a little stressed.

"Hey, that was amazing, good job!" I said.

"I'm glad you had fun. I thought the sound was a little muffled."

"You sounded great." I looked at her. "Is everything okay?"

"Not great. Kinda weird," she said.

"Ok, what's going on?"

"Well, my ex came up to me after the show. He arrived at the festival late so I had brought some of his camping stuff. Anyway, he said he was going to pick it up today but he never did. And so he asked if he could stay with me tonight."

"Oh, well that *is* weird! And you said ...?" I replied, fearing the worst.

"And I said he could, of course. Am I meant to make him sleep outside in the cold?"

"No, of course not!" And there goes that sweet, sweet opportunity, I thought, considering my own cold night ahead.

"Anyway, I have to go help pack up some things at the main stage. Let's catch up later."

"Okay. Hey, don't worry about anything. Everything will be okay in the end." I smiled, and really meant it. "If it's not okay, it's not the end!" The John Lennon quote seemed appropriate as we parted ways.

Whatever, it's cool. I'm cool. Everything's fine. But I was feeling a little rejected, that familiar cloud of darkness threatening to touch ground. So I ate a couple of tamales, bummed a cigarette from a tweaker near the psytrance stage and made my way up to the chill lounge to find some friends. I caught up with my crew, who were lounging on cushions and my troubles melted into a cuddle puddle of cacao-fueled massages as the effects of the LSD slowly wore off. By dawn our merry band had dwindled and the room was warm with mostly sleeping bodies. I hadn't found a snuggle buddy but rather than go back to my damp, cold tent I decided to grab a spare blanket and found an empty spot on a large ground pad. I curled up as the ambient tunes lulled me to sleep.

A while later, I was disturbed from my dreams as I felt someone join me on to the ground pad. I opened my eyes briefly to the dim light of dawn to discover that a slim, long-haired woman had backed her way onto my pad. I fell back to sleep. It must have been some hours later when I was woken up, because the sun had risen, the music had long since ended and the room was a lot emptier. I had been nudged awake by the motion of the woman in front of me. Since she'd taken up residence on my ground pad, she had moved closer to me until we were spooning. My arm was loosely laid across her, innocently enough, but she was now slipping out from underneath it. I felt her sit up and I opened my eyes to discover it wasn't a woman at all but a slim young man with long brown hair that had no business being that luxurious. I think we were both a little surprised. We exchanged manly nods after which, without saying a word, he got up and left. And that's how that New Year's Day started. Gender confusion and a head cold to end all head colds.

I laid back and groaned. Last night I might have forgotten that I was getting sick but this morning I felt like warmed-over death. I pushed myself up and surveyed my surroundings: far less magical than the night before. I stepped over snoring people, found my shoes and emerged into the cool morning air. As I descended from the hill, on a mission to find some tea to soothe my aching head, I decided I could not spend another night here and messaged the Cacao Fairy to see if she could find me a room in her hotel. Later that morning she replied saying that she was sorry she'd lost me the night before but she'd found me a room. *Great news!*

I was exhausted but despite my balance being affected by this impending cold and feeling like I was going to pass out at any minute, I managed to pack up my things and do a lap around the festival to say some goodbyes. I ran into Nadia near the Red Tent.

"Are you okay, brother?" she asked when she saw me. She looked concerned.

"I think I'm coming down with something," I said. I hadn't looked in a mirror but if I looked anything like I felt I could understand her concern. "I decided to book a hotel for tonight and get some rest. I just wanted to come say goodbye."

"Well, come back to San Marcos when you feel better, there's some fun things happening next week."

"Okay, I'll keep you posted," I said. To be honest I didn't know what my next move was and this statement seemed like a way to deflect having to make any plans. But something told me this might be the last time I was going to see her for a while. We shared an extra-long hug and I set off back toward the entrance gate.

I caught a tuk tuk right outside the festival and asked the driver to take me to the hotel. As we drove away I looked at the dozens of locals outside the gates, desperately trying to figure out a way to scrape together some money from the festival attendees. My head swirled with broody thoughts about waste and privilege. The drug-fueled revelry of the preceding days seemed to stand in stark contrast to the reality just outside the gates. Clouds of judgment further clogged my already stuffy head. I tried to move my attention to the aspects of the festival that had been positive, the workshops, the outreach initiatives, the educational projects that were teaching locals about sustainable agriculture and living practices. And maybe that's what it's all about? That this life is just a big, beautiful mix of all that's bright and dark, dancing together from the beginning to the end of time? Maybe learning how to *be* in that balance was my transformational lesson. That and being clear with my intentions. After all, the universe *had* given me the snuggle buddy that I'd asked for, just a slightly different one than I'd expected.

I arrived at the hotel, and to even call it a hotel was a generous overstatement. The rooms were in bad condition but the sheets were clean enough and I just needed a place to sleep off this wicked head cold. That evening I ate some soup and passed out before it was even dark. I slept for fifteen hours straight but woke up feeling even worse. I couldn't tell if it was the flu or food poisoning or a parasite, I just felt terrible, so I booked another night and then mustered the energy to go to breakfast with the Cacao Fairy before she left on the boat. And as divine comedy would have it, we showed up at the exact same restaurant where her ex-boyfriend was eating breakfast.

"Of course he's here," she whispered somewhat cynically as we approached, seeing him from across the street. "We had an argument and he left the hotel this morning with all his things. I should have known he'd be here. It's our favorite restaurant."

"Do you want to go somewhere else?" He had his back to us and hadn't seen us yet.

"No! This place has the best tortillas," she said stubbornly as we continued to walk toward him. "I told him that we kissed last night, by the way. Would it be weird for you if we joined him?" she asked as we approached his table, but it was already too late to protest even if I'd wanted to.

"At this point, no, it's *totally fine,*" I whispered. Whatever. I was sick, hungry and fast approaching the edge of being totally over dealing with other humans. But try as I might to not like him, I found it hard not to. His name was Eric and if he had any issue with my presence he didn't let on to it. He was a musician, and had the sort of cool demeanor of an old jazz cat that had been incarnated into a young man's body. When I asked him about his experience of travelling for his shows his eyes lit up with life. It was in that moment I could understand where their romantic issues lay. This man's soul was meant to be unencumbered, free on the open roads of the world where he could improvise music, delight audiences and live life in the moment. And if that meant entertaining his adoring young fangirls, I imagined he was not one to limit his own experience.

Eric paid his bill separately and said goodbye, sharing a long hug with the Cacao Fairy and a firm handshake with me. A cool cat, indeed, I thought as he exited the scene. After we finished breakfast, which did indeed feature fantastic tortillas, it was time for us to say goodbye.

"Thanks for all the good memories. And all the cacao," I said.

"Sure. I'm sorry for all the weirdness. I have really appreciated our time together. I think getting to know you helped me understand more of what I am looking for in a relationship. Oh well, I'm sorry we didn't get more time."

"Reasons, seasons or lifetimes, remember?" I replied, recalling our conversation from a few days earlier. As she turned and walked toward the dock I realized that this was probably the last time I'd see her. We'd shared a sweet, ethereal connection around this lake, cameos in each other's scripts, only to be spun back out into the rest of our lives. Who knows what forces bring humans together or what influence that remains long after they part ways? I wished her well and she dissolved into the crowd.

My final day in Santiago was a bizarre dream. It felt like my head was swollen twice its normal size with congestion so I spent the rest of the day lying down, watching Spanish soap operas, wondering how the large stain on the wall had been made and generally feeling pretty sorry for myself. By the evening I felt delirious; this sickness seemed to be morphing in all sorts of strange ways. The half-painted walls of my shitty hotel room seemed to be pulsing in sync with my throbbing head. That night a balcony on the building opposite the hotel had switched on some Christmas lights that relentlessly sent a tinny electronic version of Jingle Bells into my room. Just the first verse. Nonstop. I almost lost my fucking mind. Thankfully, I restrained myself from running into the street, scaling the wall and ripping the goddamn thing off the balcony by stuffing my ears with damp toilet paper and curling into a ball. I woke up the next day, feeling a little better and decided that I had to leave this place.

I was feeling strong enough to carry my backpack, and although there was a big full moon festival the following day in San Marcos that *"everyone was going to,"* as Nadia told me via text message, I didn't really want to head back there so I told her "definitely maybe." I was still feeling terribly sick and pretty antisocial. Besides, even if I hadn't felt like a walking plague victim, I knew that if I didn't leave this lake I might become like that Norwegian guy Erik who'd arrived ... and then suddenly it was thirteen years later. It was time to regain my sense of independence.

"Yeah man, you gotta get out of there before it's too late." Loki's words rang in my ears. I knew I had to keep moving on; however, I wasn't quite ready for the long day of travel back to Antigua so I decided to relocate to the neighboring town of San Pedro for a few days. In San Pedro I found a small Airbnb run by a crazy artist and the entire place smelled like weed. In the morning the artist made me waffles and would talk about his grand plans for the future while smoking doobies. It was the perfect place to recover from whatever disease that I'd contracted at the festival.

After two days, still congested but at least mostly functional, I was ready to hit the road, so I packed my belongings, said goodbye to the artist and took a boat across to Panajachel. I sent Nadia a message to say goodbye. "Haha! I KNEW you weren't coming back! Follow your heart, brother. Come visit me in Thailand this winter!" she'd responded.

This lake seemed to be as full of hellos as it was of goodbyes. It had only been three weeks since I'd arrived at Lake Atitlán but the amount of experiences I'd had in that time made it feel much longer. Within a couple of hours I was once again crammed in a shuttle bus, bouncing around curvy roads, back toward the charmingly bland town of Antigua.

10. To The Moon And Back

11. Meanwhile, Back At The Ranch

It turned out to be a quick but humorous couple of days. I took the opportunity to throw myself into the typical backpacker scene, shifting from my opulent-by-comparison house in San Marcos, into the budget world of hostels and the diversity of characters that come along with that.

The scene at the Bigfoot Hostel in Antigua was a little jarring after all the bliss-ball-fueled clean living of Lake Atitlán. Upon my arrival a rowdy beer pong competition was taking place and a bunch of inebriated folks were sloppily learning to dance salsa rhythms in the central courtyard. I checked into my dorm where I was given the bottom bunk in a stack of three beds. There were about four of these stacks positioned along the walls around the room, giving me a total of eleven possible roommates. Each person got a locker to put their belongings into and each bed was equipped with a reading light and electrical outlet. There was a shared bathroom down the hall with travel quotes stenciled on the walls, the cheesily inspiring "Wherever you go, there you are" kind of thing.

I had unpacked and was lounging on my bunk when a young, voluptuous black girl, who couldn't have been more than eighteen, came into the room. Her name was Zoe; she was Dutch and had just come back from a volcano adventure. We chatted for a little while as she dolled herself up, shamelessly stripping down to her panties and squeezing her ample derriere into a pair of jeans, readying herself for a night of salsa. In general, people at hostels are pretty easygoing and in many ways it felt like my childhood boarding school all over again, but with a wider assortment of genders, ages and nationalities. Zoe was on her gap year before college, travelling down from northern Guatemala and had already stopped at some of the locations I was planning to visit. In a few short minutes she listed off a string of suggestions of where to stay and what to get up to. She then invited me to go learn some salsa moves so I joined her and despite being twice her age and possessing two left feet I mostly kept up. A while later I excused myself and decided to head back to my dorm, despite a young Scottish man's notable efforts to recruit me into his beer pong team.

The following day I was walking through the central square and looking for a place to eat when I saw a quirky fellow who looked strangely familiar. He was walking toward me and seemed to recognize me at the same time.

"Hey, man. Were you at Cosmic?" he asked as he approached.

"Yeah! I thought I recognized you," I replied.

"What are you up to?"

"I'm about to go get some lunch. Want to join?" I asked. It's a good sign that you're getting into the travel flow when, with minimal formalities, you just roll with whatever shows up in the moment.

"Sure, I can always eat," he said. So we rolled down the street to a taco place that he'd heard was good.

His name was Blaze; he was a musician and he talked pretty much nonstop, but his stories were so fascinating, and his delivery so matter-of-fact, that I found myself enthralled. Blaze had long, curly, blond hair and wore mirrored aviators most of the time, even inside. He sported a brown suede jacket with tassels, a psychedelic paisley shirt, a bolo tie and faded blue jeans; he looked like he'd just gotten off stage after jamming out with the Grateful Dead. After a few rounds of some excellent carne asada tacos we continued walking around with the loose plan to check out some of the architectural relics scattered around town. Blaze was deep into yet another tale, this time about a girl who he'd met at the festival.

"So that evening we head back to her camp to find out she'd gotten jacked. And not just her money, but someone had actually packed up and taken her entire tent, her sleeping bag and backpack, too. *Even her damn shoes!* Can you believe that shit?"

"What? That's crazy, how did no one see that happen?"

"Well, I don't know about you but I thought those security guys looked a little shady."

"So, what happened?" I asked.

"Of course, I offered her to stay in *my* tent, so it turned out alright for me," he laughed. "But still, sucked for her!"

"Did she ever find it?"

"Well, that's the funny part. The next day she found it all, just as she left it. She says someone played a prank on her but I think we all know that she was just a little too high! Or maybe it was her way of getting into *my* tent ..." he chuckled. "Haha, yeah, I like that."

"Gum, nuts, cigarettes?" A small street vendor interrupted us as we were walking by.

"No, gracias." I said, waving my hand and smiling.

"Coke, weed, mushrooms?" he added under his breath.

"Damn, that escalated quickly," I remarked to Blaze, who'd stopped in front of the kid.

"Yeah, these street kids have the connections on pretty much all the drugs," Blaze said. He said something in Spanish to the kid, handed him some money and the kid handed him a pack of gum. "And if you're looking for hookers, it's the tuk tuk guys you need to talk to."

We spent the afternoon walking around town while I listened to story after story of his "conscious awakening." After years of playing rock and roll and drinking heavily he'd gone to a Vipassana course that had unexpectedly launched him into a series of out-of-body experiences. These began in his meditations but soon he discovered that he could enter trance-like states even while awake.

"So I was totally tripping out, man!" Blaze was on a roll as we walked around the ruins of La Recolección cathedral. "One minute I would be eating a burrito and the next I would be travelling through an intergalactic network of superhighways."

"Hey, it happens," I chipped in.

"Sure does," he replied. "Anyway, along the way I was informed by an inner voice that I was headed to meet with the intergalactic federation of light beings where I would be representing Earth." We stumbled up some stairs to see if we could scope a good view of the town. Blaze continued, barely catching his breath: "As you can imagine I was feeling a little bit of pressure, given that I would be debating the future of our planet and species ... *but then BAM!* I had appeared on this translucent platform, floating in some distant nebula, in front of an assembly of higher consciousness beings. I did my best; I mean, it was kind of high-stress, you know?" I didn't really know, but nodded anyway. "Then one of them said, 'Hey Blaze, we're glad you came all this way, we really are, but we just can't allow Earth to join the federation until it gets its shit together, man.' I mean it didn't really *say* that, because it didn't use words exactly, but you know, I *felt* it. Can you believe that shit?"

"Well, to be honest," I replied, "if I were part of a federation of intergalactic light beings that had figured out how to travel through space and time to mind meld with each other, then I probably wouldn't let Earth join my club, either."

"True, true," he laughed. "We got a way to go, I guess."

A while later we were walking up a steep hill toward La Cruz Blanca, a large white cross that looked over the town. Once we got to the lookout Blaze retrieved the gum packet that he'd bought from the nut seller, emptied a small nug of marijuana into his palm and proceeded to break it up and roll a joint.

"It's not the best pot, but it's better than nothing."

We found a spot in the grass and he proceeded to get royally high. My sinus system still felt like a disaster zone so I declined his offer. Besides there were some police just over the hill, so I felt a little nervous. He didn't seem to care.

"Hey, man. You know how to be invisible?" he asked, perhaps feeling my slight apprehension.

"You mean, like … *not visible* to other *people*?"

"Exactly, man." He smiled, lying back onto the grass without a care in the world. "Not visible to other people."

"Hmmm. Well, now that you mention it, no, no I don't, Blaze."

"Well, let me tell you." He took a final hit of the joint and stubbed it out on the ground. I smiled, getting ready for another story. He proceeded to tell me about this time his friend had been driving a car in North Carolina. Blaze had been sitting in the back with a duffel bag filled with pounds of marijuana. "I mean it was a giant amount of weed, man," he said. "And right when we were exciting the highway we got pulled over for a broken fuckin' tail light!"

"That sucks! What happened?" But Blaze was already telling me.

"So I said to my buddy, 'Hey man, just chill, I'm not even in the back right now.' The cop idled up next to the car. I just looked straight ahead and didn't say anything. I didn't react, I just kept looking ahead, telling myself that I was invisible. So the cop did the usual thing, you know, 'License and registration' and all that shit, and shined his flashlight in the backseat. Shined it right in *my face,* man. *'I'm invisible, I'm not even here,'* I said to myself. And just like that the cop let my buddy go with a fix-it ticket. Yeah, man, if you just don't even allow yourself to enter another person's perception, then just like that!" He snapped his fingers. "You're *invisible.*"

We sat on the hill below the white cross for another hour. Blaze told me about cloud bursting by using just the power of his mind. He told me about technologies that aliens had given to indigenous people, technologies that were capable of moving and sculpting rock itself. In return the Earthlings mined gold for use in their alien spacecraft. He told me that our species was beginning to split into at least three subspecies: the working class who were best kept malnourished and powerless; the uber-wealthy, tech-centric elite; and the all-organic, crystal-activated light beings, the latter of which he was certainly on his way to becoming.

"We need to be prepared, man. This is the time of The Great Unravelling."

Finally, after finishing another joint, we descended the mountain of La Cruz Blanca. Blaze had to go "take care of some business," presumably to buy some more "gum," so I decided to take the rest of the afternoon for myself. We were both travelling in different directions the following morning so planned to meet for dinner that night to celebrate our short but humorous friendship. As I walked back to my hostel, I thought about the state of the world. Things really did seem to be unraveling at an alarming rate and the future that our culture was facing felt rather bleak. The new story of hope and global collaboration that felt oh so tangible just a few years earlier seemed to be withering on the vine. And in its place, a perfect mirror was being held up, reflecting back to us all that was fucked up in the world. The climate was under severe threat; predictions for this hurricane season foretold of increasingly harsh storms; the West Coast of the U.S. was being ravaged by fires and landslides; cities around the world were reporting other impending disasters from floods to air toxicity and a dramatic shortage of fresh water. Power was increasingly being centralized within the hands of autocratic rulers, funded by such blatant corporate connections that they didn't even feel the need to hide it anymore. The European Union, a once-lauded example of multicultural cooperation, was beginning to fall apart as the UK and other nations considered their exits; China had removed term limits on its presidency; the U.S. had elected a megalomaniacal president who seemed bent on picking fights with everyone from Syria to North Korea; and Russia meanwhile seemed to be stirring up a lot of it with controlling tactics, cyber meddling, and bullying behavior on an international scale. Unions were crumbling, new border walls were being erected, embargoes and trade tariffs were being put in place and talks of nuclear threats suddenly made it feel like it was the Cold War all over again, now with more nations.

And all the while the disparity between the rich and the poor was growing more stark, and access to technology, healthcare and other basic human needs were becoming unattainable to many of the population. Personal debt had reached record numbers, and many had no real hope of ever getting themselves out of it. Rather than working together, people were being pitted against each other, blaming one another as the cause of the turmoil. Conservatives blaming liberals, politicians blaming the media, truck drivers blaming self-driving trucks, women blaming men, and men blaming each other. The majority of people had become so emotionally trigger-sensitive that it seemed like no one wanted to be accountable for anything anymore. Individuals couldn't throw their power and sovereignty away quick enough.

Even technology, the former golden child of human progress and its utopian promise of a better world, was now facing a backlash. Constant hacks, data breaches and privacy scandals had consumers fearful for how they were unknowingly being manipulated. Even AI, what many hoped might help save us from ourselves, was being shown to express the same character flaws, such as racism and misogyny, as its flawed human creators.

The news media had become a sensationalist echo chamber in which no one could even agree on what was *true* anymore. It was far more profitable to stoke our primal reactions by delivering shocking, if erroneous, statements in lieu of objective facts, and "*post-truth politics*" had become a proven strategy. Even the world of entertainment was stricken by disease; terrifying stories about impending dystopias played out on the big screen, and blood, violence and mayhem felt more welcome in movie theaters and in our homes than the female nipple. The endless war against terror had become big business and its ever-changing villain meant that war could now go on forever. Fervent nationalism was appearing all over the globe as displaced immigrants and climate refugees clashed with fearful citizens. Of course, governments were taking the chaotic opportunity to seize more control, all under the guise of *citizen protection,* while the people were more than happy to hand over power to anyone who promised to keep them safe. Fear of the future was running rampant; many people were too busy expressing false nostalgia over times that never even existed to notice as their democracy dissolved around them. Of course there were plenty of good things happening and people doing wonderful work but less people were talking about that stuff; it just wasn't *newsworthy. Goddamn, these were strange times!*

I tried to shake off the mood but it was just one of those days. Before dinner I called in to the first Manzanita phone meeting since before the holidays and it was immediately apparent that things weren't *"just fixing themselves"* like I'd hoped for. What's more, gossip about our squabbles had breached our gates and begun to spread throughout the valley. *"Oh, you're the people that are afraid of a beaver?"* a snarky neighbor had asked stoic Joel's girlfriend at a holiday potluck and she was fuming, certain that it had been Angela or her boyfriend spreading rumors. A local wildlife publication seized on the opportunity and published an issue with a happy beaver on its cover: "Under Threat in our Valley?" read the title of the article. While Manzanita wasn't explicitly mentioned it was obvious that our discussions had inspired it.

Things had quickly escalated beyond the beaver issue and now seemed impossible to reel back in. The already tense situation was aggravated by a time deadline on the loan that we'd taken from the former owners.

"We haven't found any new members to help pay off our debt, and while some of us might be willing to invest more to pay off the loan we are reluctant to do so without making some changes to our operating agreement and ownership percentages," Joel said. We all knew that this would almost certainly open a larger can of worms. Either way a financial and social breaking point was approaching.

The earlier members, including Teddy Bear Gabe and Earth Mama Angela, were environmentally sensitive but weren't as financially stable as the members who'd joined the project later on.

These latter members, Joel, his girlfriend and a few others included, had more funds and had already funded the majority of the project, but felt that their voices were being marginalized. I'd joined the project somewhere in between these two groups and had enough money to cover my share but not enough to help float the loan. So a conversation began about how to value the various zones and structures on the property as a means to "equalize" our investments in a more equitable way. Rather than focus on what was working or how to improve the new property, we were locked in debates over who said what and how to clean up this mess that we'd gotten ourselves into. And we thought we'd been so *intentional*! So here we go again. From living in boarding schools to artist colonies to community organizing and running social events, and now to a rural commune, my life was apparently destined to be a relentless experiment in community life. And each time, the reality of humans' inability to collaborate nicely seemed to get in the way of the dream. Despite a string of challenging situations and difficult characters I seemed unable to expunge whatever insane character trait was fueling this recurring madness.

Thankfully the call eventually ended and I left Bigfoot to meet up with Blaze, who I hoped would take my mind off things. We went for dinner at a delicious vegan restaurant called La Bruja. As we waited for our food the conversation moved fluidly between science, technology and religion.

"Most religions are archaic, man. They use stories that are thousands of years old yet still people expect them to have the same influence over us. To be as relevant. That's ridiculous! All over the world the old paradigm is crumbling and belief structures are falling away." He was on another roll.

"I'm with you," I said. "But what comes next? I mean, religion has filled an important role throughout history, so without it what fills the void?"

"That's the question, man. Science and technology are great, but logic and reason can't do it all. Besides, have you ever talked with a hardcore scientist? The mixture of staunch, unwavering belief in their style of thought? Skepticism for those that don't share their philosophy? Fear of entertaining ideas that don't fit with their methods? Does any of *that* at all sound religious to you? Have you ever listened to someone from Silicon Valley outline their vision for a technological utopia? The way that technology seems to have an answer for every problem? Have you ever thought that even though they're wearing T-shirts and jeans, they have the same dogmatic eyes of those Hare Krishnas selling you books in the park? I'm telling you man, humans just can't help but repeat things from the past, especially the things that don't work. Man, it's like we're locked in cultural déjà vu."

"Well, I'd say that reason and the scientific method are pretty good starting points." After all, I'd known many scientists, and while some of them were certainly a little set in their ways, many were still open to the more esoteric realms, at least behind the scenes.

"I agree. Many of us were taught to hate science from an early age so it's a tough sell for some but come on, it got us to the moon! Science will get us to Mars and technology might just be the thing that saves us from ourselves BUT we can't forget about our hearts as we pursue our heads. And we can't throw out the mystical just because it doesn't fit in our models. Scientific models don't explain everything anyway. Dark energy? Quantum behavior? Shit, our own consciousness?! No one's got a clue how those things work. If we don't act at least a little humble to the mysteries of the world then we run the risk of becoming just as fanatical as anyone else."

"Sign me up, buddy!" And he was right. Religion is certainly in need of an upgrade and yet there are still many aspects of all world religions that can be salvaged. There is so often this tendency for humans to want to throw everything out with the bathwater, burn it all down and start again, hoping for a different result. When instead, with a little curiosity and patience, we can explore different schools of thought and combine the best of the old and the best of the new, ushering in a new reality, born through the blending of models and beliefs. How we treat each other, how we coexist, how we believe in something greater than just our own little world. How can we *feel* why we're here, not just *think* about why we're here?

"Here's to Spirituality 2.0!" I said and we fist-bumped in solidarity.

I said goodbye to Blaze almost in the exact place in the central square where we'd met the previous day and as I walked home I thought about the interaction. He was obviously a total nut, that was for sure, and I appreciated that about him. In many ways it didn't matter so much what was true and what wasn't, so much as it mattered that we were able to talk about things freely without bristling or feeling like our psychological sovereignty was being threatened. If someone talks about crop circles you may or may not believe them, but when you suddenly feel a tightening up in your entire being, or desire to dismiss them as a lunatic, what does that say about you? Is dismissal the best way to communicate with our fellow humans? Does the propagation of an us-versus-them dynamic make them feel more connected *or further pushed away?* There's almost always some way to connect with another person, some common ground in our humanity, and as soon as we find it we can begin to establish a basis for connection.

If we can talk about our different beliefs and philosophies and learn how to be tolerant with others who might not share our worldview then maybe we might just learn how to get along. Yes, the world might be falling apart, but in the meantime there's still everyday life. What are we spending our time and energy on? What kind of food and media are we putting into our bodies and minds? How do we speak to ourselves and how do we speak to others? What energy do we bring into our families and jobs and what are we creating with our limited time here?

There are a million possible ways that it will all fall apart, and while the dystopian future warnings should be acknowledged let's make sure to pay extra special attention to the present moment. Let's be grateful for what's working, for what we have, because if it's all an illusion anyway, we might as well make it a pleasant one. And who knows, if things go well then one day we might still get invited to join the intergalactic federation of light beings after all.

12. Sweet, Sweet Rio Dulce

Seven strangers had been stuffed into the back of the rickety pickup truck. They sat facing one another, crammed onto two rows of the most uncomfortable benches you could imagine. There was no backrest, just a horizontal metal pole positioned in such a way that every pothole, which seemed to be the main feature on this dark jungle road, threatened to dislodge vertebrae or sever spinal columns completely. *And yet everyone was smiling with joy.*

That morning, still in a travel-slump from the tropical flu that I couldn't seem to shake, I had caught a shuttle bus from Bigfoot Hostel in Antigua to Lanquín, the closest town to the tiny village of Semuc Champey; I'd gone on a whim and didn't know much more about the place other than that it was adjacent to some pristine limestone pools that had recently been opened up to tourists. The shuttle bus had driven northeast through curvy, quease-inducing Guatemalan roads while I sat there, a bleary-eyed, nauseous, sniffling mess, blowing large amounts of organic material into an already soggy handkerchief. But otherwise I felt great; I was back on the road.

It was a chaotic scene when we arrived at the Lanquín bus stop but I soon found my connecting ride to my hostel—the very same pickup truck that was now hurtling through the jungle. I was headed to a place called Greengo's Hostel, on the advice of Zoe, the voluptuous Dutch girl whom I'd met a couple of days earlier in Antigua. Connecting with strangers is something that I do quite well, probably a result of being dropped into new cultures and schools repeatedly as a young boy. Sometimes finding common ground is challenging and yet sometimes it's so effortless, almost like you're meeting old friends again. This particular group of backpackers, crammed into this old truck in the middle of the Guatemalan jungle, was a perfect example of just how easy it can be. Together we traveled through the darkness, breaking from our incessant laughter only briefly as we crossed a hazardous bridge that was in severe need of some new wooden planks. And so began the memorable adventures of Semuc Champey, the most unexpectedly picturesque and entertaining time I'd had so far in Guatemala.

Almost an hour later, our spines thoroughly readjusted, we arrived at Greengo's and descended through a prison-like cinder block tunnel, crowned in various sections with barbwire. It was a little disconcerting but we soon emerged into a welcoming reception area where we met the friendly owners of the hostel, a couple of Israeli guys. After checking in we asked them about the best way to see the sights. They suggested we take their 200Q (USD$30) tour that set out the following morning. After some deliberation—after all, backpackers are a frugal bunch—we accepted their offer. We were given towels and showed us to our seven dollar-a-night dorm rooms, where our new group of friends bonded over some Guatemalan hibiscus-flavored alcohol called Quetzalteca. Our merry band of scoundrels included five women, an Israeli, a German, a Spaniard, an Australian and a Dutch, as well as three guys, me, a firefighter from Montana, and a Scottish accountant who didn't like his job very much. Over rounds of the syrupy concoction I regaled them with the story of my San Pedro volcano experience.

"That's crazy. Have you tried it? Maybe it's not acid!" the Israeli woman, whose name was Nama, said suspiciously.

"Oh yes, we tested it at Cosmic Convergence."

"And …?" Was the collective response.

"And it is definitely acid. *Excellent acid,*" I informed them. "So I know tomorrow's tour is already going to be great but perhaps it would be a wise decision for us to take some before we head out in the morning?"

"Well, that's an intriguing offer," the Scottish fellow, whose name was Michael, said. "How long does it last?"

"It comes on in about an hour. Then there's a peak a couple of hours after that and the effects mostly wear off after eight to ten hours."

"That's long!" the Israeli woman said.

"We'd be back to normal just in time for some of Greengo's homemade Israeli cooking." Which apparently they were famous for.

"That sounds fun. I'm in!" the German woman said, with a mischievous smile. Her name was Stella. She was tan, slim and in great shape. Her short shorts, which I'd first noticed in the truck, showed off her strong calves and well-toned thighs. Her green eyes, which filled me with the zeal of a temple looter, squinted when she smiled, forging the crow's-foot wrinkles that often appear as a smiley person reaches their mid-thirties. I imagined her with a whip and a pistol strapped to her thigh, like a Germanic Lara Croft. I was instantly attracted to Stella and her willingness for adventure made me even more so.

A couple of the others also expressed interest, so before heading to our cozy bunks I made plans to meet them in the dining room just before breakfast. My blanket was thin but the bed was comfortable and I soon fell asleep to the rhythmic buzzing sounds of the jungle. The following morning I woke to a beautiful misty scene outside the screened windows. I got dressed and ventured out into the sunshine.

Greengo's by daylight presented a bizarre aesthetic mix: brightly painted wooden walls clashed with concrete and steel stairways, angular cabins were met with natural bamboo details, and rather out-of-place graffiti murals of varying quality decorated the place. Greengo's smorgasbord of style was set alongside a gurgling stream, which meandered its way down from green hills and through a rural farming valley. But despite the prison-like entrance and ADD design style, our Israeli hosts were attentive and friendly and by 8 a.m. were already up and taking breakfast orders.

Four of us had gathered in the dining room, me, Michael the Scot, Nama the Israeli, and Stella the German. Stella was even more lovely by daylight, wearing a tank top and her same demure smile. We ordered breakfast and while we waited, I dropped a full dose of liquid LSD onto the back of each of their hands. We placed them in the center.

"May the day be filled with magic, mystery and of course … *a little mischief!*" I said. We licked the tiny drops off of our skin and I raised my mug of coffee.

"Salud!"

"Salud!" they all replied in unison.

The rest of the crew soon gathered and after a breakfast of shakshuka and freshly baked pitas we packed up our day packs and reconvened at the reception.

"Okay, everyone have water, snacks, camera?" asked Cornelio in a thick Guatemalan accent. He was in his mid-twenties, skinny with long hair and wore a soccer T-shirt that looked like he'd been wearing it for a long, long while. Cornelio was to be our guide for the day. Everyone was ready. "Okay, then, let's go!"

And so our band of humorous day-trippers set out, lulled by the promise of hidden caves, lazy rivers, jungle trails and the natural beauty of the local mineral pools. We'd all chosen to stay at Greengo's instead of the nearby town of Lanquín for the same strategic reason; rather than having to drive the bumpy forty-five minutes in the morning, Greengo's guests could walk directly to the caves and pools which meant that we arrived before any other tour groups.

As we walked over the hill and down to the river, we were greeted by a bunch of little girls selling small, flat, silver discs. It was homemade chocolate, which they wrapped in tinfoil sheets and then sold to tourists who they intercepted enroute to the local attractions.

"Buy chocolate! Two for five quetzals! My name is Sandra!" said one of them, running up to me. This worked out to be around forty cents each so I bought four, forking over a twenty quetzal note, and sharing them with my friends. They were sweet, granular and infused with a distinct cardamom flavor.

"Buy chocolate! Two for ten quetzals! My name is Rita!" another girl said a little further down the path. She was barely eight years old.

"Oh, no, thank you, I already bought some from Sandra."

"How much did you buy them for?" Rita asked, dejected but curious. I told her.

"Well, maybe later you buy from me. I give you *five* for twenty quetzals!" She offered before strutting off defiantly.

As we crossed the rickety bridge, the same one with gaps large enough to swallow a person, a rabble of young boys ran over to meet us.

"Hello, my name is Pedro. Buy cold beer! You pay later!" the first yelled, followed by competitive deals from the rest of them. Apparently we'd just met the chocolate girls' brothers, the beer boys. No one really felt like a beer at 9:30 a.m. so we made our way through the boisterous throng, arriving at the entrance of the park just as the acid started kicking in. Nama was giggling and the rest of us were smiling like loons. Cornelio paid our entrance fee and instructed us to put anything that wasn't waterproof into a locker. He looked at me and said I wouldn't need sunglasses, which I gave up somewhat reluctantly, convinced that my pupils, which must have been the size of saucers, would blow my cover.

We were each given a small, thin candle. *And that's when I realized that I had no idea about what was involved on this tour.* From the pictures I loosely knew it involved some caves and natural swimming holes. So here I was beginning to trip pretty hard, wearing only hiking boots and a swimming suit and holding a candle with no clue what was going to happen next. Cornelio led us up a path to the mouth of the caves.

"Hey, strong man," Cornelio pointed to me. "I lead the front; you lead the back."

"Sure!" I said, more confidently than I felt. Once inside Cornelio proceeded to light our candles. "And don't let your candle go out. It's the only light we have." I was giddy with a mix of fear and excitement as our group of nine brave adventurers embarked into the darkness.

Within a minute we were up to our necks in water, swimming through a network of pitch-black caves, holding our candles as high above the surface as we could. After a while it became shallow again and the group gathered on a flat, rocky area. Stalactites hung from the ceiling and Cornelio ran his fingers along one; they came away dark. Without saying anything he turned to Stella, raised his fingers and made two warrior marks on her cheeks. One by one we each got tribalized by the flickering light of our candles. The air was humid and the walls of the cave seemed to have a life of their own, flexing and morphing as the LSD played tricks with my mind.

"Okay, we made it through the easy part." Cornelio smirked. "Now time to be more careful. Watch your step." Michael looked at me, his eyes wide with a mix of excitement and terror.

"This is so intense, Dougie!" he whispered at me.

"You're doing great!" I whispered back. I gave him a smile and the thumbs up and we were off again, back into the cool, dark water.

We continued through caves and up ladders, eventually coming to a fifteen-foot waterfall. Cornelio reached into the gushing water and pulled out a rope.

"Okay, you go." He pointed at Chad, the firefighter. Chad handed Cornelio his candle and clutching the rope while searching for footholds, he slowly made his way up the waterfall and soon arrived safely at the top. I was next; presumably Cornelio wanted Chad and me at the top to help people with the last part of the climb, which seemed the most treacherous. As I began climbing, I was laughing so nervously that I swallowed a bunch of water and almost lost both of my contact lenses to the cascading flow. I blinked them back into place, trying to get a handle on myself. One by one we each passed our candle to Cornelio and made it up the waterfall until only Stella and Nama remained. On her second step Nama slipped and Cornelio instinctively grabbed her, extinguishing all of the candles that he'd been holding. The whole cave grew almost instantly dark, lit only by Stella's candle, which she now clutched with both hands, her face flickering in the dim light. At that moment I saw through Stella's tough German veneer, which had cracked open to expose a softer, more terrified side of her. It made me want to hug her and tell her it was all going to be OK. Instead Cornelio broke the silence.

"Don't worry! Stay cool, everyone!" He made sure Nama got up to safety before returning to Stella. "No problem, see?" he said as he used her candle to relight the others that he was clutching. He pointed at the waterfall, but she didn't move.

"I'm not giving up my candle!" Stella said defiantly, her tough veneer beginning to return.

"Okay, then we can use the ladder if you like." Everyone laughed as Cornelio led Stella around the side of the waterfall to a hidden passageway where they climbed up a rickety ladder to meet the rest of us.

After some more precarious situations, including Cornelio birthing us through tight spaces and jumping off a rocky ledge into a pool of pitch blackness, we circled back to the cave's entrance.

"One of the things I appreciate most about developing countries is the lack of safety standards," Michael said as we returned to the mouth of the cave.

"There's no way in hell they would get away with this back home."

"Seriously!" I agreed. "Everyone would be wearing life jackets and helmets and the whole thing would be regulated into monotony." We emerged into the warm sunlight and chirping jungle just as a couple of other tour groups were arriving. Permasmiling faces covered in stalactite muck, we must have been a real sight to behold.

"Watch out for cave sharks!" I hollered to the approaching group, much to the surprise of a young Asian couple, as we passed by. Everyone laughed as we descended the path, through the jungle and back down to the river.

After killing some time on a questionably safe rope swing, we were each given an inner tube for the river. Mine was laughably small and barely kept me afloat as I pushed off the shore into the crystal blue water. After some minutes of slowly floating downstream we spotted the horde of beer boys from the bridge who were now jumping into the river and pelting us with unopened beer cans.

"Buy beer, pay later, my name is Jose!" hollered one boy, whose cans had landed close to me. Even though I was still cold from the caves and not really in the mood for beer I was so impressed by his tenacity that I bought one for myself and one for Cornelio. Both the cans had "Jose" written on them in waterproof black marker, presumably so they know which little salesman you owed money to or in case they needed to be recovered further downstream. After we'd passed the beer-boy brigade we floated for a while longer, avoiding the low-hanging, cobwebby branches near the edge, until we found a good spot to go ashore. We hiked back up the river, settled our debts with the beer boys and returned our inner tubes.

"Extra-large tube, for extra-large guy!" Cornelio said as I handed my tiny tube back to him. His local guide buddies laughed.

"Very funny! Thanks guys!" I was suddenly aware that I'd been the subject of their practical joke.

We continued up the river path until we emerged onto a rocky outcrop in front of a wide and perfectly clear waterfall. Blue and orange butterflies swirled around bright flowers and the mist of the waterfall cast small rainbows over the entire scene. I turned to Stella, whose lips were slightly parted, eyebrows raised and head shaking slowly in disbelief. Even though her facial bone structure seemed, in my mind, to have taken on a life of its own, she was still stunningly attractive and I smiled back, but also wondered how I must have looked to her. But it didn't matter; I was lost for words and all I could do was clench both my fists and repeat "YES!!!" emphatically like I'd just achieved something especially remarkable. We swam out to a rock and looked back at the spectacular view and watched as the rest of the group followed suit.

Lunch was a somewhat awkward affair. We'd walked back to Greengo's and Michael could barely sit still. Stella and Nama picked at their fried rice. Chad, on the other hand, who hadn't taken any psychedelics, was talkative and ate everyone's leftovers. I ordered a simple fruit plate and shared it with the other trippers, which they found to be more palatable than their fried offerings. Luckily we were soon off again, this time bound for the natural swimming pools. It was a steep climb, weaving up a damp and slippery mountain path and old Mayan stone steps. We clambered over rocks and up decaying wooden stairways that had been built over areas where the steps had been completely worn away. Eventually, sweaty and breathing heavily, we reached a lookout where we were rewarded with a spectacular view of the limestone pools below. This bright-blue series of terraced pools was the main attraction of Semuc Champey and had previously been a ceremonial location until the locals realized they could open the pools to tourists and charge a fee for entrance, a fact which I couldn't help but feel a little conflicted about.

After taking some pictures and feasting on melons and mangoes that were for sale near the lookout, we headed down to the pools for a respite from the afternoon heat. In some places the incredible force of the water had carved underground channels, hence the name *Semuc Champey*, which loosely translates to *"Where the river hides under the stones."* A short length of rope was all that was keeping us from the edge. Cornelio said the rope was a new safety addition since a few months earlier some unlucky French guy had fallen into the rocky, cavernous opening, his broken body only to be discovered when it was spat out a half a mile downriver. That story aside, we all had a delightful time.

We swam, splashed around in the rejuvenating water and explored the shallow lower pools until the sun went down. As we walked back to Greengo's we were once again flanked by the local chocolate girls who continued to hock their foil-wrapped disks. This time I bought some from Rita who, despite her age, seemed like one of the more successful of the young entrepreneurs. Her cinnamon-infused batch was a sugary and gritty treat.

By the time we all got back to Greengo's it felt like we were old friends, feasting on homemade hummus and falafel as we shared highlights from the day.

"I knew something was suspicious when none of you wanted to eat your lunch!" Chad said, apparently unaware that we'd taken the acid.

"We *told* you we were going to take it!" I said.

"Well, I didn't know you really had!" he exclaimed, laughing. To my surprise, most of the others hadn't known, either. While I'd thought we'd been pretty obvious it was a good reminder that *no one usually expects other people to be on psychedelics.*

"It was *so* amazing!" Nama said, her leg raised up on the chair opposite. Down her side was a long, increasingly purple bruise. On the walk back she'd been distracted on the treacherous bridge and had narrowly avoided falling into the river below, saved only because only one leg, not both, had slipped into the gap. Between almost falling off the waterfall, and then through the bridge, she'd had a rough day, but remained surprisingly upbeat.

"It was unbelievable," Michael said. "I feel clearer about everything. I'm going to go home and quit my job." We all laughed.

"What are you going to do instead?" Stella asked.

"I'm going to do what I love. I'm going to become a writer!" We all clapped. It was the Spanish woman's birthday and another bottle of Quetzalteca was brought out. We smoked spliffs, drank liquor and practiced salsa dancing with each other until the bottle was empty.

After the others went to bed, I sat with Stella on the balcony, looking over the moonlit valley. At first we talked about our travel plans; her main goal was to make her money last as long as she could. Then we talked about romance; she was tired of men objectifying her, so I decided *against* telling her about her starring role in my *Lara Croft Tomb Raider* fantasy. Instead we moved on to talking about working in foreign countries and we both fantasized about how fun it might be to start an adventure hostel one day.

"It'd be mainly healthy, but we'd still have some party time ..." I said.

"I love it! I can be the project manager!" she said as we sat laughing in the moonlight for another hour. If there had been a moment for romance, I had officially missed it and we finally retired, separately, to our bunks.

The following morning, after breakfast and lounging around in hammocks, I led a group yoga class to help us recover from the adventures of the preceding day. Afterwards I walked up the road with Sarah, the Australian woman from Greengo's, to a small house where we attended a chocolate-making class led by a local girl named Ana. Ana, who happened to be Sandra's older sister, outlined the entire process from raw bean to foil disk and said that Sarah could now join her team. Apparently I hadn't made the cut.

Most of us had decided to stay a third night before taking off on our next adventures. It was pizza night at Greengo's and over the deliciousness we talked about the state of the world and how privileged we all felt to be able to explore these spectacular places off the beaten track.

"How lucky we are to be able to come out here, to get out of our bubbles, to look back on where we came from, and to consider where we're going," I said. "The fact that we even get the opportunity to spend time thinking *about how we think*? How fortunate is that?" Everyone agreed. "Man, I feel like it's my obligation to share what I find out here with as many people as I can."

"Yeah, thanks for sharing the LSD, at least!" Nama squealed and everyone laughed as one of the Israeli owners placed a few more bottles of beer in front of us.

"So what's the deal with all the barbed wire and concrete?" Stella, fueled by a few beers and feeling curious, asked him.

"For the safety of our guests," he said.

"Have there been any threats or hostility from the locals?" I asked.

"No," he replied. "*Because we have the barbed wire!*" We didn't press him any further. Was there an actual threat? After all, sometimes these slices of paradise felt safer than they actually were. Or was this the effect of bringing two ex-military brothers from a country where conflict was such a part of the national identity?

Early the following morning we caught the pickup truck back to Lanquín and from there we scattered into smaller groups. Some of us were headed southwest toward Antigua, some north toward the ruins of Tikal, and the others southeast toward Rio Dulce, a supposedly relaxed location near the east coast of Guatemala. Stella,

Michael and Nama had all decided to go to Rio Dulce, so on a whim I decided to change my route from Tikal so I could join them instead. It was a good opportunity to let instinct guide me and see what happens when I didn't *over*plan. I also had developed a nice little crush on Stella and wasn't quite ready to let her go just yet. I smiled at the strange way the world works, realizing that I never would have met this delightful group of friends had I not gotten sick and had to delay my departure from Lake Atitlán.

It proved to be a smart decision; the trip wasn't too tough and that afternoon we arrived by shuttle at the pretty riverside town of Rio Dulce. We had lunch at a waterside café where we learned about a hostel nestled deep in the mangroves, accessible only by boat. The place had great reviews so we hopped in a boat that offered to take us there. Casa Perico was run by a German expat named Peter and the hostel was immaculately rugged. A series of raised boardwalks extended into the surrounding mangrove jungle, branching off to a variety of accommodations that were built on stilts to avoid flooding from the swell of the river in the wet season. After checking in, we borrowed the rowboats that Peter made available to guests and rowed out of the mangroves and over to a platform on the river that provided a peaceful place to spend the rest of the afternoon. Later that evening, after an early dinner we all retired to the mosquito-covered dorm beds above the dining room.

I used the following morning to catch up on communications and spent some time researching what it would take to buy a motorcycle as there seemed to be plenty of cheap ones for sale. However, it seemed that in order to take any vehicle across the border it would need to be registered in my name and unfortunately registration would take a few weeks. I cursed myself for not researching these details when I'd first arrived in Guatemala. I had received my motorcycle license seven years earlier, with the loose plan to Che Guevara my way around South America but had ultimately ended up abandoning the costly plan, opting instead to take buses and hitchhike through Argentina, Chile and Bolivia. So I hadn't actually *ridden* a motorcycle since getting my license but the dream of two-wheeled freedom was still alive and I remained intent on making it happen on this trip.

That afternoon we decided to take a boat back to the center of Rio Dulce and explore the surrounding area. We caught a bus that had a bunch of chickens on it, apparently headed to market, hopping off a short while later to find a hot-flowing waterfall west of town. The waterfall turned out to be hotter than any shower I'd had in the last few weeks so we took our time in the water, sharing stories and insights from our different cultures.

"We're like the foot soldiers of diplomacy," Michael said in the accent of a youthful Sean Connery. "Building bridges between people from different backgrounds and cultures. Doing our best to be good representatives for our countries along the way." We all nodded.

"I love coming to places which people at home tell you are unsafe only to find that they are often much more friendly and safe than you were told!" Nama replied. Everyone agreed.

"And I love moments like this," I said as we stood with our backs to the waterfall's edge, letting the warm water cascade over our shoulders. "Surrounded by new friends, experiencing something magical. I take pictures with my mind so I can return to these moments whenever I want in the future." I raised up an invisible camera to my face, closed one eye as I framed the others. "Say cheesy!"

It had been a sweet time in the eastern Guatemalan town of Rio Dulce. On our last day we rowed Casa Perico's old boats back out to the swimming platform one final time where I taught a wobbly yoga class. Meanwhile my flirtations with Stella had progressed nicely and by that evening we were cuddled up together on the couch. At one point the electricity went out, which seemed to be a regular evening occurrence, so we took advantage of the sudden privacy to pull even closer, giggling as the lights came back on. I think we both knew it was borrowed time, which made our connection all the more sweet. That night a storm hit Rio Dulce and we shared her small dorm bed, making out like teenagers and enjoying each fleeting moment.

The next morning our merry band parted ways. Michael was bound for Honduras, where he planned to write about the political upheaval that had been brewing for a couple of months. Police and private security forces were clashing with citizens who were protesting a disputed presidential election that they claimed was "stolen" by the victor, Juan Orlando Hernandez. Stella and Nama were going back the way I'd just come from, toward Antigua and then over to Lake Atitlán. My heart wanted to remain with Stella but my head told me it didn't make sense to return to the same place I'd just come from, so I'd planned to continue east instead. I wanted to explore

Livingston, a port town on the eastern coast of Guatemala where the Garifuna Afro-pirate culture was still very much alive, the last place of its kind in the country. And from there I had no plan. Four weeks into my trip and I was entering into the "wander and discover mode," seeking out the raw and rough edges, finding hidden paths that lead to unpredictable interactions and untamed natural beauty. Michael was right, in places like this, the adventurous can enjoy experiences that would never be permitted in the developed world. Caving by candlelight, slippery jungle ladders, navigating bridges with missing planks, buses shared with farm animals ... *the vibrance of a life less regulated!*

As I drifted off to sleep, intertwined in the arms of this strong German woman, I thought about how the more I learned to communicate from my heart, the more I was able to quickly and authentically connect with others, and when the feeling was reciprocated, it felt like falling in love over and over again. The sweetest new friendships pop up along the road in the form of these smiling international gems. To travel is to experience a life lived in the moment.

While some moments bring you together, other moments offer the practice of non-attachment. And so the lessons continue, to deeply connect, only to disperse amid hugs, a volley of information and future aspirations, as we continue our ephemeral journey along the open road.

13. Boat Of Malcontent

By the time I woke up, the others had already left and I was alone.

"Let's meet up again soon for more adventures. Maybe come visit me in Oregon sometime?" I had said sleepily to Stella as she had said goodbye.

"To be continued ..." she whispered in my ear as she gave me a final kiss. Parting is indeed such sweet sorrow, I thought as I drifted back to wild dreams of exploring the world with my Germanic Lara Croft.

Michael and Nama had also left on the early boat back to Rio Dulce, so after breakfast I packed up in silence and waited for a boat that was heading the opposite direction, toward the coast. Instead of excitement, I felt a longing for my new friends, aware of a sudden vacuum where previously there had been lively connection and laughter.

A while later I was on a boat bound for Livingston, sharing my feelings with a Canadian guy named Brian.

"Sometimes it happens when travelling, buddy. You wonder if you'd be happier if you did something else, went somewhere else, or were with someone else," Brian said.

"I like people, don't get me wrong, but I need to feel free," I replied. "Even when things are going well, I just can't help but wonder *what comes next?* What else is out there? This explorative nature can draw people toward me just as easily as it can push them away. And so I develop these shallow relationships, cut short by a desire to explore new locations, new communities and new behaviors. And maybe that's just how I am?"

"Maybe," Brian continued. "And it's not necessarily wrong, either. Are you driven by excitement and curiosity, or are you driven by something else? Perhaps fear of intimacy or some insecurity?" To be honest, I wasn't always sure. At times my actions felt driven by excitement, while at other times they were driven by an underlying anxiety, a discomfort with my surroundings, whoever or whatever they might be.

"Sometimes it's hard to know," I admitted. "Anyway, sometimes relationships just run their course, you know? It's time to move on. I don't carry any hard feelings, that is just how it is." As the words came out of my mouth I wondered if this was fair, kind or even *true*.

"How do you think that makes people feel?" Brian asked.

"In the past, when I drifted away, some friends took my behavior personally," I replied. "Sometimes, much later on, they told me that they felt rejected and I hadn't even realized it. But it was rarely ever about them. Sure, I felt guilty that they felt bad but that doesn't really inspire me to rekindle the relationship. The relationships that work best for me are the ones that pick right back up where they left off, rather than the ones that dwell on how things *used* to be. Let's talk about all the things that we've been up to and the things that we're excited about, you know?"

"And how would it make you feel to be on the other side of the relationship? If you felt rejected for not being so fun and exciting all the time?"

"Good question. Probably not great." It was true and I felt my heart pang for a moment; yes, I'd certainly been on the receiving end before. The whole situation was made even more hurtful in this new era of social media where you are still "connected" so can see when an estranged friend *reads* your messages but chooses not to *respond*. I might try to tell myself that they are just busy, and maybe that's true, or maybe they'd cast me aside just as thoughtlessly as I had cast others aside. "Well, maybe I'm just an insensitive bastard who can't seem to maintain close relationships!" I said, half-joking and half-beginning to feel like this might be true.

"Ha! Or maybe it's completely natural and humans aren't built to handle so many relationships!" Brian laughed as we approached the port of Livingston.

"Anyway, don't beat yourself up about it, buddy. You can't be friends with everyone."

By the time we reached our destination my sore throat was back with a vengeance, revived by the relentless wind and damp travel conditions of the journey. Livingston, a town only accessible by boat, is a colorful mix of cultures set among deserted beaches and crumbling architecture. The Garifuna, who make up a large part of the population, are said to be descended from pirates and slaves that had escaped from boats bound to other parts of the Americas. Brian and I walked away from the dock, passing walls covered in murals, and found a backpacker's hostel called Casa de Iguana. It wasn't yet noon but a group of young backpackers had already started some drinking games and Brian decided to join them. Instead I decided to go for a walk to find a local gym that I'd heard about. I dropped my belongings in a cramped dorm room and headed back toward the dock and up the main street.

"Hey, you look cool, mon!" an old Garifuna man who was leaning up against his bicycle said to me.

"Thanks man, you do, too." His knit hat contained a vast amount of dreadlocks and he had a smile on his face and a twinkle in his yellowed eyes.

"Where are you going to?" he asked.

"I heard there was a gym around here?" I replied.

"Ain't no gym anymore, mon," he said. "Besides, that ain't no way to explore Livingston! Let's walk and talk!"

And that was how I found the fascinating character known as Philip Flores. Or perhaps he'd found me? At first appearance, wearing tattered clothes and shoes I had almost dismissed him as a homeless man but as the discussion continued he turned out to be an incredibly sharp and socially engaged local resident. "Come with me and let me take you on a tour to see *behind the scenes*, the REAL Livingston, mon."

For a moment I considered whether or not this was a good idea. He didn't feel threatening and there were plenty of people around so I wasn't concerned for my safety. "Sure, why not?"

We walked down the main street and after a while veered off into some narrow alleys, through backyards and past rickety structures. I wondered where he was taking me but everyone we passed said hello to him, which kept my safety concerns at bay. Any remaining suspicions dissolved when we passed a backyard playground and one of the kids came up to give him a first bump.

"Hey, little man!" he laughed as the child scampered back to the janky rusty swings.

"Why do so many things look in disrepair," I asked, noting the broken roofs and general disorder that was visible in every direction.

"Hurricane, mon! People don't have no money to repair things." Philip told me that a big hurricane had recently hit and the town was still recovering from the destruction, giving it a raw, gritty feel.

Along the way he shared stories of hanging out with Jerry Garcia and the Grateful Dead, and Ken Kesey, the writer and Merry Prankster, when they had come to visit Livingston back in the seventies. Apparently, they enjoyed his company so much that they had even flown him out to Oregon to visit them. He'd since been an avid supporter of the Ducks, an ice hockey team, so was excited to hear that I was from Oregon, and then somewhat disappointed that I wasn't more aware of the team's current status. I changed the topic by asking him about the Garifuna and their way of life.

"All is not well in Livingston, mon. What they don't tell you in your guidebooks is that we're still oppressed. Believe that!" We had woven through a maze of tightly packed houses onto an open grassy area overlooking the coast. In the middle was a cross and we stood there talking for a while, looking out onto structures that appeared to be either falling apart or half-built, it was hard to tell.

"The other local people, they don't hire us black people for jobs. Everyone walks by each other, nice enough, sure, but these people don't care about us. Even the government isn't helping repair after the hurricane. It's like we're a forgotten place." It made me think of Puerto Rico, which had recently been hit with a super hurricane and largely left by the U.S. government to fend for itself.

"That must be rough. Well, I feel grateful to have found you and gotten the behind-the-scenes tour!"

"You are lucky, mon, cause it's my day off!" He smiled.

"What do you do for work?" I asked.

"This, mon. Behind-the-scenes tours. I'm in *Lonely Planet.*" I laughed. And then he pulled out a piece of paper from his pocket, a photocopy of a page from the *Lonely Planet* guidebook, and sure enough there was his name, the first mention under the "Top Things to do in Livingston": "Get a tour with Philip Flores, should you be lucky enough to find him." He laughed as he read it out loud before carefully folding up the paper and putting it back in his pocket. He told me about what he was up to in the community and asked for a donation to his charitable project that helped feed local children so I gave him USD$20. I felt happy that rather than ignore him and pass on by I had stopped to listen and been able to share this special interaction with this old, weathered Rastafarian.

Before we parted ways he pointed me in the direction of a cemetery that I'd been interested in visiting. The Livingston deceased are encased in concrete and buried above ground in brightly colored tombs so when the floods come the bodies won't dislodge and float to the surface. Many of the tombs were disintegrating, their jagged, concrete edges hanging precariously over eroded earth. The only other person in the cemetery was a Swiss woman, who I struck up a conversation with and agreed it was a rather bizarre place. We were going the same direction so continued on together, walking up a largely deserted beach, past some beachside bars that looked abandoned except for the occasional scrawny-looking jungle chicken. Further north we followed a path that led away from the beach to some unimpressive waterfalls and pools called The Seven Altars. There we discovered a decorated hut centered around an altar upon which was resting a painting of a very black Jesus, head adorned with dreadlocks and holding a cross. The caretaker of the shrine didn't seem overly thrilled to see us so we didn't stay too long. On the walk back I realized that there wasn't really a lot happening in Livingston and that the best thing for my mood was probably to keep moving on as swiftly as possible. The protests in Honduras, which Michael had gone to write about were causing road and border shut downs and besides, the weather in the Bay Islands was looking like endless rain so it made the most sense to head into Belize and continue northward. From northern Belize I could re-enter Guatemala to visit the Mayan ruins at Tikal, where I wanted to learn more about Mayan history.

I got back to the Iguana just as the evening drinking games were getting underway. The game amounted to downing shots of rum to win points for your country, the score being tallied on a blackboard behind the bar. Brian, who was already slurring his speech, was well on the way to achieving a win for Canada. Meanwhile, a rather plump young woman was in the small pool splashing around in all her clothes. I wasn't really feeling the scene. I'd heard from Philip Flores that there was some live music nearby so after a shower decided to leave the drunken festivities of the Iguana and walk into town to find it. Back at the main street I strolled by a café where two attractive women were eating ice cream and drinking champagne. I liked everything about that scene.

"Hey, I recognize you!" I said to one of them. I didn't really but this was my go-to line when I wanted to break the ice but couldn't think of anything more imaginative.

"Maybe, from the boat?" one said in a French accent. "Did you arrive from Belize this morning?"

"Hmmm, no. I arrived from Rio Dulce," I replied. "I'm on my way to Belize tomorrow, though. But funny, you look familiar!"

"And maybe not," she said, smiling. I decided to change the topic.

"Well, I'd love to ask you some questions about Belize. Perhaps I could join you for an ice cream?"

They laughed, almost certainly aware of my ploy but invited me to join them nonetheless. The women were both in their late-twenties and turned out to be a humorous pair. One was obviously the wild one while the other was more sensible. As they told me their stories from Belize it was obvious that the sensible one, Claire, consistently had to keep Elise from getting into trouble. Story after story, Claire would roll her eyes as she recalled the mischievous actions of her friend.

"If Elise wasn't climbing statues in the public square, she was getting drunk with locals or smoking pot in the church bell tower!" Claire said.

"Mais non! I wasn't so bad!" Elise exclaimed. She was a woman, but still maintained the insubordinate nature of youth; even without knowing her for more than a few minutes I felt sorry for what she'd no doubt put her poor parents through. Elise had the kind of eyes that you might see in an untamed stallion that simply will not allow its spirit to be broken. Even her lustrous brown hair, which was clipped up at the back, resembled a mane as she tossed it around, laughing and seemingly impervious to the dismay of her friend.

After we'd finished the ice cream and champagne Elise said she wanted to go to the dance clubs on the beach. Claire said she wanted to go to sleep so we walked her back to her hostel. And then of course, being the gentleman that I am, I offered to accompany Elise and we strolled off toward the beach. In addition to being a wild woman she was also an exceptionally gifted photographer, and seemed to be able to capture the most candid and intriguing images of local people on her smartphone with a quick, barely noticeable flick of her wrist.

After being caught trying to sneak into a surprisingly fancy quinceañera, Elise's idea of course, we escaped the bouncers by fleeing down an alley. We circled back to the main road and followed the music to the rougher side of town, where even though it was already past midnight the party was only just getting started. Over the next few hours, we danced at a few of the beach clubs. They were mostly filled with locals who were smoking copious amounts of ganja and getting super freaky on the dance floor. I'm not talking just dirty dancing—the women were literally propped up against walls, men relentlessly grinding against them. The night was hot and only a small amount of clothing was keeping people from having full-on sex on the dance floor. Elise loved it and true to form acted completely, and wonderfully, inappropriate. She would dance into the middle of the gyrating couples, twerking her way up against the women. She would flirt with the men, only to grab their large joints right out of their fingers to steal some puffs. Elise proceeded to get stupendously high. By about 2 a.m. I felt all partied out and besides, I wanted to get some sleep before catching the ferry to Belize the following morning.

"Hey, I think I'm going to head out," I said to Elise.

"Okay, I'll come with you. Just let me get my things."

"Sure, I'll wait outside."

I waited. Ten minutes went by and no Elise. I peeked my head back in and perhaps unsurprisingly she was in the middle of yet another frenzy of action. Who was I to tame this wild child? She'd given me her phone number so I sent her a message, wishing her well, and wandered back to the Iguana. Surprisingly, Brian was still standing at the bar—well, half-standing at least—and when he eventually recognized me, he proudly slurred that he'd "Won for

Canada!" What a nut he was. But a nut with some wisdom. I thought back to our conversation earlier on the boat. Had I been a bad friend when I bailed on Elise tonight? Wait, had she bailed on me? Oh, fuck it, who cares? If everyone just took a little more care of themselves, we'd all be better off! "What a privileged white man thing to think, you asshole," I said out loud to myself as I stumbled up the steps to my dorm room.

Early the next morning I woke up and despite brushing my teeth twice I could still taste the rum in my throat as I loaded up my backpack. To my surprise Brian was also awake and looking remarkably pulled together. It turned out he and a friend he'd met at the Iguana were heading to Belize on the same boat so the three of us huffed it over to the ferry terminal.

At around 9 a.m., just as the boat was leaving the dock, I got a text message from Elise:

"I just got home!" it read. "We missed our boat to Rio Dulce and Claire is so mad at me. AGAIN! Haha! What a crazy night. I don't even remember when you left!" This was followed by a string of emoticons. I imagined her tossing her hair and laughing as she wrote it, as her friend Claire shook her head. I was glad to hear that she was at least safe and I replied to her message with a photo that I'd taken the previous night; it was of her, riding the smiling bartender like a horse. What a memorable mess of a wild stallion she was! And what a memorable twenty-four hours in the bizarre and gritty Garifuna town of Livingston.

14. Just Belize In Yourself

"Everyone needs a little loving, a little regular physical touch sometimes, you know?" Once again I was on a boat, lamenting my shadowy feelings to my new Canadian friend, Brian.

"True. And yet some people seem to need it *more* than others," Brian said with a hungover slur. He might be young, and he might have an alcohol problem, but nonetheless he was right.

I was sitting in the middle of the row and Brian was sitting on my left. And in between us was a passed-out local kid who couldn't have been more than eight years old, head on my shoulder and completely fast asleep.

"Yeah, I see that," I replied. "I mean take my dog, Tux. Weaned way too early—at four weeks, the shelter said. He wasn't much bigger than my fist when I got him and was so nervous that even an out-of-place cardboard box would spook him. Over time he relaxed a little, but to this day he's still pretty anxious."

"Yeah, buddy, what happens at the beginning of life has a big impact." Brian said.

"Did you ever hear about that Russian baby experiment?" I asked.

"No?"

"Well, I forget all the details, but basically they figured out if babies don't get enough physical contact in the days and weeks immediately after their birth they can die."

"No way, that's a fucked-up experiment," Brian said.

"Seriously. We're either not hugged enough or we're hugged *too* much. Either way, we all get messed up somehow. That's life, I guess." It wasn't a long ride and I looked out toward the approaching shore of Belize. The kid woke up and looked at me, a little embarrassed. "But it's not all nurture." I continued, "I mean, look at twins in a cradle. One's giggling and drooling on himself while the other is kicking and screaming. They might share genetics, but have tiny differences in the way their brains were formed."

"Maybe it's just their soul?" Brian asked.

"Yeah, science or spirituality? Or a mix. Still to be determined," I replied.

The shore was fast approaching and we'd soon be arriving at the Belizean port town of Punta Gorda. Brian had turned to his buddy to discuss the next part of their itinerary while I sat in a soup of my own misery and self-pity. Maybe it was the effects of my own hangover but I still couldn't shake my shadowy feelings. My inner voice jabbed at me, a familiar nagging, asking me just what the hell I thought I was doing with my life. "You're only running from yourself!" it said, and if the voice had a head it would have been shaking it disapprovingly. I thought back to a course that I'd taken a few years earlier called Dialectical Behavior Therapy (DBT), which was basically a more scientific name for mindfulness. I closed my eyes and reminded myself of the training. "You're doing just fine, buddy. You have everything you need. These feelings are temporary and in time they'll pass on by," I told myself, practicing some slow breathing to calm my nervous system down. "And hey, *at least your sinuses are finally clearing up,*" I thought, conjuring some humor to encourage my bitchy inner critic to fuck off.

"Where are you heading when we get to Belize?" Brian asked me, jolting me out of my mini meditation/depression showdown.

"I think I'm going to Placencia. I want to get up to Tikal in a week or so, and will cut across northern Belize. What about you?"

"We were thinking the same thing." Brian and his friend were chill, easygoing guys and it was probably a good idea to not isolate myself, especially not in this misery slump I was feeling, so we shared notes on bus timetables and places to stay.

In Punta Gorda, on the advice of a friendly local, we ran down the street to catch a chicken bus bound for Placencia. The bus was an old American school bus, one of many that are brought down here after they get retired in the U.S. They were named for the fact that there were often people travelling with chickens, which was apparently a regular thing in Central America. A twenty-something French girl called Annabelle had sat down behind me so we struck up a conversation. She was also going to Placencia so we invited her to join us.

Immediately, Belize felt cleaner and more civilized than Guatemala. Less trash and not so many hustlers trying to sell us stuff. After a slow, couple of hours' ride we were dropped at a small town called "Independence and Mango Creek." English is the national language of Belize and U.S. dollars are the accepted form of currency. From Independence and Mango Creek we paid a few bucks for a water taxi called the Hokey Pokey, which took us across a small stretch of water to nearby Placencia.

Placencia was immediately strange. It was a little *too* clean. While there were some relics of Garifuna culture, it felt sterilized. As we walked down a pedestrian pathway that ran parallel with the ocean, we passed vendors selling chintzy items like conch-shell earrings and tacky beaded bracelets with Rasta colors and words like "Ya Mon" woven into them. While there were some people of color, it seemed like most of the inhabitants were older expats, many of them looking rather despondent and miserable. As I passed one cheesy-looking American tourist I said hello but he didn't respond so I grabbed him by the shoulders, looked him in the face and yelled: "Wake up!"

Okay, I didn't actually do that, but goddamnit I wanted to, if only just to summon some sort of sign of life out of him. People like this were one of the problems with the world, I thought darkly. Here they are in a beautiful tropical place, bellies fat from eating and drinking too much, walking around like overweight, neo-colonial zombies.

"This place looks like it has a margarita happy hour!" Brian was smiling and pointing toward the beach at a way-too-scrubbed-clean restaurant called the Tipsy Tuna. "We should come back here after we find a place to stay, eh?" Goddamn Canadians, they're just so damn nice and easygoing all the time, I thought. I decided to hold my tongue and not tell everyone that Placencia felt like a beach resort that had been loosely inspired by Livingston, designed by Mickey Mouse and purged of all the black people. *Whoa, dude. Chill the eff out!* I told myself, aware that I was orbiting around a black hole of shittiness.

As we continued down the path we passed a group of drunk American women on a bachelorette vacation. I hated this place already. Most places were either booked or too pricey for our group. Turns out Belize was at least double the cost of Guatemala. A little further down we arrived at a place called Anda Di Hows which was literally under a crazy woman's house. But it was right on the beach and the lady was nice enough to make room for us.

"I have two spots left in the dorms for USD$20, a tent for USD$12 and a hammock for USD $10," she told us.

"I love hammocks!" Annabelle exclaimed, clapping her hands together.

"Well, I have a sleeping bag so I can take the tent," I offered.

"We'll take the bunks," Brian said, pointing at his buddy.

After we checked in, the Canadians and Annabelle went to the Tipsy Tuna for margaritas. Intent on reversing my mood I went to find a gym to get my blood flowing. I walked back out to the main road, to the first of two gyms that had popped up on my smartphone map. The first one brought me to a locked door on the second floor of an apartment building so I continued to the next option called "Evolution Gym," which sounded more promising. Eventually the route veered off the main road and down a residential street. I got to the end of the block and looked at my map, realizing that I'd somehow passed it. I retraced my steps to find a chain-link fence with a faded sign hanging from it. In the front yard of a rundown house sat two burly looking locals, smoking a large joint and taking apart an exercise bike.

"Welcome to Evolution, mon!" one said, waving me into the yard, I opened the gate and stepped inside. "You want some?" He offered me the joint.

"No thanks, just checking out the gym," I replied.

"Ya, mon! Check it out!" He handed the joint to his friend and approached me. "I'm Thomas, let me give you the tour!" Thomas proceeded to show me around a series of rusty equipment that lay strewn around his front yard. Some of the barbells were actually just metal poles that had been set in buckets of concrete on either end.

"And we also have classes!" Thomas said proudly. He pulled a dusty chalkboard from behind an unplugged fridge, revealing a list of scribbled activities. "Boxing, cycling, weightlifting …" he read. "What do you need, mon?!"

Evolution cost $10 a day and I thanked Thomas for the tour, indicating that I might return later. I was truly inspired by his enthusiasm, if not his gym, and I decided to walk back down the beach and find a place to do some yoga instead. After a while I walked by a dilapidated beach shack that looked incredibly out of place in between a newly remodeled house and some garishly painted beach huts. In comparison to its neighbors the shack, which was almost certainly abandoned, looked as if a creative beach spirit had blown together a rustic dwelling out of parts of other old shacks and some driftwood. But I liked it, it had a strong character, bucking the norm like a homeless person who stubbornly refused to leave Disneyland. So I stepped onto the creaky porch and peaked through the boarded-up windows. The living room was empty besides some bedding heaped in the corner and some trash strewn about the place. It looked like it might have been a squatter's residence but the porch was flat enough and had a great view so I laid down my mat and began my yoga practice.

I was mid sun salutation when a Rastafarian guy appeared from some trees next to the house and went into a side door. After a few minutes he came back out, returning from the way he'd come. He didn't really pay much attention to me so I just continued doing my yoga. As I was wrapping up, an older white couple straight out of the summer catalogue of J. Crew approached from the direction of the beach huts.

"We've never seen anybody on this porch before," the woman said. She was American. "Are you staying here?"

"No, it just seemed like a nice place to do some yoga."

"Oh, well *we* heard it used to be a drug den," the man said. "But we always thought it would make a nice property with a little clean-up and paint job."

"Let's take a look, honey," the woman said, strolling up onto the porch. They both peeked through the boards.

"Oh, this could be just *wonderful,*" the man said.

"Seems like there's a lot of development going on here," I said.

"Oh yes, we began buying property here ten years ago. It's really gotten *so much nicer*." She smiled, nodding at the gaudy huts. "We just finished renovating those," she said proudly. "Well, enjoy your yoga."

“Thanks,” I smiled. A fine example of neo-colonialism in progress, I thought to myself as they strolled off down the beach. But this time my judgment all felt lighter. The yoga had helped lift my mood.

I had told Brian and the others that I’d meet them at the Tipsy Tuna that evening so after a nap and a shower I headed back out. On my way to meet them I came across a pizza place called Chachi's. There was some great jazz music coming from upstairs so I ordered a slice and decided to explore. As I reached the top of the stairs the jazz band came into view and to my surprise I saw an old friend of mine, right at the back, drumming his heart out. His name was Chachi and somehow without making any plans I’d stumbled upon his restaurant! We saw each other and exchanged surprised smiles. After the show we went down to the bar to get a drink.

“What a surprise, man!” he smiled. “Seeing your face in the crowd. I heard through the grapevine that you were coming down here but forgot to follow up.”

“Haha, yeah, I knew that you were somewhere down here but forgot to find out where.”

“And here we are! Well, cheers!” Chachi raised his glass. I asked what he was doing here and it turned out he’d come down to visit and a friend of his had offered him the opportunity to run this place.

“It’s been fun. But it’s kind of a weird place. I think I’m getting ready to go home. Or just go somewhere else.”

“Yeah, it *is* a little weird. What’s the deal with the old white zombies?”

“Haha. Yeah, that’s one of the reasons this place isn’t quite what it used to be.” He laughed. “Some are expats. Others are property developers. Others are just escaping the winter. Whatever they are, many of them seem to be living out their days in a fog of the easily accessible pharmaceuticals.”

Chachi had to get back to work so I grabbed another slice and walked over to meet Brian and the others. The scene at the Tipsy Tuna was as cheesy as I expected but I was a few drinks in and my initial reaction was receding, replaced by more jovial inebriation. I found the Canadians, who had made friends with another couple of Canadians, two nice women, who were sitting at the table next to us.

After my third rum and coke, as I made my way over to the restroom, I locked eyes with a stunning tanned young lady and promptly walked right past her and into the restroom. As I stood at the urinal I amped myself up. "Don't overthink it, buddy. Just go say hello." I looked in the mirror, smoothed down my beard, pushed up my eyebrows and left the bathroom.

"Well, hey there," I said as I approached her.

"Well, hey there," she replied, mimicking me. Her name was Coco. American. Probably in her early twenties. We immediately fell into a super easy interaction. I told her about my trip. She told me about coming to Belize to spend time with a long-lost brother. Something about her birth father leaving with him when she was a baby. Amazingly, she'd been in town for a couple of months yet had not yet explored anywhere else in the surrounding area. I joked that she should let me kidnap her and whisk her away on an adventure. She laughed, flashing a perfect smile and tossing her head back. I bought drinks for the Canadians while we traded contact info and I told her I'd catch up with her later. After a slew of card games, nachos and cocktails we were ready to call it a night. It seemed that Coco had already left so I drunkenly commended myself for getting her number.

Back at Anda Di Hows my tent was smaller than expected. I think it was actually a kid's tent because I had to sleep in it diagonally and my head and feet *still* poked the fabric walls. Also, it turns out that sand is much harder to sleep on than you might think. After a poor night of sleep, and being less than enthused to stick around, I decided that I'd continue on to my next destination, Hopkins. Over breakfast, I said goodbye to Brian and the others, who were heading out on a tour to some lagoon or other to see some turtles or something. We planned to keep in touch and maybe hook back up in northern Belize.

Once I was on the bus I messaged Coco and to my delight she responded almost immediately. She said she was sorry for disappearing the night before, something about her brother getting too drunk, but said she was interested in taking a little side trip so to let her know how Hopkins was. *Well. That. Is. Just. Fantastic. News,* I thought.

Later that afternoon I arrived in Hopkins, a dusty beach town that had more of a raw, authentic Caribbean vibe, which I instantly appreciated. My hostel, The Funky Dodo, was easygoing and upon checking in I met a rugged-looking older man who'd rented a motorcycle and told me about some great local adventures he'd been on; I made a note of the rental shop's location. I messaged Coco and told her that *"Hopkins is awesome and you should come visit tomorrow so we can go on that adventure we talked about."* Again, she responded quickly and told me she'd look into bus schedules.

Ten minutes' walk down the dusty street I found the motorcycle rental shop which was run by a badass, Dutch woman. She gave me the rundown and told me about a nearby national park that was worth visiting. She also told me that she had a small Airbnb behind the motorcycle shop. It only cost a little more than my hostel bunk so I told her that I'd be back the following morning to rent a large, powerful-looking dirt bike and that I'd also like to book her Airbnb for one night. The game was on! As I strolled back down toward my hostel, Coco messaged me that she was coming the following day around lunchtime and was excited for our adventure. I smiled at how my plan was all coming together. A beautiful young lady was coming to visit me, I had my own room and I was ready to explore the rugged, rural landscape of Belize by motorcycle; now I just needed to remember how to ride one.

As the afternoon went along I got increasingly anxious. *What if I'd forgotten all my lessons?* In my mind I tried to recall how the shifting mechanism worked. It was basically like a manual car, just using your hands for the clutch and feet for the gears. Pretty simple, right? I hadn't promised Coco anything about a motorcycle yet, so I talked to the hostel owner about the possibility of renting bicycles instead. He was a large, jolly fellow and eager to help.

"Oh, that's a long bicycle ride. It will take you a few hours to get there and back, most of the afternoon probably. You'd probably be coming back in the dark. I'd *definitely* recommend going by motorcycle." So, motorcycle it was.

That evening I went to see some beach-drumming but the real entertainment was watching the local Garifuna men hit on much older white women. I was always impressed with how most black guys seemed so much more unabashed in the expression of their sexuality. As for me, I was feeling a little out of practice. Is this an innate skill? Can I learn it? *Can I learn it by tomorrow?*

The next morning, I nervously walked down the road to pick up the bike. It was a powerful beast and the owner sensed my apprehension.

"When was the last time you rode, again?" she asked.

"Oh, it's been a little while. A few years since I got my license. Since then I've ridden a couple of times." I didn't tell her it had been only on automatic scooters, not on an actual motorcycle.

"How about I jump on my bike and join you for a quick spin," she kindly offered.

"That would be great!" I said thankfully. We started our bikes and I immediately stalled mine out. On the second time I got it running and we took off down the road and after a few minutes of bumpy gear changes I began to get the hang of it.

"Good job," she said. "Use the clutch to control your speed a little more." She instructed me to do some slow U-turns. "Now you got it. Look at where you want the bike to go," she said. And soon after that she left me at a dusty intersection and went back to her shop. My lesson was over.

I picked up my backpack at the Dodo and rode back to the motorcycle shop. After getting set up in my clean—but more importantly, private—new apartment, I rode over to the bus station to wait for Coco. She arrived a short while later, wearing bright pink hot pants, a bikini top and a smile as big and bright as any anime character. In the light of day she looked even younger than I remembered, probably in her early, early twenties. Instead of focusing on how I'd been in my teens when she was born, I focused on the fact that I possessed the experience of an older gentleman.

"Hieeee!" she squealed. We hugged. Not too long but long enough that I inhaled the fragrant smell of her freshly showered hair. Wait, was that creepy?

"Surprise!" I said, stepping aside and gesturing to the mighty red-and-black Yamaha dirt bike behind me. "I hope you're ready for an adventure." I hoped we both were.

"Oh wow! I am! I've only been on a motorcycle once before!" I decided to refrain from saying, *"Me too!"*

"Well, let's roll," I said, instead. I threw a leg over the bike, handed her a helmet that I'd brought for her and she hopped on the back, her tanned legs straddling me and sending a thrill through my body. We took off with relative smoothness, down the main road and out onto the highway, Coco's pink hot pants fluttering in the wind.

Coco held on tightly as we turned into the Mayflower Bocawina National Park and headed into the jungle. The road was gravelly and full of potholes, but eventually after a white-knuckled journey we made it; if Coco had been nervous, she hadn't let on. There was a variety of waterfall hikes to choose from but I heard that Antelope Falls was by far the most spectacular, so we paid a small fee at the entrance and began a leisurely hike along the trail. But before long we were climbing on a narrow path, grappling with vines and roots as we ascended a steep series of waterfalls. When we finally clambered out of the jungle and arrived at a lookout, we were rewarded with sweeping views of the valley from which we'd emerged. The water flowed down from the mountainous jungle above us, cascading into a large pool before gushing over the precarious rocks near where we stood, finally disappearing down into the valley below. The valley itself lay spread out into infinity, a rich carpet of greens layered with ever more greens, endless amounts of lush foliage painted on the landscape as if drawn by a child who only had a green crayon.

A little further up from the lookout was a secluded pool where we cooled off and had fun by staging a mock photo shoot under the waterfalls, taking pictures of each other posing and flexing in the brisk water. Eventually we pulled ourselves away from the Edenlike surroundings and began the hike back down the mountain.

We got back to the motorcycle and rolled out of the jungle just as the sun was setting. I rode into Hopkins, feeling victorious with a beautiful woman on the back of my ride, a beautiful woman who still had all her limbs and skin fully attached to her body. *It was a good day.* And it was to be a good night. A night for celebration.

When we got back to the apartment Coco rummaged through her bag and pulled out a bottle. "Surprise!" she said. "I hope you like rum!"

"Well, I think we deserve a drink or three after that successful expedition, I'll get some mixers from the market across the street." By the time I got back she was freshly showered and just wearing a towel. She looked more radiant than ever.

"Well, don't you clean up nicely!" I said.

"Your turn, smelly!" she grinned as I pulled off my admittedly odorous tank top. She poured us a couple of rum and cokes as I continued to undress down to my underwear. I took my glass into the bathroom and left the door open just enough for her to peer in, you know, in case she felt so inclined.

"Do you know how I can tell that it's going to be a party night?" I asked as I stepped into the shower.

"How?" she hollered from the living room.

"I'm drinking a rum and coke in the shower."

"Well, here we go!" she said giddily.

And oh my, did Coco like to party. On our way out the door she filled a water bottle with more rum. "We might need this," she said mischievously as she slipped it into her bag. We found a seafood restaurant and immediately befriended a nice, quiet Swedish couple who were on their honeymoon. We ended up joining them and when they asked how we knew each other Coco spontaneously made up some crazy story that we'd met in a Mexican border town where she was eluding the authorities.

"You know, *nothing major*!" she'd said when the couple looked at each other a little nervously. "Just a misunderstanding over tax evasion, really." She grinned that enormous grin. "And now we're getting married!" she said, raising her glass. "Well, cheers!"

"Ah, memories!" I exclaimed romantically, now nicely buzzed. "On to more important matters. I heard that there was a mini-golf tournament going on tonight." I knew Coco was up for it before she even clapped her hands together with glee.

"Well, we weren't going to stay out very late …" began Swedish husband.

"Oh, imagine the fun it would be!" Coco exclaimed, grabbing the arm of Swedish wife.

"Well, I guess we could play a round or two," Swedish wife smiled.

We finished dinner and walked down the road to Windschief Beach Bar and MiniGolf. The tournament was already long over by the time we arrived so we decided to make our own tournament. We rented clubs and balls and got some more drinks. By this point Coco and I were on a bender and even the Swedes had loosened up. Coco was heckling each of us and when it was her turn she exhibited a flagrant disregard for any rules. Each hole was themed with historical or geographical significance, as explained on the back of the scorecard, which I made sure to read loudly and in a dramatic tone. Eventually, despite Coco's lamentations, I was crowned tournament champion, which I celebrated by pole-dancing with a palm tree while the others did penalty pushups. Of course it all made complete sense at the time.

Long after the Swedes had left, after some boisterous rounds of foosball and after most of the expats at Windschief had made attempts to hit on Coco, we left the bar and began walking home, arm in arm.

"What a day!" I said.

"And what a night!" Coco said, hugging herself closer to me. *What a night, indeed!* I thought.

"I think I need another shower," Coco said as I unlocked the door of my apartment.

"Me too," I said. Now was my chance. "You know, shower time happens to be one of my *favorite* times. Perhaps we could save some water and share one?" I grinned, setting the stage for romance. *And. Then. This. Happened:*

"What? Eww, gross!" she replied and I laughed. Then she laughed. And then suddenly I realized she was serious so I laughed again, this time to mask my own disappointment. And just like that the magic was over. Any sexual energy that had been building up rushed out of the drain somewhere down near my root chakra. The bathroom door closed, along with any possibility for romance. I brushed my teeth in the kitchen sink and crawled, defeated, into bed and Coco crawled in a short while afterward. The few inches that lay between us that night might as well have been a mile.

When I woke up Coco was gone. It wasn't a complete surprise; she had told me she was going to catch an early bus, but I didn't really think she would follow through after the night we'd had. But sure enough she had set her alarm and caught the bus out of town. All that was left was a throbbing headache, a raspy throat and the bitter taste of sexual frustration. "And that, my friends, is just a great example of what rejection feels like!" I exclaimed, fist-bumping the air, as I crawled out of bed. The only thing to do was really laugh at the ridiculousness of it all; that and the note that was stuck to the mirror:

"Thanks for the fun times! Had to take off early. Safe travels!" Followed by a string of hearts. Friend-zone hearts.

During mini-golf the previous evening I'd arranged to hitch a ride with the Swedish couple up to Belize City where I'd catch the afternoon ferry to Caye Caulker. I had my bags packed and was waiting in front of the motorcycle shop when they arrived.

"Where's Coco?" Swedish husband inquired as I hoisted my bag into the back and slumped into the rear seat.

"Oh, Coco," I said, remembering the fictitious dinner conversation. "She left this morning for Placencia."

"Is everything okay with you guys?" Swedish wife asked, concerned.

"Haha! Yeah, everything's fine." They were both a little taken aback. "She isn't really wanted for tax evasion. And we aren't getting married. In fact I just met her two days ago." They laughed as we drove down the dusty road and out of Hopkins.

A sudden tropical downpour made driving slow. I was lying down uncomfortably in the backseat, working through my hangover and inner shadows. Someone had stuck a Chiquita banana sticker to the roof of the rental car. Did you know that the Chiquita company used to go by a different name? Yep, you guessed it, The United Fruit Company, the same company that helped instigate the Guatemalan civil war decades earlier.

I still couldn't shake my gloominess. I missed my friends back home. I wondered if I had made the right decision in my travel route. I wondered what might have happened if I'd just had one more day with Stella, my *Tomb Raider* fantasy girl from Rio Dulce? If anything, my interaction with Coco had made me even more attracted to that strong and confident German woman, who embodied elegance even through her backpacker facade. She drank, but not excessively. She was mischievous, but not brash about it. I thought about the unabashedly sexualized Garifuna men at the bonfire the night before and wondered if I had been assertive enough with her. I decided to share my romantic frustrations with the Swedes.

"Well, you know, European girls can be a little more traditional than American girls," Swedish husband said, glancing at his wife after he said it.

"What do you mean?" I asked.

"Well, they usually expect the man to make the first move," he said, carefully watching his wife's reactions. "I mean, as independent human beings, women are completely welcome to also make the first move if they like," Swedish husband said, hedging his bets. Swedish wife nodded her support.

"People have to be clear with what they want," Swedish wife said.

I thought about this for a while. The world was in total uproar over sexual harassment allegations that had been recently sparked by the #metoo movement, a social media phenomenon in which no celebrity, executive or politician was untouchable. The movement was also causing a huge amount of sexual confusion in both men and women. Most men were completely terrified about expressing themselves sexually for fear of overstepping any boundaries and meanwhile women were complaining about the lack of strong, confident men. But I thought I *had* been pretty clear. Hadn't I?

"So how do men strike a balance between asserting themselves and being respectful?"

"Well, just be honest," Swedish husband said.

"Yes. But also know that sometimes women just want to feel taken," Swedish wife said.

"Okay, so men today need to be both honest AND assertive?" I offered the Garifuna guys at the bonfire as an example. They laughed.

"Honest and assertive … *and respectful!*" she laughed. "It depends on the woman, too. We are complicated sometimes!" Wasn't that the truth.

The Swedes stopped at the zoo and invited me along but I told them I'd stay with the car. Despite being crammed in the back I fell into such a deep sleep that when I woke up we were already driving again. I'd awoken from a bizarrely disgusting dream in which I was eating tacos, full of limp lettuce. But instead of taco shells it had been slices of jellied ham that I was peeling off a cylindrical stack like those blank CDs that you used to buy back in the day.

"We're almost there. Hungry?" Swedish husband said, passing me a bag of fried plantain chips. And I was, despite the revolting taco vision, so I took a handful.

"Thanks." I said, shaking off the dream and choosing not to attempt to analyze its cryptic meaning.

It was still raining when they dropped me off at the ferry terminal. "Hey, take care of yourself, Dougie!" Swedish husband said. "And be careful of flirtatious tax evaders!" This time they both laughed. We shook hands and I stepped out into the rain, running into the terminal with just enough time to catch the last ferry to Caye Caulker.

As the shore of Belize City receded, I recalled the highs and lows of the last twenty-four hours. I was still a little bummed out but not totally consumed by Coco's rejection. After all, not everyone *has* to like or be attracted to me. There's plenty who are, I told myself. I tried to list things I was grateful for. I sent some text messages to family and friends. I practiced some breathing exercises, long inhales and exhales. I told myself that I was awesome a few times and even *sort of* believed it.

The infinite possibilities of being on the road can make it tempting to jump from place to place, person to person, propelled by a subtle yearning, a desire to achieve contentment. It can be so easy to blame my environment for my mood. When I'm in the mountains, I think about the beach. When I'm at the beach, I think about the lake. When I'm alone, I want to be with people. When I'm with people, I want to be by myself. It can be an exhausting cycle until I just settle down and remember how to just *be content* with who I am, where I am and what I have. I took another deep breath and reminded myself how fortunate I was to be out here, able to explore my inner and outer world.

It was raining on Caye Caulker. Puddles filled the sandy streets and the lady at Go Slow Guesthouse had just bitched me out for leaving my backpack in the wrong place. Despite the aggressive nature of the hostel owner I decided to stay for two nights and the following day the clouds parted for just long enough to take a tour boat to see some sharks and manta rays. I snorkeled up close to the creatures, peering into their strange looking eyeballs, trying to imagine how they saw the world. Did they feel joy and happiness, pain and suffering in any comparable way to us? I'm pretty sure they didn't really question their place in everything or get too bent out of shape if they got rejected.

"I wonder what they're thinking about," I joked with the captain of the small boat as I climbed back on board.

"The same as any of us, mon. Food and sex!" he laughed. He was probably right.

My cold had returned in the form of a dull sore throat. The forecast for the next few days was continued rain and I felt the urge to keep moving west toward Tikal, so later that afternoon I sat in my bunk at Go Slow and planned my departure for the next day. The plan was to take the ferry back to Belize City and catch a bus to San Ignacio near the border.

That afternoon I'd run into the Canadian women from the Tipsy Tuna at a yoga class so we all decided to go for a shrimp ceviche and lobster dinner. After the feast we hit a local dive bar, the Barrier Reef, where there was a dance competition taking place between the foreigners and the locals. It was funny, and a little bit embarrassing, to watch my pasty compatriots display their lack of rhythm on the dance floor with such inebriated gusto. But everyone was having fun, especially the local guys and the white chicks, although the local women and white guys didn't seem to be nearly as sexually compatible. After the competition one of the Canadian girls turned to me and drunkenly admitted how much she loved black men so I played Cupid and introduced her to a very handsome Belizean man who I'd made friends with at the bar. Soon they were getting freaky on the dance floor and I decided to duck out and get an early night in preparation for my return trip to Guatemala.

The journey to the small town of San Ignacio included a brief, gritty stopover at a bus station in Belize City but was otherwise uneventful. San Ignacio sits near the northern borders of Belize and Guatemala and is mostly known for a couple of Mayan sites, including the ruins of Xunantunich and a network of caves where the Maya conducted their ceremonies. I decided to book a tour to Actun Tunichil Muknal cave, also known as the Cave of the Crystal Maiden, but despite being flaunted as adventurous and challenging it was not nearly as thrilling as our excursion in Semuc Champey. Our group, which consisted of myself and a group of Canadian retirees, waded across rivers, through muddy paths and eventually into the dark caves, this time equipped with helmets and headlamps. Our guide was a muscular Belizean guy named Patrick. He was relentlessly flirtatious with the older women on the tour, especially the chubby ones, while they giggled and blushed.

"Jenny Craig ain't got no business down here in Belize, you know what I'm saying, mama?!" He asked this question at least half a dozen times over the few-hour tour. "You ladies like cacao? Well, I'm two hundred and ten pounds of chocolate love!! Yah, mon! Talk to me, mama!" Patrick was less friendly with their husbands, who smiled awkwardly as they stumbled along behind their tittering wives. Eventually after weaving under stalactites and over stalagmites we came to a small, calcified skeleton, the remains of a young girl known as the Crystal Maiden. It was the final, sparkling evidence of a sacrifice that had happened around 1000 AD during some of the most challenging and drought-stricken years of the Mayan collapse. Skeletal legs akimbo I couldn't help but wonder if rape had been part of the sacrificial proceedings. If so, it still hadn't done much to stave off the impending drought.

San Ignacio had plenty of cheap, greasy street food and I met some fun German kids at a fried-food stall that evening. I was well aware that I was eating and drinking too much in an attempt to numb myself out of my mild depression. And then in a moment of gross self-pity I realized that I was turning into the same despicable foreign zombie that I had so despised just a few days earlier in Placencia. I just needed to buy some property, paint it gaudy colors, get a Valium prescription and the transformation would be complete.

I made a note to myself that for the rest of my trip I would prioritize healthy destinations and activities. I saw a pattern that when I could stay in one place a little longer, buy my own food and cook for myself, I tended toward a healthier style of living. And staying healthy usually helped keep me positive and upbeat. And when I was positive and upbeat I stopped blaming things and inevitably felt more complete within myself. So I wasn't feeling my best but I also wasn't feeling like a neglected Russian baby just yet. But still, what does a guy have to do to get a little physical touch these days? I laughed to myself as the bus drove across the Belizean border gates, back into Guatemala.

15. Downfall At Tikal (Part 2)

"Want to buy some crack?" my wild-eyed driver asked me as we swerved through the cobblestone streets of Flores.

"I think I'm okay for now," I replied, gripping the rails of the doorless vehicle a little more tightly. *"But thank you!"*

Frenetic energy of my driver aside, I was immediately charmed by the quaint and colorful town. Flores is the closest jumping-off point to the Mayan ruins of Tikal and sits on a lake that is connected to the shore by a two-lane, raised road. I had booked an Airbnb on the island's northern shore but when we got to the address, there was no house, only a dock with a few water taxis idling in the gentle water. I messaged the host but received no response, so I paid the twitchy tuk tuk driver and decided to wait around near the dock. It was getting dark and the water taxi men, who seemed even more questionable than their tuk tuk compadres, were of little help so I decided to head over to a nearby restaurant. Finally, the host arrived and together we hopped in a water taxi and started making our way across the lake.

"Your Airbnb profile gave me the impression that your place was on the island of Flores."

"Yeah, I thought it'd be easier to just put the location as the water taxi dock," the guy said. He was an expat and immediately had a dubious vibe. You know, the kind of person who only has stories about how they've been screwed over? "So after years of effort my business partner completely screwed me. Well, screw that bastard ..." one story ended. "And after all I'd done for her, to just leave town and ghost me. That bitch!" ended another. Yeah, he was one of those guys, and complained about an endless variety of topics as we puttered across the lake.

Upon arrival the place seemed nice enough but once inside we were met by a bunch of other guests milling around a dirty kitchen. I was shown to my room, which didn't even have a door, and the bed was a small, uncomfortable futon, rather than the "cozy queen" that had been advertised in the pictures. The window opened right onto the porch where the host smoked cigarettes and complained loudly to any guest who would listen. For ten dollars a night I didn't expect too much but even so this was a bit more of a subpar experience than I had in mind. So that night, while lying uncomfortably on the lumpy futon, I found another place, making sure this time it was actually on the island, and booked it for the following day. The next morning, despite my sore throat which had returned with such vigor that I now had a swollen, golf-ball sized lymph node protruding from my neck, I packed my bag, told the guy his place his was lousy and was moving back over to Flores. "Goddamn backpackers, cheap bastards with their complaints and crappy reviews ... *screw 'em!*" he ranted to no one in particular as I left the house.

After getting back to Flores, I met up with my next host in the central square. He was a very pleasant, local man who showed me back down the hill to a brightly painted, two-floor apartment right in the center of the island. He made sure I was comfortable, showing me where everything was and soon after he left I began exploring the town. As I walked the perimeter of the island, I was surprised to discover that a large portion of the lakeside street was actually underwater. I asked some locals and apparently the lake had risen significantly over the last couple of years. I walked across the bridge, over to the mainland where I found a gym, got a haircut and went to a bustling market where I stocked up on some healthy groceries. On the way back to my apartment I stopped into Los Amigos Hostel, another suggestion of Zoe's from back at Bigfoot Hostel in Antigua, which apparently offered decent tours to Tikal. I booked one for the next day and then made myself some dinner and read about Nicaragua, where I was planning to spend the majority of the second half of my trip.

The following morning I woke up early and ate a heroic portion of oatmeal. I hadn't had the most social couple of days, which meant that I hadn't met anyone to rope into a psychedelic conquest of Tikal. But it felt like a very special opportunity and I felt experienced enough to manage myself amidst a group of strangers, so after a brief moment of deliberation, I placed a drop of LSD on my tongue and walked over to Los Amigos to catch the tour bus to Tikal.

I didn't expect the journey to Tikal to take as long as it did; two hours later we were still on the bus and I was, as the kids say, *tripping balls.* I'd made friends with the entire back of the bus, including an Indian couple, a fun Kiwi guy and what seemed to be a group of Irish soccer players in full uniform. We were all in a jolly mood once we arrived at the first checkpoint. Armed guards silently watched as we got off the bus and stood in a line to get some sort of receipt. I smiled from behind my sunglasses, which were the only things keeping my pupils from frisbeeing out of my eyeball sockets. *No one expects you to be on acid,* I reminded myself. I'm just another smiling tourist, excited to be here. *So. Effin'. Excited!*

After that mini-ordeal we crammed back into the bus and drove on to the next checkpoint, where we had to produce the previous receipt in order to get our ticket. Finally, at the last checkpoint, we exchanged our tickets for wristbands. Of course I found the inefficiency of the whole situation utterly hilarious, made even more so when it started pouring gobstopper-size raindrops on our heads, and that's when the colorful ponchos were handed out.

As the horde of bright blobs ventured into the forest, Rodrigo, our militaristic tour guide, took the opportunity to point out various types of plants and animals, stopping at stunning views of the richly textured structures. The buildings, which had once been brightly painted, were now mottled hues of stone, mold and moss. When I'd first tried LSD years earlier, I had expected to see all sorts of visions and creatures, just like the movies depicted. But in my experience my visions were less cohesive, and more like a gossamer overlay of iridescent cobwebs and motion trails. My depth perception became more erratic, and at times my visual field flattened completely, becoming a two-dimensional tapestry of constantly evolving patterns and color. Everything I looked at seemed to be alive, to be breathing, somehow connected to my own breath. Closing my eyes was no escape from the visual chaos, the inside of my eyelids exploding into morphing patterns, intricate mandalas and recursive fractals. My thoughts came fast and splintered, a disorderly mess of past, present and future, all vying for my attention at precisely the same time. My body felt strong, more flexible and energized, but also jittery, like I'd had too much caffeine. This effect, combined with the already slippery terrain, made my legs feel like jelly and it was all I could do to stay upright as we traversed the landscape.

Rodrigo's voice came back into focus. He'd begun explaining how the Maya had inadvertently been the architects of their own demise. From environmental degradation to overpopulation and greed, their empire became bloated and drunk on its own grandiosity and began to collapse.

"Over time the Maya could no longer rely on their rulers for prosperity and guidance; their culture was in a death spiral and the rulers were powerless to stop it. The old style of rulership, long steeped in the traditions of construction, warfare and ritual, proved to be less adaptable to the times and kings began to be replaced by ruling councils of elite lineages." Rodrigo's command of the English language was impressive and I wondered what his role had been in the military. "However, rather than help the situation, this only further fanned the flames, prompting more power grabs, and inadvertently served to expedite the downfall of the Maya. Within a couple of generations huge swaths of the Mayan empire lay abandoned, and by the 9th century many of the classic cities, including Tikal, lay empty. Dated carvings ceased and squatters moved into the temples and palaces. For the next few hundred years there was a lot of movement of people around the area, as they attempted to adapt to their ever-changing world. Some new cities even sprung up where there were still untapped resources. Those cities often showed a defensive design, indicating a lifestyle in which warfare was increasingly prolific. Sadly, scholars believe that most of these cities collapsed for the same reasons as those that had preceded them.

"By the time the first Spanish arrived in 1511, the Mayan civilization was already greatly reduced and weakened." Rodrigo continued, "Even so, the Spanish brought back stories of rich and prosperous cities and well-stocked marketplaces to their financial investors in Europe. It was these locations that became the main targets of the conquistadors, and while there were some attempts to coexist at first, it was the European desire for gold and other resources that ultimately dissolved any potential for peace. The Maya resisted Spanish conquest for almost two centuries but in 1697 the last independent Mayan city, Nojpetén, fell to the Spanish. The remaining Maya continued to survive in small remote villages or on the move, and while they were largely confined by proximity to water sources, they were still able to resist the conquistadors and did pretty well to defend themselves.

"The final blow to the great Mayan empire was that indigenous people had never developed immunity to European diseases, so when they were exposed to them it became an unintended, but highly effective form of biological warfare, and the Maya eventually lost most of their remaining population from sickness. The surviving population was forced into submission and exploited by Europeans for materials, labor and other resources." Rodrigo let the heaviness of the moment linger. All the while, graphic imagery was appearing in my mind's eye, flashes of chaotic scenes spun from Rodrigo's words. "Mayan culture was seen as savage to the Spanish, who largely dismantled it by burning books and converting the survivors to Christianity and enforcing other European cultural practices. The natives were forced to learn Spanish and the European writing system, so within a couple of generations their ability to write and decipher their own hieroglyphics had all but vanished.

"It wasn't until the first couple of decades of the 20th century that we began to understand more about the Mayan's mysterious culture. Funding for new archeology projects emerged, allowing for large-scale excavations to be undertaken. Up until the late 1900s the Mayan numeral system was still a mystery and the meanings of the hieroglyphics and details of deities and religious ceremonies continued to be only imaginative at best. At that point the prevailing theory of Mayan culture was that they were a peaceful, forest-dwelling people governed from largely vacant cities by astronomer-priests." Rodrigo paused for effect. "But we were *quite* wrong about that.

"By a stroke of sheer luck a few decades ago, four manuscripts appeared. These codices were unearthed from collections from different parts of the world, carefully protected and hidden over time. Eventually analytic comparison of these artifacts led to the Mayan script being deciphered, and what we discovered completely dissolved our previously held beliefs. The Maya were not such peaceful people as previously thought. Their rituals even included bloodletting and human sacrifice."

By this point we'd clambered over a series of ruins, out into the grand plaza at the center of Tikal, and were standing at the foot of the Temple of the Moon. "Kidnapped warriors or members of elite families from neighboring cities were sometimes tossed down these very steps," Rodrigo said, pointing at the steep incline of jagged limestone. "Cheering crowds would gather to witness the display of their city's power."

In an effort to lift the heaviness Rodrigo told us more about the structures, about the many Mayan accomplishments and how they were probably the first inventors of basketball. We were then let loose for twenty minutes to explore the plaza, but despite the dark tale of the Mayan downfall I found myself giggling like a lunatic, not because I was an insensitive asshole, but just at the sheer irony of the situation. Here I was, watching a bunch of humans in colorful plastic ponchos, slipping and sliding on structures that were built by a civilization that had collapsed due to many of the same circumstances that our own civilization was now facing. The rain poured down as my emotions, all of them, simultaneously, streaked through my perception at an incredible speed. I laughed out loud as I began climbing the steep steps of the Temple of the Moon.

OK, so that brings you, the reader, up to date, back to the beginning, or more accurately back to the middle of this meandering tale. A bunch of factors, including big-city burnout and a mischievous beaver, had all eventually led me to the steep steps of this Mayan temple in Guatemala, high on acid, laughing to myself in the rain. *So, let's continue ...*

Breathe. My legs felt wobbly. Breathe. One leg in front of the other. *Breathe.* The view from the top was spectacular, a thick carpet of lush jungle stretching as far as the eye could see, pierced through in various places by the pinnacles of Tikal's towering limestone temples. After catching my breath, I struck up a conversation with an Indian couple, who were on their honeymoon, and before long the conversation had turned to Mayan culture. "I'm so curious about how it must have felt back then. I mean, I wonder what it *feels* like to be on the waning end of a civilization," I said. "How was day-to-day life for the Maya as they reached their end ..." My topic of conversation seemed to have become as heavy as my mood.

"Oh, I've never really thought of that," the young woman said. I could tell I was bumming them out so I decided to shut up for a while.

Internally I was spiraling into a dark hole of thought. Could the same thing happen to us? Could our civilization collapse as easily? What would societal devastation look like on such a massive scale? I imagined the great cities of the United States being abandoned, any survivors returning to agrarian and hunter-gatherer lives. And then what? Invasion from abroad? The Maya just happened to be at their weakest when the Spanish arrived, but now foreign powers can just sit back and watch as the United States self-destructs, waiting for the right time to swoop in to stake their claim. My only dark consolation was that since environmental degradation was happening on such a huge scale nobody, and no country, would be left unscathed. I wondered how many times different versions of this same story had played out and what sort of evolution it would take to break free of the cycle. Was there some glitch in our own human design, a self-destructive loop that was hardwired into our very psyche? Why are we never satisfied until we've squeezed every resource dry? I wasn't sure how much time had passed but in case you can't tell, I was experiencing a little bit of a mid-LSD panic attack, falling into one apocalyptic rabbit hole after the other.

"Hey, we better get back to the group," the Indian husband said cheerfully, breaking me out of my misery, and we carefully descended the steps.

It was getting dark by the time the group had all gathered back in the plaza. The howler monkeys were making their presence known with boisterous eruptions and the insect orchestra had struck up its evening chorus. Once everyone was accounted for, we began to walk back the way we came.

"Watch for snakes at this time of the day!" Rodrigo hissed. I think he was joking but in the descending darkness, and still under the influence of the LSD, every shadowy root looked like a goddamn slithering snake as we made our way through the jungle and back to the bus.

The question remained in my mind as we slowly, and damply, drove back to Flores. *How would it feel to watch your culture fall apart?* Maybe like us, the Maya had plenty of distractions to take their mind off things, day-to-day stuff like entertainment, romance, art, drinking, drugs and all the other stuff that humans occupy their time with. *Did the Maya actually have drugs? I think the Egyptians did ...* Anyway, when tragedy hits you in the face, it can be incredibly transformative, but when it unfolds over hundreds of years maybe it doesn't feel so threatening; people don't have to admit that it's actually happening. Even the Spanish conquest had been a somewhat slower process than I'd originally thought. Maybe that's one difference to what we're facing today; things were slower, more localized back then. Now plenty of people are talking about how global collapse could come about. We're being made aware every day, through a relentless barrage of news sources, how we are laying the groundwork for our own demise. But there's business to run, sport games to support, movies to watch and tropical fruit available all over the world, any time of year. Isn't all that far more enjoyable than having to admit the fragility of our own existence?

"I've seen success, I've seen wealth and the things it can buy," the Indian husband said. I'd ended up sitting next to him and in an attempt to take a break from the inside of my head I'd asked him about his life. Apparently he'd sold a software company and now lived a pretty lavish life. "I've had a yacht; I've had all the fun. And I've also seen the emptiness, the bottomless hole that all these things aren't able to fill. I used to think that maybe this next thing, this next object or next level of wealth might be where I would find my sense of peace and joy, yet it always remained just out of reach. No. More stuff will never fill the hole." It was so fascinating to meet someone from a totally different culture going through many of the same realizations. "Health, friends, family ..." He nodded at his sleeping wife. "These are the true signs of wealth."

Back in Flores the Kiwi fellow was wrangling people for happy hour but I was pretty exhausted and over-socialized so I said my goodbyes and set off for my apartment, only to get completely lost in the maze of cobbled streets. After walking in circles, I eventually got my bearings and found my way home. When I got inside, I stripped off my still-damp clothes and flopped down on the couch. I took a deep breath. I had made it back from the Tikal expedition with both my shoes still on my feet and my body more or less intact. My mind, on the other hand, remained a boxing match, and I had ringside seats as my optimism and fear let each other have it.

I decided to take my mind off of things by checking out what was happening in the world. In retrospect this was possibly not the best idea in my current emotional state. My email inbox was full of bad news and I found myself lost in string of climate concerns, nuclear threats between the U.S. and Iran, and continued sex scandals from the church to Hollywood. Even the world of technology was looking increasingly grim. More data scandals had influenced international elections. Self-driving cars had just killed their first person and now the whole industry was facing significant pressure. AI was being used to swap famous people's faces onto porno, using a new technology called *deepfakes,* threatening a future where fake news could be deployed with relative ease. *Dark fucking times,* I thought, shaking my head.

I clicked the next email and the previous distant threats touched ground into my immediateness; things back at Manzanita continued to move toward a breaking point. Remember the beaver, and how certain members supported its arrival, and others less so? Well, the *beaver-hesitant* group had offered to provide the remaining part of the funds that would prevent us from defaulting on the loan and losing the land. However, in order to do this, they required that certain terms be met. It seemed like the only option we had, so yep, the can of worms was being opened.

What terms? Well, as is typical at the start of business ventures, everything had been all friendly and trusting and huggy. However, in an effort to swiftly close the deal on the property, members had thrown in whatever funds they could afford. Maybe some details weren't explicitly clarified. Maybe some loose promises weren't kept. Instead of placing blame on any single individual we—rather maturely, I will say—chose to blame it on a collective inattention to detail. Well, sure enough, after a short-lived honeymoon period, the details began to bubble to the surface; some members had paid relatively little for fully habitable cabins while others had paid significantly more for piles of rubble with a view.

In an attempt to equalize this discrepancy a spreadsheet was created that included all sorts of variables, analyzing each structure's square-footage and state of habitability as well as other amenities like road access, power, plumbing and Wi-Fi connectivity. And at first everyone was supportive of the equalization strategy—that is, until the spreadsheet made it apparent that the *pro-beaver* group would stand to owe a significant amount more money than they'd each invested at the beginning, money that none of them had to offer. But the *beaver-hesitant* group wouldn't agree to pay off the loan with the former property owners until this equalization issue was resolved.

Everyone was unsure of the next move. But one thing was certain, we were all getting some deep insights into the right—and wrong—way to launch an intentional community.

If a clear shared vision is the crucial first step when starting a community project then the next most important thing to do is to get on the same page *financially*. Ideally every member has a comparable amount of savings so that there aren't financial rifts; for example, when one group of members wants to invest in improvements but the other is barely scraping by month to month. It's not to say that this dynamic can't be resolved, especially if those without the funds can funnel their skills and energy into a sweat-equity arrangement, but it's certainly easier to clarify these relationships up front by being transparent with financial investment and expectation. Despite good intentions, clear financial transparency wasn't quite our modus operandi in the early days of Manzanita, and now, with just a few short weeks before I was scheduled to return, the community was facing a serious and as of yet unresolved loan deadline. Our weekly meeting was in a couple of days. For now, I just turned off my phone.

It was late by the time the LSD wore off. As I made myself a bowl of oatmeal heaped with fruit, I thought about the intense experience that I'd subjected myself to. Psychologists say that LSD can amplify psychological conditions and it certainly seemed to bring my bipolar tendencies to the surface. One minute I was laughing like a lunatic and the next dwelling on my own demise. Something within me craved it, though, as if to test myself, to see if I'd made progress in my ability to self-soothe and balance my own psychology. Moments like today made me wonder if I had. For some reason, I loved to run myself ragged in the quest for some sort of transformational experience. One therapist told me that I have a proclivity for what he calls "exposure therapy." And he might be right. *But did it always have to be so goddamn blunt?* Maybe in time I could learn to be a little more gentle on myself?

As I slowly munched my way through the oatmeal, I considered what I was going to do next. I really had no idea. My romantic self longed to see Stella the strong German woman again but it was a long way back to Lake Atitlán and my explorer self told me to forget the girl and continue the adventure. I was examining my calendar when I realized I was at the exact halfway point of the travel insurance I had purchased; *it felt like a sign*. I began to think back to the last six weeks, which had been a deep exploration into the past, a history lesson into U.S. intervention in Central America and a deep dive into Mayan culture, and the legacy it left both in the form of monumental structures and in the tale of its own unraveling. Simultaneously it had been a journey into my own past, unearthing unresolved aspects of myself and other things I wasn't even aware of. All the while, the world seemed to be spiraling out of control and an altercation that was instigated by goddamn beaver was threatening my life back home.

I was mid-spoonful of oatmeal, when in a glorious moment of clarity, I had an epiphany. I realized that at the core of it all I was being way too hard on myself, an old tendency that had snuck up in a very subtle way to bite me in the ass once again. Life is already challenging enough without needing to be such a judgmental asshole to myself. This was, after all, a vacation from what had been a tough year, and a time to enjoy life and prioritize my own health, happiness and well-being. And then just like that, I stood up from the couch and raised my spoon into the air: "I hereby transition from dwelling on the past *to looking toward the future!* From the darkness to the light!"

What I needed was some actual rest and relaxation, some sunshine and drier air for my sinuses to recuperate. Was this a cop-out to my original plan? No, screw it! Who besides myself was keeping tabs on me, anyway? As a storyteller my biggest struggle is often changing the story that I've written inside my own head. I might become attached to the way a scene is *supposed* to unfold, to the desired arc of a particular relationship or the imagined significance of a chance encounter. In this case I had romanticized the idea of traveling down through Central America on a motorcycle. That hadn't quite taken shape and in its void I felt a frustrating sense that I was somehow missing out on something, missing out on some story that I had wanted to tell instead of the story that was actually happening. In a moment of joyful reframing I realized that this change of plans was actually a *great story*, a story in which treating myself kindly would become an integral part of the plot.

And that was it. It felt like removing a backpack after a long hike. I felt light and carefree again. I was done being regretful of travel decisions. I was done acting miserable and dissatisfied with the present. From here on I would find gratitude for wherever I was, for whatever I was doing and for whoever I was with. I would return to my original plan to head south toward Costa Rica, visiting intentional communities along the way.

Extended traveling can repeatedly present us with a quick succession of novel challenges. In each instance we can learn to navigate these experiences by getting increasingly stressed or *increasingly graceful.* When I feel grounded and maintain my mind, body and spirit connection through yoga, meditation, exercise, journaling and healthy eating, I tend to be far more content. I'm able to make new friends more easily and to enjoy new experiences more fully. It's valuable to review the factors that lead me to diverge from this solid foundation. Departure from this proven path often begins with a period of hyper-extroversion or manic energy, moving too fast, taking on too many things without having enough of my own space or the time to process and integrate my experiences along the way. Then, from this shaky foundation I no longer feel complete within myself and begin scrambling to fill the growing hole inside of me. If left unchecked I begin blaming my environment and reaching for distractions such as food, drinks, sex, adventure, basically anything I can grab to prevent me from feeling what I am feeling.

I have always stumbled along this path but I am grateful to finally be catching myself before the cycles get too out of control. In these moments I stop, take stock of the situation and proceed as mindfully as possible. I don't need to *blame* anyone or anything. I don't need to numb out. Each challenge is a teacher, a way to learn how to best support ourselves. How can I learn from this experience? How can I be more creative in this moment? If I determine what it is that I need can give it to myself, instead of reaching for it elsewhere? When I'm not scrambling I can look beyond my own immediacy, to see what I'm doing with my life and to consider how I can use my energy to be of service to the world. *Isn't that nice?*

As a testament to my new vow of self-love I picked up my phone, pulled up my calendar and added "Be Extra Nice To Dougie" every day for the entire next week. I washed my bowl and made my way up the spiral staircase that led to my bedroom, where I lay down and began to make travel arrangements. First, I decided that I would just chill out and take it easy on myself for a few days in Flores. Within an hour I had nixed the idea of a strenuous overland journey and booked myself a flight instead; in a few days I would fly to Nicaragua and take a bus south to San Juan del Sur, where the weather was warm and sunny and the beaches were said to be beautiful. I booked a place to stay for a few days, from where I would research intentional communities and healthy locations and chart the next part of my Central America expedition. *And the best part?* I even tracked down a motorcycle rental place in San Juan del Sur and put down a deposit on the last bike they had available. The dream of two-wheeled adventure would finally be made real.

There had been so much inspiration and growth on this trip already, and I once again felt the excitement stirring; the second half of my trip would be less about the past and instead focus more on the present, what *is* working and how we are creating solutions and healthy visions for our future. Some people say that Nicaragua is the new Costa Rica, still budget-friendly and unexplored by the masses. As I fell asleep my mind swirled, imagining all the places where we can create resilient communities, retreat and wellness centers, permaculture and appropriate technology showcases, food forests and more. I imagined beautiful structures, integrated with the environment, alternate building techniques and *awesome tree houses, of course!* The ideas grew and morphed as I drifted off to sleep.

A few days later, despite getting lots of rest and maintaining a healthy diet, I was still plagued by this sore throat and on the day of travel I woke up to one of my eyes stuck shut with yellowish goop, so as part of my new self-care initiative, I promised myself that I'd visit a doctor as soon as I got settled in San Juan del Sur. Despite my disgusting condition I still felt excited about life again; I was excited for the stories and adventures that were waiting for my brand-new, shiny self. I was even, and somewhat prematurely, excited to return home again. Despite the unfolding drama, and also perhaps prematurely, I still felt confident that things would work out at Manzanita. At the very least, even if it fell apart, I could write a great book about it. Yep, I was officially ready for anything the universe could throw at me.

I caught a tuk tuk to the airport and checked my large backpack. I was so full of ideas and future aspirations that when I had packed my bags I completely forgot about the small dropper of magical breath freshener that I'd stashed in my toiletry kit, bringing it right onto the plane with me in my carry-on backpack. But airport security never expects you to be smuggling large amounts of acid. Or do they?

Act 2: The Nicaragua Part

16. Sounds Like Some Hippie Crap

"And then this one. Also me in Colombia with my girlfriend." Avianca Flight 7979. I was sitting next to Maurizio, a swarthy Italian man, probably mid-sixties. He was stocky and had leathered skin, and a thin gold chain glinted through the chest hair that protruded from his mostly unbuttoned shirt. He was showing me photos of his travels through South and Central America. These particular photos were not of Mayan ruins or colorful colonial structures, no, these were mostly nude photos of his innumerable voluptuous "girlfriends" that he'd romanced along his journey. Sometimes he was in the pictures, usually wearing only a small, testicle-hugging speedo swimsuit. I've always been the kind of person that people feel comfortable opening up to and it was no different for Maurizio. During our short friendship, I'd heard all about his family. He had a couple of kids with his best friend back in the 90s. He and his baby mama, Rahzel, lived at different apartments in the same Tuscan town, sharing parent duties one week on and one week off. And now that the kids were all grown up, he travelled the world eating delicious food and indulging his favorite hobbies: salsa dancing and sex with a harem of women spread out around the globe. People often talk about how developing intimacy with a monogamous partner is the righteous path of meaning and fulfillment. Maurizio, however, seemed to be living a perfectly enjoyable life, the details of which he was more than happy to share with me.

"And this one, ooohee, this one!" He made that typically Italian hand gesture, flat hand, palm up and a couple of chop motions thrown in for effect. "The Colombian girls, my friend. *Peligrosa*!"

Maurizio continued to share pictures of his exploits up through Panama, Costa Rica, Guatemala and Mexico. He wasn't particularly good-looking or charming so he was either a fantastic salsa dancer, or these women were all prostitutes. The next picture popped up and it was mostly just a shot of his penis, standing erect in front of a rather bushy and dark-lipped vagina. "But these ones are not for you!" He laughed a wheezy smoker's laugh, coughed and smiled to himself as he snapped shut his old-school flip phone.

"So, you tell me now. What are you doing?" Maurizio asked.

"Well, first of all, thank you for sharing your adventures, Maurizio. I'll have to go to Colombia sometime!"

"You must!" He laugh-coughed again.

"I'm spending the winter down here in Central America. So far I've been exploring a lot of Mayan culture and foreign involvement in the area. And now I'm getting ready for some relaxing time. I want to try surfing in Nicaragua. Just chill out for a little while, you know?"

"Oh nice! The ladies in Nicaragua." He placed all the tips of his fingers to his lips and kissed them. "Bellissima. And great cocaine in Nicaragua."

"Good to know!" I exclaimed, although cocaine was not my drug of choice. It brought back memories of those late nights in Los Angeles during which everyone was totally blitzed, waiting for their turn to talk about something they felt was *incredibly* important. "I'm going to rent a motorcycle down in San Juan del Sur and tour the country a little bit, exploring communities and permaculture projects."

"What it is, *permaculture*?" Maurizio asked.

"Well, it's short for *permanent agriculture*, although the concept is probably more accurate to think of as *permanent culture* these days."

"And so, what is it?"

"Well, the basics of permaculture are to observe the patterns of nature and to figure out how humans can live and grow food in a sustainable way."

"Aaaah, *si*, sounds like some hippie shit, my friend!" he replied, followed by laughing and coughing. And to some degree he was right. I'd taken a permaculture course after my yoga teacher training in Thailand and all of the twenty or so participants were definitely on the hippie spectrum. There were the long, dreaded-hair types wearing colorful clothes and that rich musky scent that was created by mixing body odor with essential oils, to the less-overtly hippie types like myself who still enjoyed topics regarding the environment and sustainable practices but stopped just short of crystal consciousness and chemtrail conspiracies. Long hair or not, we all shared a disdain for the extractive, wasteful behaviors of *The Man.*

"Haha, maybe," I laughed. "It's hard to deny that the word *permaculture* sounds like something a bunch of hippies do in the woods instead of getting a *real* job." And that may be true, at least if what constitutes the idea of a real job is something that adds ever-increasing, bottom-line value to the capitalist economy. To the hippies this notion of a "real" job meant making stuff that people don't need, advertising stuff people don't want, or sitting down at a desk pushing bits of information around on a computer as their bodies slowly deteriorate.

But permaculture is actually a fascinating thing and as the environment suffers, it will become increasingly important. It was first coined in the late 70s by a couple of guys in Australia to describe a holistic system of living in balance with nature, and by *holistic* I mean a system that takes into account *all* of its inputs and outputs. At its root, permaculture strives to design systems that work *with* an environment, rather than forcing systems *upon* the environment. Thanks to a relatively simple and well-designed corpus of information, as well as a culture that priorities teaching students to become teachers, permaculture has grown at an astounding rate. You know when hipsters, those mustachioed, hat-wearing heralders of the cultural zeitgeist, start posting pictures of micro-farms planted in abandoned city lots and talking about learning to can exotic berries for future jamming of artisanal loaves, you know when *that* happens, things are becoming more mainstream.

But permaculture is far more than a hippie movement or a hipster catchphrase. One of the founders of permaculture, Bill Mollison, said: *"Permaculture is a philosophy of working with, rather than against nature; of protracted and thoughtful observation rather than protracted and thoughtless labour; and of looking at plants and animals in all their functions, rather than treating any area as a single product system."*

And so in many ways permaculture is not a new thing at all, but an old intelligence, rediscovered and continually infused with new technologies and current scientific understanding. In 1870, around fifty percent of the U.S. population was employed in some aspect of agriculture. As we began to industrialize farming practices people began to leave the farms to work in growing cities and to pursue other areas of interest, like art, philosophy and science. And this is good; after all, it is a sign of a thriving culture when it can support artisans and scholars. However, after World War II, a strange and unfortunate chicken-and-egg scenario unfolded. The Baby Boom generation began to arrive and the population swelled. One way to maximize efficiency of food production was to farm monocrops, millions of acres of corn and wheat processed by specialized farm equipment to manage the unparalleled harvests. However, monocultures are extremely vulnerable to pests and the lack of rotational farming practices is incredibly destructive to the soil.

In a seemingly unrelated concurrence, the former bomb and nerve-gas factories of the war were no longer needed to produce such large amounts of munitions. Well, as luck, or at least divine comedy would have it, science came to the rescue in a brilliant capitalistic love story. The chemical companies were able to tweak their nerve gas, intended for humans, into pesticides and herbicides, and the process for creating bomb fuel was easily tweaked into creating fertilizer, which helped dying soil continue to produce. And so finally, thanks to access to cheap and abundant oil we replaced farm labor with giant machines run by fossil fuels. To feed the growing population, as well as to create vast profits, farmers were given subsidies to produce these monocultures and they quickly became entrenched in a system in which they no longer had any choice but to remain if they wanted to compete and support their families as farmers. And so over time, much of farmers' deeper understanding of agriculture, just like the meaning of Mayan hieroglyphs, began to disappear. By 2008 less than two percent of the population was directly employed in agriculture and one-third of the topsoil of the planet had vanished into sand and dust.

Besides being destructive on our bodies, the industrialized food system has a huge impact on our minds—and not just for those immediately exposed to chemicals. Some pesticides have even been able to be shown to alter our DNA, which means their effects will be passed down to future generations. In permaculture, you look at all inputs and outputs to judge the merits of a system. How much oil are we consuming by eating what we're eating? How much are the farming practices that produce our food also producing water pollution, air pollution, disease and even extinction? It's enough to make you gag on your small bag of airline pretzels.

In U.S. cities, many citizens live in what are called food deserts, vast areas of urban sprawl that have minimal access to fresh produce. Many of those who live in food deserts get most of their food from processed sources. This means that they're just not getting enough nutrients. Unhealthy people are unhappy people, the perfect targets of advertisements claiming to be selling the next great thing that will make them feel better, if only for a brief, shining moment. I don't necessarily think it's a big corporate conspiracy as much as the resulting effect of compounding selfish schemes to extract profit and energy from human beings themselves.

Of course, it's a really big and complicated system to change. And it's pretty depressing for people to think about, so besides the most sensitive and responsible portion of a population, most people tend toward whatever is cheap, easy and not too upsetting to think about. Of course *real* change can happen in a few ways. Legislation is often slow and not even completely effective as lawyers and lobbyists weave through corporate loopholes. When change can be made fun, hip or even sexy; those techniques all work well. But one of the best inspirations for change is of course a deep and sweeping crisis. Cuba is an interesting case study for the latter and a good example of how to adapt when access to cheap fossil fuels is cut off.

When Cuba lost its Soviet support most of its industrialized monoculture farming practices fell apart. Cubans had no choice but to convert parts of their urban landscape into productive micro-farms, which saved lots of money by minimizing the need to transport produce over large distances. Cuba then employed old farmers, who still had the knowledge, to teach them how to plough with oxen, fertilize with manure and to save seeds for crops that would be more resilient. Many years later one-third of the nation's fruits and vegetables are now produced on urban farms.

But the people hold great power so it doesn't *have* to take a deep crisis to create meaningful change. What I loved about the permaculture course was that in a ninety-minute class we were allowed five minutes to discuss the problems and the rest of the class was dedicated to solutions. This was a beautiful inspiration for how to think about all areas of life. Permaculture is not just about sustainable farming practices but also represents a whole lifestyle design of living in harmony with yourself, plants and other humans. Nature is not wasteful. It's had millennia to create balanced systems so it's at least worth examining for inspiration. By incorporating permaculture design practices, we can create solutions that are both low impact on the environment and encourage regeneration of new, nutrient-rich topsoil. As we become less reliant on external systems, we put power back into the hands of the people. It's for this reason that permaculture is sometimes called a "quiet revolution," a subtly subversive yet incredibly powerful movement.

"When people become able to feed themselves and teach others to do so, we reclaim a lot of our personal sovereignty," I added as I wrapped up my soliloquy.

"Definitely some hippie shit!" Maurizio offered. "So you think we're all going to become farmers again?"

"Ha! Maybe some of us. But we don't all need to. There's at least something that makes us feel good when we know where our food comes from. And it connects us more to our food when we see what it looks like before it's trimmed, sanitized and hermetically sealed in plastic. Working outside together, sharing what we grow and cooking and eating together. This builds social connection and even though it can be tough sometimes, being *interdependent* with your local community feels good."

"It's true. You know in Italy we call this the *slow food* movement. We don't eat fast food. We love to eat. No rush, sometimes lunch lasts four hours. So I understand. America is like a teenager—'*Look, everything is about me!*'" Maurizio grinned. "But it's okay, you'll learn. Remember Emperor Nero in Rome? We all learn in time."

"Seriously. I don't know exactly where the hell America is heading. Where the world is heading. What I DO know is that it's all unravelling right now, that's for sure. Things all over the planet are so fucking crazy right now that there's no longer any way to deny it. What used to be done secretly is being flushed out into the open. Our deepest shadows are coming to light and some of them are getting elected. How's it going to end? Who knows?"

"*Que sera, sera.* Nobody knows, my friend."

When I was learning to ride a motorcycle, my teacher told me, "Focus on where you want the bike to go." And I think about that all the time. So many people are so caught up in what isn't working. They're so caught up in the latest scandal or sensation. It's like they are watching a slow-motion train wreck but they can't seem to turn away. And people focus on all this crap so much that suddenly their world is completely made up of it. Look at our president. Many people laughed and teased him, and yet the more attention they paid, the more attention they literally *paid* to get him elected, and then they watched the insanity morph into this reality.

"So what are we going to do about it?" I asked.

"Ah, eat, dance and make love." Maurizio smiled, and laughed-coughed again. And maybe he was right.

A while later we landed in Mexico City, where I was to catch my connecting flight to Managua, Nicaragua. I said goodbye to Maurizio, who was continuing down to Colombia for some final romance before heading back to Italy. We'd arrived late so a representative from Avianca led a few of us through some back corridors until we popped out at another security checkpoint where we had to get our bags x-rayed once again. I took off my belt, shoes and put my things in the little plastic tray. I walked through the metal detector and was waved over to the x-ray conveyor belt.

"Your bag, sir?" a short, matronly security guard asked as she pointed at my backpack.

"Yes," I replied, suddenly remembering my magical breath mints and swallowing deeply.

"Please." She motioned me to a side table. My stomach began to fold in on itself. *Probably just my chargers, cables. Maybe my extra-large battery pack*? I thought to myself. She unzipped the backpack and began to take things out. A small sack of my electronics. She peeked inside and put it aside. A hoodie sweatshirt and then my mesh travel sack of toiletries.

"This is also yours?"

"Yes."

She unzipped the toiletry bag and began removing items, setting each down on the stainless-steel surface of the table. Her fingers emerged with toothpaste, dental floss, deodorant and then holding the small white bottle filled with green fluid, which contained enough LSD to get everyone in this security area high for an entire week at Burning Man. She twirled it in her fingers and looked at me.

"For fresh breath," I said innocently. "For kissing." Her dark cheeks blushed a little and she put it down next to my toothpaste. Finally she pulled out a small silver object from the sack, my nail clippers. She slowly slid out the tiny, blunt nail file. "You can't take this part on the plane," she said.

"Ha! No problem!" I said, perhaps a little too cheerfully. She proceeded to bend the poor-quality piece of cheap metal until it snapped off. One by one she replaced the items in my toiletries bag and then placed it back into my backpack.

"Have a good flight, sir."

"Thank you, you, too," I said without thinking. As I walked out of the security area, I realized that no wonder airport security guards were always so grumpy. All they did was watch people travel to exotic destinations all day while they had to stand around, bend off people's nail-clipper files and deal with annoyed travelers who replied, "You, too" even though they weren't going anywhere except back home after another shitty shift. This traveler, however, felt as light as a feather as he floated along toward his gate, free as a bird, bound for the sun, fun, and mischief of Nicaragua.

17. San Juan Del Sur, Why Not?

Did you catch that movie where the guy gets hypnotized and then right when he's in a state of bliss, the hypnotist has a heart attack and keels over, dead? Well, the guy remains completely blissed out for the rest of the movie, unaffected by the stresses of the world, and everything just naturally works out for him. And that's how I felt in San Juan del Sur.

Even when I landed in Managua and a clean-cut, clipboard-carrying guy lied to me that I'd missed the last shuttle to the bus station and that I needed to take his friend's taxi; even when the taxi driver's other friend grabbed my bag, walked me to the bus and then demanded a tip; even when the ticket collector on the bus charged me way too much for an express bus that was not only *not* an express bus but which didn't even go to my destination; even when another taxi driver convinced me (again) that I'd missed the last bus to San Juan del Sur and I would need to take his ride; even though it had taken many more hours AND cost me more than if I'd just taken a direct taxi from the airport; even through all of it, this string of naive mishaps, I remained in a state of bliss. Maybe it was the warm and sunny weather, or maybe my new state of mind, but the very next morning I could breathe freely, my sore throat had almost disappeared and the swollen gland in my neck had begun to recede.

San Juan del Sur is a surf town by day and a party town by night. The streets were a mix of young, flip-flopping westerners in board shorts and bikinis and unperturbed locals going about their day. Scooters zipped by and local vendors hollered to advertise their goods. Signs hung outside shops offering surf classes, board rentals and shuttles to one of the many nearby beaches. And if you didn't feel like going to the beach, there were endless restaurants, all-day happy hours and a string of resorts that felt far more fancy than their prices otherwise indicated. It was the perfect place to recuperate.

I bought a new fedora and spent the first couple of days lounging around various locations, sipping agua frescas and jumping into gleaming pools. The evenings in town were warm and the relentless wind of the dry season whipped through the intricate mazes of telephone cables and threatened to tear off rattly tin roofs in its wake. After sunset I strolled around town, graciously turning down drugs from the cigarette boys and sampling street food at the myriad of curbside *comedores*. Old señoras served up heaping plates of BBQ meats and fish alongside the staple rice, beans and plantains. The plastic chairs and tables of the comedores also provided a great forum for people-watching. The street scene was mix of locals and foreigners of different ages, moving between beachside bars and cheap eateries. As always in developing countries I found it impressive how many members of a family could balance on a small, underpowered scooter. And meanwhile back in the United States, SpaceX had just launched a Tesla Model X Roadster into outer space that played David Bowie's "Space Oddity" over and over again on its way to Mars. What a bizarre world we live in.

As I mentioned before, my usual strategy for arriving as a stranger in a strange land is to find the yoga studios and healthy restaurants, to look at their message boards and to find out what "high vibe" things are going on. While San Juan del Sur definitely caters more to a young, party-going surf crowd, there were a couple of yoga studios and one vegan restaurant to check out. The one message board I found had pretty slim pickings, although there was evidence of some permaculture communities and ecovillages that existed in the vicinity.

A couple of days after I arrived I met Nelson, a local surf instructor with a big smile and wildly curly hair that was barely containable under his flat-billed cap. The word on his hat read "Nica," which stood against a sunset surf scene. And this pretty much summed up Nelson perfectly. I took him up on his offer to take a surf class and we headed out to Maderas beach. While extremely friendly, Nelson actually spoke very little English apart from a couple of phrases, which made instruction rather challenging. "Easy for you" was one of his main phrases, which he used to describe almost every wave, and after a few throatfuls of salt water and a chipped tooth, it caused me to lose some trust in his idea of what was easy. He was also somewhat distractible, often flirting with young ladies from Chicas Bravas, the all-female surf camp that also practiced at Maderas. "Party tonight!" Nelson would holler. This was his other main catchphrase, whether or not any party was actually happening.

It might have been the plethora of bars, perpetually drunk tourists or the same, old and not very attractive prostitute that approached me each night asking, "You want sex?" but I quickly realized that the town itself wasn't quite what I was looking for. I craved a little less distraction, some healthy home-cooked meals and some more quiet surroundings to help me re-engage with my personal yoga and meditation practice. Whenever I neglect exercise, meditation, writing and reading I begin to feel anxious, so I was grateful when, through an ad at the local yoga studio, I discovered an apartment for rent just outside of town in a yoga community called El Camino Real. It seemed like a calm, quiet place where I could settle down and put some time into researching this next portion of the trip, so I booked the place for a week. It was close enough to town that I could pop in as needed but I'd be away from all the distractions. And I definitely wouldn't miss the town's juice vendor who would relentlessly yell, "Jugo, jugo, jugo!" at all hours of the day.

The morning that I was moving to El Camino Real I jumped out of bed, because this was the day I would pick up my much-anticipated motorcycle. As I approached El Gringo's rental shop, I saw it out front. It didn't matter that it was underpowered and slightly smaller than it looked in the pictures, it was a gleaming beacon of freedom, a black and red body wrapped around chrome detailing. It had a few dents and dings in it, war stories it kept close to its oil- and gasoline-fueled soul. "Yamaha" was written on its side but I knew its real name was El Rojo, the fiery mechanical steed, the legend of the open Nicaraguan road. This was the moment I'd been waiting for, the dawn of an adventure in which I rode off along dusty roads into the sunset, my cares blowing away in the warm winds of the Nicaraguan night. In other words, probably nothing the tattooed, expat owner of El Gringo's, hadn't already seen countless times in the faces of men much like myself. He was a cool character and gave me some tips about how to deal with possible checkpoints or shady scenarios. After checking my license and signing some papers the shop owner gave me a helmet, the keys, a firm handshake and I was on my way.

Now it's important to note that the traffic rules in Nicaragua are more like traffic *suggestions* and inevitably the more powerful vehicle gets the right of way. This meant that motorcycles were somewhere in the middle of the hierarchy between small cars and motorized fruit carts. I avoided stray dogs, erratic bicyclists and swerving car drivers that didn't use any signals. I was free, and after picking up some groceries I arrived at El Camino Real, a glistening jewel in the hills overlooking the bay. I parked my bike and was waiting next to the crystal-blue pool taking it all in, when my hostess, Tania, came to meet me. We sat down by the pool and she began to share a little bit about herself. Tania was a yoga and surf instructor from France, who lived in the community with her husband and young son and daughter. Previously they'd been a nomadic family but had moved to San Juan del Sur a few years earlier in an attempt to establish roots and give their kids a little more stability. As she talked I took her in; she was tall and lean, probably in her late thirties and her clear and calm eyes connected with mine easily as she talked. A tribal tattoo swirled down from one shoulder—a subtle clue to a wilder side, perhaps? She showed me to my casita, a sweet little apartment just across from the pool. It had its own bathroom, a compact but neat kitchen and was breezy and quiet.

"Well, thank you, Tania. I'm really in need of some healthy, quiet time so this is perfect," I said.

"Ah, it's no problem," she said in her sweet French accent. "I am very happy to have you here; I think we'll be friends. And we can at least try to keep it *mostly* healthy, n'est-ce pas?" She smiled as she extended the key on one finger. Was it just the French accent or was she flirting with me? Who knows anymore? Besides, she was married anyway so I decided the best idea was for me to give up my pursuit for female attention altogether.

I'd downloaded a bunch of travel guides onto my phone, and spent the rest of the afternoon catching up on some travel reading. Did you know, Nicaragua is known as "The Land of Lakes and Volcanoes"? Well, it is to some people and while most of the volcanoes that run along its west coast are considered inactive, smoke and the occasional spurt of lava is still very much a reality for some of them. There is an abundance of opportunities for hiking, camping and swimming in hidden crater lakes and there are some old colonial towns that promise at least a healthy dose of cultural inspiration if needed. I also stumbled upon a website called *NuMundo* that lists all types of intentional communities and ecovillages so I began plotting them on a Google map. And so, the Nicaraguan adventure route began to take shape.

All the while, at the back of my mind there was the loose idea that I was researching locations for other community projects, a place where I might return to visit during the chilly Oregon winters. I enjoyed imagining vibrant hubs of alternative living, showcases of permaculture design and natural building concepts, venues for healthy retreats, unique rental experiences and all sorts of mind, body and spirit-centric stuff! Yep, while my fledgling community project at home stewed in its own deep crisis, I still couldn't help but think the answer to everything in some way centered around community. But whereas I'd been in a pit of despair just a few days earlier I was now living on a cloud, sailing through a sky of deep clarity, understanding my purpose and place in it all: To live in and build experimental communities, because apparently I just can't help myself. These recurring cycles of despair and excitement used to be overwhelming but these days I've learned how to deal with them. When times are dark, I tell myself that they'll inevitably pass. And when I start getting overly excited, I just take a breath and remind myself that it doesn't all have to happen this minute. If it's a good idea it will still be a good idea tomorrow. And next week. And maybe even next year. After enjoying the sunset by the pool, I took the evening to cook, read, journal and generally settle my ass down.

I woke up to the sounds of birds and howler monkeys in the jungles outside, like some sort of tropical version of my cabin back at Manzanita. I did some yoga, ate some fresh fruit and was feeling increasingly grateful about how the first half of the trip had unfolded. My Guatemalan sinus onslaught had almost completely cleared up and my flirtation with insanity at Tikal seemed like a distant, humorous memory. Later that morning I was lounging at the pool, working hard on my tan and daydreaming about where the next few weeks would take me when Tania appeared, wearing a bikini top and cutoff jean shorts.

"Bonjour, Dougie!" She pronounced it "Doogie" but I didn't correct her. Really anything she said in that sweet, French accent sounded delightful. "I see you have some good tanning, aujourd'hui!"

"Yeah, these muscles won't tan themselves, you know?" I joked, and she laughed. "What are you up to?"

"Nothing so much. I'm going into the center. Do you need anything?"

"I think I'm all good. Merci, Tania!"

"Okay." She paused for a moment. "The children are at a friend's house tonight so I was thinking of making some curry in case you want to join?"

"That sounds just lovely!" I replied.

"Great, let's say 7 p.m., chez moi! You can help chop vegetables!" She waved as she glided down the steps away from the pool. "À bientôt!"

When I arrived that evening at Tania's place I was greeted on the porch by a short, dark-skinned fellow who I assumed to be Tania's husband.

"Hi, I'm Dougie," I said. "Are you Tania's husband?"

"Haha, no, no. I'm Fernando. A friend of Tania's."

"Oh, well, nice to meet you, Fernando." We shook hands. His hands were small and rough. Tania appeared, barefoot and wearing a loose-fitting blouse and the same jean shorts from earlier that day.

"Alo, Dougie!" She said as she came to the door. "So you met my friend, Fernando? Ah, good. He is a great surf instructor, one of the best! You should take a lesson with him while you're in town."

"That sounds great."

"Sure, any time. Tania has my number." He slipped on his beat-up flip-flops. I kind of felt like I'd walked in on something and was still trying to figure out the dynamic when Fernando continued: "Okay, I have some business to take care of. I will see you later." He gave Tania a hug and was off.

"Merci, Fernando!" Tania said as she waved me in. "Welcome! So, it's Friday and I thought before we cook, we could have a cocktail. Would you like some rum?"

"Well, a sunset cocktail on a Friday sounds absolutely appropriate, why not?"

"Absolument!" Tania moved into the kitchen and set about pouring a couple of stiff rum and cokes.

Drinks in hand we moved back to the porch, which overlooked the bay.

"I thought Fernando was your husband for a moment."

"Ha!" she laughed. "Fernando wishes this!" And laughed again. "No, Jean-Claude is my husband."

"And where is Jean-Claude this evening? Is he still at work?"

"Hmm, I don't know, let's see …" She glanced at her watch. "No, I think he's probably sleeping."

"Oh, he's not in San Juan del Sur?"

"No, he's in Asia for work. He stays there for three months at a time."

"Wow, three months! That's a long time to be away from home."

"Yes, it is." She didn't seem too upset by it and instead moved into the realm of the completely unexpected. "Hey, we are all very healthy here at El Camino Real most of the time. But it's Friday and Fernando just brought over some very nice cocaine."

"Oh really?" So *that* was what was going on.

"Yes, would you like to try a little?"

"Well, when in San Juan del Sur …" Now, like I say, snorting cocaine has never been a favorite pastime of mine but my willpower was apparently no match for a beautiful French woman who was offering me drugs. Apparently the plan had gone from chopping up vegetables to chopping up lines of cocaine.

We went into the bathroom of the master bedroom and Tania emptied out the small bag onto a mirror. There wasn't a lot so she spread out four lines and split the first one between both her nostrils. I did the same. We stood there for a moment, looking into the mirror at each other and laughing like mischievous teenagers. "More rum!" she clapped.

We headed back to the porch where we continued our suddenly much more excitable and important conversation. We talked about traveling and the nomadic life. Tania and her family had only been here for a year but she was already getting antsy.

"I don't know. Is it because this place isn't perfect?" she asked. "Or is it because we think the next place might be?"

"Exactly!" I said. "It's that familiar lure of travelling, we can blame any problems on the place and just keep moving along to the next one. When is the problem not actually with the place, but something within us?" I asked. "That's why it is important to settle down for a while, to see how we're doing, and then to proceed."

She looked out across the bay and took a long inhale of a cigarette that she'd produced from a small box on the patio's table. "Well, we're trying to at least give it a chance. But I envy your freedom. I used to be like that."

"Well, I am grateful. And it comes with its own challenges. What feels different about this trip compared to previous trips is that I do have a place to go back to." I told her about Manzanita and about the beaver issue, which of course she found hilarious.

"So at least you HOPE you have a place to go back to!" she said. She had a good point.

We took another trip to the bathroom, bare feet gliding across the cool tiled floor, to inhale the rest of the white powder into our heads. More rum followed, along with cigarettes. An unexpected night of rum, cocaine and nicotine.

We were back out on the porch, loosened up by the rum and energized by the cocaine. It didn't take long until the conversation turned to her marriage.

"So how do you guys make it work?" I asked. "I mean, with being separated for months at a time."

"How we make it work?" She paused for a moment. "Well, do we make it work?!" She laughed but there wasn't any sadness present. "Have you heard of monogamy?"

"Of course," I replied.

"Well, we are not monogamy."

"So it's an open relationship?"

"Yes. But more of the 'don't ask, don't tell' variety."

I told her about my own history of non-monogamy and she took a special interest, especially in how my former partner and I had been so communicative about everything.

"I like that idea. But for now, he does his thing and I don't ask."

"And what about you?" I asked.

"And me? I'm fine," she said, but she said it quickly, almost defensively, and I wondered how fine she really was with it.

The conversation moved on and she gave me some interesting insights that really only an expat would know. For example, she said not to buy drugs from the cigarette boys—apparently they didn't have good quality cocaine—and told me which restaurants were constantly giving people food poisoning. It was almost midnight when we finished the bottle of rum. And then, more unexpected delights.

"So I was wondering," she began. "I'm probably not going to be able to go to sleep for a while. And I thought maybe you might want to keep me company?"

"Well, that sounds nice," I replied, trying to keep my cool and suddenly aware of the bitter and smoky taste in my mouth. "I'm going to get my toothbrush."

I walked over to my casita where I picked up my toothbrush, and a couple of condoms--you know, just in case. When I returned the lights had been turned off and the inside was dimly lit by a few candles. And then Tania appeared at the door of the bedroom. She approached me, put her hands on my shoulders, pulling me toward her and kissing me deeply. I was out of breath from the stairs and a little taken by surprise. I pulled away.

"So how many Airbnb guests have you seduced with promises of curry?" I asked. She laughed.

"Actually, you're my first," she said seductively.

"Are you serious?"

"Yes! I am completely serious!" A little more innocently this time.

"And how many men have you been with since you got married?"

"I have only kissed one other man! It's true that I don't usually do this!"

Whether she was telling the truth or not I decided to believe her as it made the whole affair that much sexier, and she lured me into the bedroom. We stood facing each other. I stroked her toned arms as she unbuttoned her loose blouse, revealing the gentle curve of her cleavage. I let my hands fall down the soft slope before parting her blouse to expose her soft breasts. Her nipples stood delightfully at attention, and as I playfully took them between my thumb and forefinger she moaned, her legs seeming to give way ever so slightly as her blouse slipped off her shoulders, falling to the ground. I unbuttoned my shorts as she pulled off my shirt, the tempo of our foreplay increasing. I kicked off my shorts, my underwear already straining under the growing force of my erection. I led her to the bed, and sat on the edge, pulling her toward me, kissing her breasts and belly as I freed her of her jean shorts. She was wearing a thong, the last, impossibly tiny piece of material that stood between us. I turned her around, teasing her as I slowly pulled the thong down, now free to explore the growing wetness between her legs.

Whether I was Tania's first Airbnb conquest or not, she made love with the graciousness of a lover who has been starved of affection for far too long. The fact that we had that in common made the interaction all the more sweet. We took our time, giving each other's bodies our complete attention. We made love for a long while, no doubt fueled by the mixture of rum and cocaine, until we finally collapsed in a heap of sweat, laughter and satisfaction. We cuddled for a while before finding our own comfortable space in the bed, content on a light touch of elbows and feet, before falling asleep to the sound of the San Juan del Sur winds sweeping around the house.

When I woke up, Tania was in the kitchen making us some breakfast. She had some work to do but invited me to a beach later that afternoon where she and her kids were meeting some of their friends, so I gave her a kiss and returned to my place to do some writing. A few hours later I headed back up to Tania's place. Her kids were home and after gathering all the things we loaded up in Tania's SUV and headed south to a secluded beach called El Yankee.

Eventually their friends arrived, another family, and the kids set about playing in the surf. I felt like I needed some exercise so I decided to say my goodbyes and walk down to the next beach, Playa Hermosa. There was no direct route along the beach so I had to walk back out to the main road, which made it a significantly longer walk than expected but gave me the opportunity to scope out some properties for sale along the way. While researching Nicaragua I'd read that the country is still a victim of its own bad image from earlier years but all that was quickly changing. Most attractively, foreigners can own property here without needing to have a local partner. And the prices are low, like it was in Costa Rica ten or fifteen years ago. You can buy an acre of land on an empty plot with water and power hook-ups near a beautiful beach for around $30k. If you want to build something from scratch, construction labor is cheap, especially if you bring the design and act as your own project manager. On the other hand, a well-equipped, already built house can be found for well under $100k and even cheaper if you want to go off the grid, permaculture style, or move further away to less developed areas. Obviously if you want things like a pool and spectacular vistas of lakes or the ocean then it's going to cost a bit more but it's very affordable especially if you have time to hit the ground and interact with the locals instead of going through the more established real estate agencies.

It was getting late so I was grateful to hitch a ride the rest of the way along a particularly hilly section of road, thanks to a friendly Latvian couple, and I just made it to Playa Hermosa for sunset. It was aptly named, a stunningly beautiful beach, a strip of sand sandwiched between breezy trees and perfect surfing waves. A few bars lined the beach, offering lounge chairs, hammocks and drink specials to the chill tourists that had gathered for sunset in this remote little corner of the globe.

The next few days were kind of odd. Despite having received some good sexual satisfaction I was *still* feeling anxious. My meditations were totally distracted. Would I have enough time to do everything I wanted? What were the driving conditions going to be like? What would happen if I got into an accident? *Trying to clear my mind!* My new bathing suit feels too tight. Had I been eating too much? I also should probably buy a rash guard before I surf next time so I don't get wax in my chest hair again. *Holy crap, I can barely keep my mind focused and calm for more than thirty seconds.* I wonder if I'm over my travel budget? When I finally got the money conversation out of my mind I began thinking about my romantic interactions on this trip. When I hadn't had any I felt upset. Now I'd had some and I started wondering if I'd been good enough. I mean I was her first lover in ten years! What if I had been terrible? It seemed that she enjoyed it but she's a yoga instructor and I bet yoga instructors have some crazy flexible sex full of tantric eye-gazing and soul-connecting. *Goddamn it, I can barely keep my mind straight!* Then I was thinking about Maurizio. Was the quest for intimacy and deep connection really worth it? Or would I find simpler satisfaction in short, clear-cut sexual encounters? Does part of me long for a slowly unfolding romance or is that something society has put in my head? *Holy crap, can my mind stop racing already?* And then the meditation bell on my phone rang and I was left sitting there, feeling a little frazzled and wondering if other people are like this or if I was particularly fucking crazy. At least I'd tried, I consoled myself.

I thought about my mind state over a breakfast of beans, avocado and tortillas. Aren't we humans a funny bunch? Even once we have our basic human needs met, many of us still scramble about, trying to fill this great emptiness with all sorts of things. But to "Know Thyself," as Pythagoras said—at least I think it was Pythagoras—is a huge and noble endeavor. I often thought of Maslow's Pyramid, a graphical representation of a hierarchy of needs, including such things as food and shelter near the bottom, and working up toward community all the way to self-actualization at the top. Few people know that by the end of Maslow's life he added another layer above self-actualization, a pinnacle that he called self-transcendence. It made me think back to that mystical teacher Chaty, in her wooden pyramid at Lake Atitlán and the conversation she and Maslow might have had. There felt like a correlation in that it's hard to move up to the next stage without having the foundational needs met first. And yet while so many of us have all our basic needs met we still feel like we're struggling and have a hard time knowing what we need to feel better. I thought back to traumas of my childhood, the bullying, the shouting, the constant feeling that something bad was about to happen. I'd learned to leave my body, to numb the pain, but the ripples of anxiousness remained, locked in my body's memory. Wouldn't it have been nice if I had been taught to give myself what I needed in those moments, to assure myself that I was safe and that everything was okay? Wouldn't this sort of emotional education have served me so much more effectively than quadratic equations or dates of medieval battles?

It was my last day before leaving so I decided to take my mind off things and hop on El Rojo for some exploring. I travelled down gravelly back roads lined with tropical plants to a place called the TreeCasa, a resort with a pretty pool, great drinks and friendly people. I made friends with a couple of young boys who reminded me of myself when I was little. We went down on the water slide in every single way imaginable, until the sun went down and their lips were blue. Afterwards, their mom bought me a drink and thanked me for letting her get some relaxation.

I checked my messages; Tania had invited me out to meet her friends over pizza so I headed back into town to meet her and a bunch of other young mothers. I soon gathered that almost all of their husbands had developed problems with alcohol or cocaine while being down here, so most of them skipped happy hour. In fact, one of their husbands hadn't been seen in days.

"Where is he?" I asked, somewhat surprised by the casualness of it all.

"Who knows?" his wife said. "The last time this happened he ended up appearing after a week of wearing the same clothes. Apparently he'd been to Panama and back." It was fascinating to hear these women talk, all united by life in this strange place, just trying to do the best they could do for their kids. One of them, Debbie, had a twelve-year-old daughter and had actually helped launch the local expat school.

"I've seen a bunch of younger kids around town, but where are all the other older kids? Where are the expat teenagers?" I asked.

"You're seeing them get made!" Debbie said, gesturing at the flock of white kids running around with slices of pizza in their hands. "This is the first batch! Each year my daughter gets older and I need to add a new grade to the school so she can keep attending!" How fascinating to be living in a place so recently discovered by expats that you could witness the first wave of expat teenagers coming of age. These were truly expat pioneers, driven by curiosity. Or at least by sunshine and a darn cheap lifestyle.

Meanwhile Tania was getting a little bit tipsy and flirtatious, playing footsy with me under the table but I felt that it was better to just keep it platonic in front of her friends and kids so I once again said my goodbyes and went to get a large gelato to take my mind off romance.

Later that evening I phoned in to the weekly Manzanita call and things were still hanging in the air like a bad fart that no one wanted to admit to. The equalization issue was still unresolved and everyone was now considering whether they even wanted to continue with this project at all, with more than a couple of members saying they were willing to walk away, foreclose on our loan and cut their losses. I couldn't tell if it was a bluff but this would be a truly terrible direction to take. I tried to console myself by eating all the artisanal Nicaraguan chocolate and drinking all the red wine that I had left in my casita.

It was late but I'd eaten so much damn cacao that I was still wide awake when suddenly the electricity went out. This was followed a few minutes later by a knock on the door. It was Tania, wearing a robe and holding some candles.

"Hey, the electricity just went out so I thought I'd come check on you to make sure you're okay."

"Oh, that's sweet of you," I said as she came inside. She placed a few candles around the room, each one casting shadows around the casita. She returned to me, slipping her silky robe off of her shoulders on to the floor. No more words were spoken.

After an impassioned final session of lovemaking, we lay in bed and I decided it was a perfect time to clear the air.

"Hey, I wanted to make sure that you felt okay about everything before I left."

"Okay?" she said, smirking. "I feel great. You appeared out of nowhere, and brought me to a different world, if only for a short while."

"I'm glad to hear that. I mean, if you don't do this sort of thing very often, I want to make sure that your experience was good."

"From the first time I saw you there was something I was attracted to. And then, you are a wonderful lover, too!" It was a well-timed bump of egoic satisfaction.

"Well, you are going to get the best Airbnb review that you've ever got," I joked as she put back on her robe. She laughed and we kissed once more before she slipped back out the door and into the night.

There was something about the exchange that felt so good. I thought about that diabolical Russian baby experiment, and while I wasn't sure if adults were quite as detrimentally affected, I still felt grateful that she'd given me the touch and human connection that I craved. Meanwhile I had taken her on adventures through my stories. I had been a worthy lover and reminded her of what freedom felt like, to be a wandering nomad with no attachments and the whole world in front of me.

The next morning, I strapped my bags onto El Rojo and said goodbye to Tania. Despite a brief interlude with illicit temptation in San Juan del Sur I was feeling healthy and prepared for the adventures that lay ahead. My time in this little town had taught me two things: the first, that good things happen much more easily when you just stop searching desperately for them, and the second, with a chipped tooth as my proof, that I was not a naturally gifted surfer.

18. El Rojo And Infinity Island

I was sitting at El Pital, a secluded, self-proclaimed chocolate laboratory that I'd discovered down a jungly dirt road on the eastern side of Isla de Ometepe. The island lay a few miles from the western shore of Lake Nicaragua, the largest body of fresh water in Central America. Shaped like the infinity symbol, the island is further characterized by two volcanoes, one called Maderas and the other, Concepción, situated at the other end of the island. Locals say that the twin volcanoes represent the rocky masculine and earthy feminine energies of the island. El Pital lay at the foot of Maderas and there I sat on a bench made from an old surfboard while sipping a chocolate superfood smoothie and enjoying the sunset colors as they washed over Maderas' western foothills. It was my fourth day on the island and I was especially grateful for not having caused anyone egregious bodily harm.

The departure from San Juan del Sur had been an adventure unto itself. I had no lodging reservations, just the open road and a loose plan to head north to León via an inland route. The plan was to head back south to San Juan del Sur a couple of weeks later via a coastal route and to explore the beach towns and a few intentional communities along the way. I wondered if I might find a place where I finally felt balanced. Somewhere a little more mischievous than San Marcos, but a little healthier and more vibrant than San Juan del Sur. My first stop was Isla de Ometepe.

So I had left El Camino Real, zooming down small roads on El Rojo, a Bluetooth headset in my ear feeding me turn-by-turn directions and feeling as free as a smiling loon. Halfway to the coast it had started to drizzle but I was decently protected; my bag and torso were waterproofed and although my pants and shoes got a good soaking at least the rain was warm. There was something exhilarating about not knowing where I was going to end up that night, but the lunchtime ferry would get me over to the island with more than enough time to figure it out. Traveling had changed in the last couple of decades since my first solo international adventure; the smartphone in my pocket, many times faster than the computers that had put a man on the moon, now had constant access to satellites to map my position anywhere in the world. Get a cheap international data plan and any foreign land became instantly accessible by anyone with even a basic grasp of technology. Besides Google Maps, which pointed me toward hotels, pharmacies, and all sorts of other locations, an endless array of apps offered the latest exchange rates, sightseeing suggestions, phrase books and other useful travel tools.

More tech-savvy travelers such as myself, could even summon apps in which translations would appear through augmented reality, and as you held your device up to foreign signs and menus the text shifted and morphed on the screen into your language. The way we documented our travels with crisp photos and videos, combined with an essentially limitless amount of storage space as well as the ability to share this with anyone at any time, completely changed the way we traveled. Many activities that used to be found only through deeper research or interaction with locals were now easily 'discovered.' For better or worse, most of the world was now open to the majority of the selfie-snapping, experience-consuming traveler eager to claim their slice of social media fame, if only in the form of an epic profile picture.

Even social interactions between travelers had changed. Gone were the early millennium days of computer-terminal-lined walls of "cyber cafes," many of which had been replaced by cafes that now provided Wi-Fi and snacks. Even in hostels, people sat together, consumed by their devices at least until lured offline by the next peak experience worthy of documentation. It is the age of the self-centered influencer, the experience junkie. But overall, I reasoned with myself, it was surely a good thing that more people than ever were experiencing life outside of their home bubbles, learning about how different cultures live and bringing pieces back home to share, returning to their old lives as more expansive versions of themselves.

At least that's the story I'm telling myself, I thought as I faithfully let my headset guide me into unknown territory while I steered El Rojo through the rain.

When I arrived in Rivas, a windblown brushstroke of a town whose main feature was the ferry terminal, I was delighted that the one remaining bungee that hadn't been stolen in San Juan del Sur had somehow managed to keep my bag in place. I had arrived a little earlier than expected so I decided to walk around while I waited for the 2:30 p.m. ferry. A little while later, I was staring over the remnants of a rather unappealing sandwich, across the grey waters of Lake Nicaragua to the two protruding rocky breasts of Ometepe, when I heard a rather loud French-Canadian man telling his friend that the 2:30 p.m. ferry had been delayed due to a mechanical issue. I went back to the ticket office and exchanged my ticket for the next ferry, which left at 4 p.m. Around 3:30 p.m. I rode out to the ferry dock and was told to wait off to the side, along with some other motorcycle riders, as the dilapidated red, white and blue ferry began to fill up. Before long, it was so crammed that a dozen men, intent on getting their fridge-loaded truck onboard, had lifted the truck up, puzzle-piecing it sideways into the last remaining space on the boat. And just like that, the ferry crew began raising the ramp and waved us away. On cue a tropical downpour began.

The small group of motorcyclists exchanged frustrated looks and profanities, mounted their rides and begrudgingly rode back down the pier. The ticket office where I'd bought the original ticket was now closed but a different company's booth had opened, now selling tickets for the 5 p.m. ferry. Of course, they didn't honor the other company's tickets so everyone had to now buy a second ticket. More frustration and profanities were exchanged but I gave in and forked over a few more dollars.

The rain continued as we returned to the dock and waited. The 5 p.m. ferry finally arrived and the same process began to unfold. The ferry was three-quarters loaded and yet the motorcyclists were still not being allowed on. The frustration was growing as the horde of motorcycles, now about twenty strong and all jockeying to be first in line, waited with their engines idling. And all of a sudden, when the crew member directing traffic got distracted by a large approaching school bus, a small woman on a tiny moped made a move, zipping toward the ramp. In an instant, following her lead, a bunch of us took off, making it up the ramp into the boat while narrowly avoiding skidding out on its slippery surface. Hearing some shouts behind me, and concerned I would be caught and ejected from the ferry, I quickly wove through the cars, found a spot, locked my bike and disappeared into the crowd that had gathered inside the last ferry of the day.

Before long, I had struck up a conversation with a Nicaraguan doctor who was dedicated to sharing both the revelations of his Christian faith and lamentations of how poorly doctors were paid. Eventually, he excused himself, apparently nauseous from the choppy water and I turned to my cell phone to find a budget hotel on the fast-approaching island. I found one near the Moyogalpa ferry terminal and booked myself in for the night.

Because of the confusion at Rivas, the ferry docked at a completely different terminal than I expected it to, in the small town of San José del Sur and a twenty-minute drive from Moyogalpa. So I mounted up and followed my headset's directions, weaving down a dark, wet road until I finally found my hostel. After I'd dropped my bags and changed into some dry clothes, I returned to the lobby of Hostel Casa Moreno where I ran into the same French-Canadian guy whom I'd overheard while waiting for the ferry earlier that day. He wore a soccer jersey with the red and white Canadian maple leaf emblazoned on it. Within a few minutes he'd roped me and a young Australian girl who'd been glued to her phone in the lobby, to join him for dinner and together we strolled toward the town's center.

This guy, David, was a short, thick fellow and possessed the sort of comically obnoxious character that on the one hand I found hard to deal with, and on the other I couldn't help but be fascinated by. He dominated the conversation with large hand gestures and a relentless monologue so I sat back with a beer and bummed a cigarette from Gaby the Auzzie. Unable to get a word in edgewise we both seemed content to sit in silence and behold the self-promotional glory of David's worldly exploits.

"So it was unbelievable, man," said David, who had the nasally twang indicative of the Quebecois. "I was one month into hiking the Appalachian Trail when this wolf pup, who couldn't have been much more than a year old, became pretty sure that I was his mother. I named her Niya and from then on, we started travelling together. We protected each other. Once Niya fought off a rattlesnake—I'm serious!" The waiter arrived and we managed to place rushed orders, a variety of local fare, in between David's exuberant storytelling.

"At one point these people tried to threaten Niya so I pulled out a crowbar that I travelled with"—why he was hiking with a crowbar was anyone's guess—"and threatened them off! Later that day Niya caught us a turkey. A fuckin wild turkey, man! So I defeathered it, removed its guts and strapped it to my backpack. As I reached the next camp I found the same damn bastards who'd threatened Niya. Imagine, I arrive at camp with a wolf, crowbar in one hand and a turkey in the other! Well, they quickly became my friends and we had a feast on the Appalachian Trail!" And so it went on.

After a deep and heavy sleep, I awoke to David's voice emanating from the lobby where he was telling some poor soul about his "most amazing breakfast recipe, man!" A short while later he came into the dorm. "We're all going to breakfast!" he exclaimed to the remaining sleeping inhabitants and I joined him, despite myself. After a coffee and scrambled eggs across the street we all parted ways, me on my motorcycle and David on foot, still wearing his Canadian T-shirt and hiking poles strapped to his backpack. We left Gaby where we first found her, in the lobby of Casa Moreno, smoking cigarettes and laughing at her phone. David had invited me to hike Vulcán Concepción and I wasn't sure which would have been more challenging, the rocky, muddy hike or his tireless chatter, so I had politely declined. I was quickly discovering that a wonderful thing about travelling by motorcycle is that at any point you can just smile, make your excuses, and hit the road. None of that awkward "Oh you're also going to *there, too?* Maybe we can all go together!" Don't get me wrong, that sort of travel can have delightful and unexpected results, as my memories from Semuc Champey reminded me, but some people can be tiresome travel companions and it was nice to have an escape vehicle.

I headed south on the west coast, with Volcán Concepción on my left, toward the slim central part of the island where I'd cross over to the eastern side and on to the lower incline of Volcán Maderas. The roads, which I'd heard were so rough, were in fact mostly smooth, curving gently as I enjoyed the moist air and morning sunshine. I was on my way to a 10 a.m. tour of Zopiloté, a unique permaculture community that also doubled as a hostel and restaurant. The southeastern side of the island had a welcoming flavor, with colorful signs that promised coastal lodging, delicious food, organic chocolate and other enticements for weary travelers. Eventually I arrived at Zopiloté and turned into a parking lot near the road. I loaded up my backpack, locked up El Rojo and started walking up the rocky path. And kept walking. And walking. Fifteen minutes later, and after helping a huffing and puffing older woman with her completely inappropriate-for-adventure rolling suitcase during a particularly rough stretch, I found myself on a neatly maintained stone path that led to the front desk. Just beyond was a large amount of smiling, happy backpackers sitting and yammering away in the dining area. I was greeted by a dreadlocked, tanned woman and the smell of freshly baked bread. I inquired about a room.

"You are lucky! We have one room left, but it still has to be cleaned. The tour has not yet started, so if you like you can leave your bag here and afterwards we can show you to your room."

A small and friendly group had gathered for the permaculture tour and after some introductions we set off. On the way out of the dining room we passed the front desk where the older woman with the rolling suitcase now stood, red-faced. The woman at the desk looked at her apologetically.

"I'm sorry, we just booked our last room," she said. A slice of guilt welled up inside me. But I let it go, not guilty enough apparently to make any gallant offers. After all, I used to be the guy with the rolling suitcase and we all have to learn somehow.

Zopiloté was spread across many acres and could host up to eighty visitors at any one point. The property extended up the side of Volcán Maderas, crisscrossed by small paths that linked together dwellings and other structures, each showcasing natural building styles and sitting adjacent to neatly tended gardens and fields. Apparently much of the food that the restaurant served was made from ingredients grown right here on the land. The whole project was run as a business and also hosted workshops and other gatherings as a source of revenue. The community aspect was integral to its function as many of the things that needed doing were done by shrewd travelers looking for work trade in exchange for lodging.

After the tour I went back to the front desk to get my backpack and then to my room, which was back up the volcano on a property called Elsewhere Land that annexed Zopiloté. I was happy to get there just before the rain began again, and even more happy to find out that

Charlotte, a curvy young woman who had also been on the tour, was my neighbor. After I moved into my room, which was only slightly larger than the bed, we struck up a conversation.

"Oh, not *another* French Canadian!" I joked after she told me where she was from.

"Why do you say that?!" she exclaimed. I told her about David.

"Well, he sounds charming," she said, and we both laughed. "There's a lot of Canadians travelling now. The freezing temperatures back home make the winter a great time of the year to travel." Charlotte was as far as you could get from David and was quiet and demure in how she interacted. Her features were as soft as her voice, round and smooth. She looked sporty, too, poured into a pair of black yoga pants, which hugged her womanly form.

"So, what adventures do you have planned for Ometepe?" I asked.

"Oh, I don't know, I heard there are some waterfalls on the other side of Maderas."

"I've heard the same. There's also a pretty unique kayak experience that cuts through the center of the island."

"I heard that part of the island is hard to get to."

"Well, what do you think about jumping on the back of a random guy's motorcycle who you just met on the side of a volcano?" I said confidently. She laughed.

And just like that, the following day's adventure was born.

Later that evening, after a game of Bingo in the dining area, a burly guy in cool motorcycle pants and a beaten-up jacket checked in to the hostel. I struck up a conversation, asking him about his motorcycle, and he showed me pictures of a powerful KLM model, as I tried to avoid feeling a little emasculated by the sheer size of his machine. Fabian was from Belgium and possessed the sort of manliness that made me sit up a little straighter and throw my shoulders back a little more.

"So, what have you been up to on Ometepe?" I asked, changing the subject from motorcycles before I had to offer up El Rojo's limited specs.

"Well, I just went around the southwestern side of the island," Fabian said.

"Oh really?" I asked. "How was that? We're doing that tomorrow."

"Well, it was more challenging than I expected," he said in a serious tone. "Not a great road, would be tough with a weaker bike. And I'm glad I didn't have my girlfriend on the back!"

"Haha!" I swallowed deeply. "Good to know!" Another round of Bingo started but I finished my beer, said goodnight and hit the sack.

The following morning, after a power breakfast of oats, honey and superfood seeds, Charlotte and I set off down the hill to the parking lot, loaded up on El Rojo, hit the road back toward the intersection and then south along the southwestern shore of Ometepe. Between the two of us we had pretty much maxed out El Rojo's load capacity and Charlotte bobbed on the back, holding on to me tightly. Fabian had spooked me a little, but by now I'd had some good practice and at first it seemed like the section to the waterfall wasn't too bad after all. And then, almost immediately as that thought passed my mind, the reality set in. The road became terrible. Luckily, along much of it there was a narrow band that other bikes had apparently smoothed out but El Rojo repeatedly bottomed out on big bumps as the wheels scrambled for traction over loose rocks. The trick was you had to go slow enough to be safe but fast enough to have the momentum to stay upright. This is where a powerful bike is preferable, and a weak one, with a shitty clutch and a passenger on the back, driven by a novice, is less so.

Besides the odd mangy dog and occasional oncoming vehicle that played chicken to stay on the smoother parts of the rocky road, we eventually made it to the entrance to the Cascada San Ramon waterfalls, the highest falls in Nicaragua.

"You can ride the motorcycle further up to make the hike shorter," the guard at the entrance said. "Or you can leave it here and have a longer hike."

"Oh, you know, I could use a nice walk!" I blurted. It was only when we got off the bike and I uncurled my fingers that I realized how hard I'd been gripping onto the steering bar. I'd never been so happy to be on my feet again—well, at least since not killing myself or Coco on the ride to Antelope Falls back in Belize. Charlotte and I had a spectacular few-mile hike up to a waterfall, cooling off along with other adventurous folks who'd made the long climb.

"You know what, Charlotte?" I asked as we dried off on the edge of the crystal-clear pool.

"What?" she asked, squinting in the bright afternoon sunlight.

"I pride myself in my ability to design a good adventure," I said with a mock air of self-aggrandizement. "And my adventure-guide instinct tells me that if we leave now, we can make it to a sunset kayak trip before heading back to Zopiloté." It would mean driving back some of the rocky road after dark, but it felt too tempting to resist.

"Hmm, I need to be careful with my money. I'm leaving tomorrow for Popoyo and I still need to pay for another night in the dorms at Zopiloté. I hadn't budgeted for also going kayaking."

"Well, I have an idea," I smiled. "I have a large bed" — embellishing reality just a wee bit. "Why don't you just stay with me tonight and then you don't have to pay for a dorm. And then instead you can afford kayaking!"

"What a gentleman!" she laughed.

"Not enough of a gentleman to pay for your kayak, apparently!"

"Good, because I wouldn't allow you to."

"Now I wish I'd offered! Just a warning, though, I snore loudly, sleep naked and move around a lot." I kept my face serious just long enough for it to become awkward. She was taken aback for a moment. "Ha! I'm just kidding." Her face eased up. "But I don't mind if you do. Sleep naked, I mean." She laughed again and after a short consideration, cool as ever, Charlotte agreed to my financially creative and gentlemanly plan.

We dried off, descended the mountain and hopped back on El Rojo. The ride north back along the same road didn't seem quite as treacherous as it had earlier and we only bottomed out and fishtailed a couple of times.

Within an hour we arrived at the Rio Istian kayak launch, and while we waited for our guide to ready our vessels his mother served us a fine meal of rice, beans and charbroiled chicken. A short time later we were each in a kayak paddling north, following the western shore of Ometepe toward the middle of the island. Once there we found a small, almost invisible inlet, which allowed our kayaks into the interior of the island and we were soon paddling up Rio Istian, a river that sits between two volcanos and cuts through the middle of an infinity symbol-shaped island that sits in a giant lake—surely the only place in the world you can do that? There was not a single other tourist in sight and for a while we were quiet with our thoughts, disturbed only by the sounds of our paddles gently lapping the water. I took in the rugged beauty of the scene and felt humbled, incredibly small and insignificant in comparison to the large volcanoes on either side of me. Our guide for the adventure, Jorge, led us through mangroves and up secluded waterways that were shaded by overhanging trees, pointing out birds and monkeys along the way. Deeper into the island the surface of the water became so thick with plant life that our oars came up tangled in clumps of leaves and roots. We were floating on a thick, green carpet and Jorge enjoyed dislodging bits and pieces and flinging them at me, much to Charlotte's amusement.

"Accident! Accident!" Jorge laughed as I splashed him back.

We circled back and eventually reemerged into Lake Nicaragua just as the sun was setting, reflecting rich hues of purples and pinks off of the calm surface of the lake and framing the two kayaks in front of me, a dreamy scene of melting peach and strawberry sorbet. I smiled to myself, satisfied by the perfect timing of it all as we made our way back to the launch.

Besides El Rojo's erratic clutch, which occasionally popped out of first gear and into neutral, we made it home safely. It was dark by the time we got back to Zopiloté and we were welcomed like heroes with a feast that had been prepared in our honor! Well, at least it felt like that. In reality Zopiloté's weekly pizza night was in full swing. But once again I was returning from a grand adventure with an intact lady friend, and that was enough of a reason to claim heroic status, drink beer and eat a well-deserved pizza. A couple of hundred people had gathered and were laughing, drinking and eating pizzas that were flying out of a large earthen oven at an impressive rate. Pizza servers whizzed around the large open-air courtyard, calling numbers and hunting for pizza owners. It was a scene of total disorder but somehow it all seemed to work and pizzas found their correct bellies. Afterward, despite stuffing ourselves we danced to the beat of a drum circle that had sprung up around the fire pit. We were both so tired when we got back to my room that I barely remember my head touching the pillow. A couple of times during the night I was the big spoon. And then I was the little spoon. And then when I woke up, Charlotte had left for Popoyo as planned, leaving only a faint floral smell on her pillow and the memories of our shared adventure. It was refreshing not to have felt any need to pursue romance, just the appreciation of good company, if only for an ephemeral afternoon.

And so here I was, sipping a chocolate superfood smoothie at El Pital. A girl was practicing a slack line that was strung up between two trees while an incredibly well-toned young man, probably around nineteen years old, had paddle-boarded out onto the calm, lapping waters of Lake Nicaragua. I appreciated how calm and quiet this island was in comparison to San Juan del Sur, which was only a couple of hours away but felt like an entirely different world. I had spent the day catching up on some communication back home, planning the next leg of my journey and figuring out the cryptic schedule of mainland-bound ferries. I also arranged a morning tour of an intentional community called InanItah, which I'd hit on my way back north to the ferry terminal.

One of my reasons for this foray into Central America, albeit an admittedly loose one, was to explore existing intentional communities to see what was working. InanItah, which was apparently quite successful, was run by a woman named Gaia whom I had met some weeks earlier at the Cosmic Convergence festival on Lake Atitlán. I was looking forward to finally hearing a community success story. How had they been successful? How had they overcome challenges? What solutions and inspiration could I bring back to Manzanita—that is, if there was any Manzanita to return to—as a bright point of illumination and inspiration for our struggling community. I read up on InanItah, crafted some questions to ask Gaia and got an early night back at Zopiloté, draped by a questionably effective mosquito net and lulled to sleep by the rhythmic sounds of the jungle.

19. The Myth Of Community

The road to InanItah made the trip to the waterfall look like a beginner's motorcycle class. Gaia had initially provided walking directions from Zopiloté through a series of rural paths, but almost certain that I'd get lost, and already being tight on time to catch the early afternoon ferry, I opted to pack up my bag, load it on El Rojo and track the place down on motorcycle instead.

After heading north for some way I turned left at a large white rock on the side of the road, which the helpful dreadlocked woman at the front desk of Zopiloté had told me to look out for, and I was soon skidding up a path of mud, loose rock and the remnants of some old stone steps that looked like they'd been around for millennia. At least I didn't have anyone on the back this time. The struggling beast was barely powerful enough to stay upright on the steep path and I cursed myself for not choosing a more off-road model.

After narrowly avoiding some rather startled chickens who clucked and flustered themselves away into a nearby shrub, I arrived at InanItah. As soon as I arrived, I realized that something wasn't quite right. I parked the bike near a natural earthen structure that turned out to be a community kitchen which was open on all sides to the fresh air. It was lunchtime and some people had gathered. I began to introduce myself and said I was looking for Gaia. I'm a pretty friendly guy and can talk to just about anyone. I'm also empathetic enough to realize when I'm not very welcome, and most of the people seemed pretty disinterested in me. I wasn't offered any food that was being served up and was told to wait around and Gaia "would probably arrive sometime soon." Eventually I found a nice resident who I struck up a conversation with until Gaia arrived and greeted me. Gaia was a strong woman, in her late-forties, with dirty-blonde hair and piercing blue eyes that immediately hinted at her story: she'd been through some shit and survived to tell the tale.

"You made it up the hill on a motorcycle. Good job!" she said. "Remind me, where did we meet again?" It was apparent that she had other things on her mind than me and my visit. I told her that we'd met at her talk about creating intentional communities a few weeks earlier at Cosmic.

"Oh, yes I remember. To be honest it's been a bit of a challenging time, so please excuse me. Will you join us for lunch?"

"I'd love that," I replied. Once I'd been welcomed officially by Gaia I could feel the others in the community begin to relax a little. So often with these remote places people tend to become overprotective and wary of outsiders. I'd seen it happen before in other communities. People say they like people, and like living in community, but in many cases once they've got their little piece carved out, their protective and even anti-social instincts kick in. Even back at Manzanita, a place that had been a retreat center and welcomed hundreds of people, there had been a lot of talk of how to create boundaries with the outside. And to be honest, some of that is good, you don't want just anyone to show up. But when and if they do show up it's nice to welcome them with at least a little congeniality. Somewhere between an open-door policy and the concrete-and-barbed-wire fence of Greengo's was probably the right amount.

From what I'd heard, InanItah was a great example of an intentional community, in that it was formed with an intention in mind, one that unites a community in a shared set of values, clear mission, way of life and other such goals. I asked Gaia about how it had been formed.

"InanItah was consciously created to be an earth-based spiritual community and transformational living and learning center," Gaia told me. "We were inspired by the path of freedom and aliveness. Our vision is to raise spiritual and environmental consciousness and create space for individual and collective transformation."

"And how do you achieve that?" I asked, aware that she'd probably been asked this sort of thing a hundred times over the years.

"There's a current expansion in human consciousness going on and a collective urge for a practical spirituality. We are responding to this by offering classes, workshops and gatherings to integrate the internal human landscape with the environment," Gaia continued. "We co-create the opportunity to live in community and in harmony with nature and to consciously transform ourselves."

It all sounded pretty great, so why did I sense some subdued nostalgia in Gaia's tone? She seemed a little busy but still kindly offered to take me around on a tour and answer some of my questions, so after a good lunch of quinoa and organic veggies we went on a walk. The place was as beautiful as it was remote—teepees, thatched huts and other structures were dotted all around the land. I asked her about them.

"Each building at InanItah is a unique handcrafted work of art, constructed using natural building techniques and made from locally available stone, timber, clay soil, straw and grasses. When people are here, they can stay in one of our unique private cabins, the shared dormitory, or camp outdoors. We live off the grid, relying on solar energy, human engineering and appropriate technologies to supply our electrical and comfort needs." As we walked, I asked her about how it all started and she continued her story.

"My partner and I bought InanItah around ten years ago and began building. The vision was to create a largely self-sustaining and locally-sourced permaculture and tantra community and offer workshops and retreats." Now I sensed some remorse, possibly even resentment in her voice. Her piercing eyes softened up for just long enough for me to sense another side of her, a more vulnerable side. "And now after ten years we're breaking up. He's got a new lover and thinks we can just all go right into being friends! I don't think it's going to be that easy."

"That is tough," I replied, genuinely feeling her frustration. "So, what are you guys going to do?"

"InanItah was born of my fiery spirit and Paul's watery soul, much like the fire and water volcanoes that come together to form Ometepe," Gaia explained, her gaze once again assuming a protective, defiant quality. "Well, in the same way that each of the volcanoes stands free of the other we will now independently hold space at InanItah during different seasons."

A fiery spirit, indeed. You could tell as much from the way Gaia carried herself as she walked through the community, commanding a powerful presence and doling out instructions as she went. She was the kind of woman who you wanted to keep on your side.

"So now we are each here in six-month increments. I'm just finishing up mine, and he's arriving soon so I'm getting the place ready for the trade-off. Some people will stay, many will go. And a bunch of new ones arrive with him."

Well, that explained the vibe I'd gotten upon arrival and the slight freneticism in the air. When business partnerships become entangled with romance, it can be a risky recipe for longevity. Apparently she had wanted to bring in other business partners in the earlier days but Paul hadn't wanted to. "Some of those people put in a huge amount of work, but eventually, after not being awarded any ownership, they left the project." It rang a familiar bell in my mind, back to some of my own early business endeavors where the selfishness of some individuals had derailed the project for all. "Without a path toward some sort of ownership people don't often give it their best," Gaia had continued, "and their efforts eventually are exhausted."

"I completely understand what you mean," I added, and decided to steer the conversation into more productive territory. "So, what are the ways people can get involved here?"

"Everyone who comes to stay here does at least a couple of days of work a week. Some of the longer-term community members pay something for their lodging but eat for free and are also involved in half work days. There are a few tiers. We call them Explorers, Collaborators and Space Holders, all with different responsibilities. There's occasionally movement between the tiers but people tend to settle into their roles."

"And so how do you support the project financially? Do you sell things that you make or grow?"

"We don't really make any products here. Money comes in through people staying on the land or through the events and retreats that we host."

"And how do things function in the community? Is there a schedule? How are any disagreements handled?"

"Each morning we offer optional daily yoga and meditation and in general things work pretty smoothly. Of course, altercations happen in a community so we have what we call Transparency Circles each morning where people can check in in case anything is coming up as well as discussing projects that are on the roster for that day. Generally, afternoons are free and sometimes there are community evening plans." I noticed that as she focused on the things that were working, of which there seemed to be many, she began to settle down. She'd obviously helped build so many things over the years, crafting pieces of a community culture that was still evolving, even if in unexpected ways.

I began to realize that perhaps it was me who had arrived with a somewhat misplaced energy, and that what I'd originally taken to be unfriendliness at the kitchen was actually just an unclear energetic exchange. I was an outsider on a tight schedule, intent on gleaning information. As far as they were concerned, I had descended upon their community, a community in transition, that seemed to move with the slower speed of nature. InanItah made me miss the quietness of my cabin back at Manzanita.

At the top of the land, Gaia pointed out a carved petroglyph that flanked an entranceway to a couple of pools from which you could see the slopes of Volcán Concepción on the other side of the island, its summit shrouded in mist. I wondered how David, the odd little French-Canadian man, had fared. Had he made it to the top? Regardless of whether he had or not, I imagined that he was loudly telling some people somewhere all about the experience. I was glad that despite having a tendency to talk a lot, I still knew when to shut up and listen to others.

We passed a wood-heated hot tub and Tonto, InanItah's pet pig, on the way over to Gaia's hut, where she busied herself packing and cleaning up. I sat on the deck, looking out across the valley framed by lush foliage and bright red flowers that punctuated the landscape. As we talked I felt her begin to open up to me more, once again letting her guard down a little bit.

"To be honest I'm not even sure where I'm going. I didn't really think it would end up like this." We talked about different models of community organization, from holacracy to sociocracy, and who was doing it right. Some of the most well-known communities were Damanhur in Italy, Oroville in India and Findhorn in Scotland. "The reality is that all communities have problems." She continued, "The successful ones just work through them. There's some good stuff happening in the U.S., too. As well as some of the biggest egos I've ever seen. But also some of the most interesting things happening, from a business perspective." She took a breath. "I guess ego and business often go hand in hand, even in community. Do you want to see my new project?"

"Oh, I'm not sure I have time, I'm trying to make the after-lunch ferry."

"Oh, it's close. Right next door, in fact," she said, a wave of optimism coming over her. "Once we broke up I decided to buy a twenty or so acre plot of land next door. You actually need to walk through InanItah to get to it."

"And how's that working out for everyone?" I asked somewhat humorously.

"Well, then Paul bought twenty more acres next to that one." Admittedly property here was incredibly cheap, but I didn't inquire further about how that all was going to work out. "There's actually an amazing five-acre property near the main road for USD$20,000 in case you know of anyone interested." At that price it was certainly intriguing but it also made me wonder: with Nicaragua being one of the few places that foreigners could purchase property, how much of this island gem was actually foreign-owned, and how did that impact the place?

"Does InanItah work with the local community?" I asked.

"We have a non-profit educational organization that works closely with our community to provide live-in, sustainable educational experiences, workshops and classes, as well as social and educational programs for the local Nicaraguan community." I admired Gaia for the thoughtfulness and work she'd put into this project. "Come on, let's go."

We left her hut and walked up the hillside, over a fence and into an adjacent field that had sweeping views of the island all the way to Concepción and beyond, birds swooping in the afternoon breeze. Near the top of the field a team of builders, some local and some foreign, were assembling a roof on top of a round structure. "To be honest, I'm not sure exactly what I'm going to do with this place. But in the meantime, I'm building a small structure. It'll have an amazing view, don't you think?"

Gaia began giving instructions in fluent Spanish. It was getting late and I still had to ride halfway across the island to catch the afternoon ferry, so I thanked Gaia for her time.

"You know how to find your way out?" she said. Her guard was back up and she was in project-manager mode. I wondered if her fiery spirit, her relentless desire to build, was at the same time both her strength and her way to deal with her hurt. As I followed the path back down the hill, back through InanItah, I felt grateful to have had such a deep insight into this fascinating community and how it came to be. I said goodbye to some people who were still mingling around the kitchen, hopped on El Rojo and bumped and skidded my way back down the steep, rocky trail.

Once I hit the pavement I tightened the stressed bungees that held my backpack to El Rojo and set off toward the ferry terminal. As I rode along, past the quaint little hostels and restaurants of Playa Santa Cruz and the tiny town of Santo Domingo, I thought about the visit, which had provided some good insights into the challenges that these communal experiences face. As Gaia's tale illustrated, it took huge amounts of energy to start and sustain these projects, and their success is still never guaranteed. And yet people all over the world continue to try to make it work.

An hour or so later I steered into Moyogalpa, the rusty, pastel-toned town of restaurants and storefronts where I'd stayed a few nights earlier. A handful of peeling passenger and cargo boats were bobbing gently around the dock. As I waited for the ferry to the mainland, I checked my email. My eye immediately and unavoidably locked on an email to the Manzanita list: "Wave 1 Loan Offer." Our weekly phone meetings had become increasingly tense ordeals, a dreaded two-hour contusion in everyone's week. During our last meeting, in an attempt to soften our communications Teddy Bear Gabe had established the terms Wave 1 and Wave 2. Wave 1 represented the earliest members, who also happened to be part of the *pro-beaver* group, while Wave 2, the *beaver-hesitant* group, was comprised of the members who had joined the project a few months into the planning. I'd somehow been the only member to avoid being lumped into either Wave so did my best to continue my role as an inter-Wave diplomat and lift the mood by providing stories and inspiration from my travels.

"It seems like every community struggles," I had replied, in an attempt to stem the despair back at Manzanita. "What makes a good community is how they navigate the storm."

To all of our credit we were still attempting to resolve the problems and keep the community intact, and the "Wave 1 Loan

Offer" email offered a solution. Remember how everyone had just thrown in whatever money they had at the beginning of the project? And remember that an equalization strategy had been drafted but Wave 1 didn't have the extra funds needed? Well, this email was an offer from Wave 2 to loan Wave 1 the funds they needed to meet the equalization terms. Surely if we could work that part out then we could work the rest out, too?

Of course this solution might solve one problem but it also created another. Wave 2 didn't have enough money to both loan Wave 1 the funds they needed to equalize AND to also pay off the loan with the former owners. We just needed more time to figure it out. Time we didn't have.

20. Granada Nights

I don't know what it is, but there's something about Nicaragua that just makes me want to throw my good behavior out the window and get downright rowdy. After all, when a bottle of rum costs USD$3 and a pack of smokes costs USD$1.50 it's almost like you're *losing* money if you don't partake. So here I was, lying on a raggedy couch, my throat scratchy from a night of drinking and smoking, and my chest hair sparkling with glitter. A couple of hours earlier, I found myself in a treehouse, the uninvited guest at a bizarre wedding and witness to the strange tradition of penis limbo.

The motorcycle ride from Ometepe to Granada had been smooth, besides a short rainstorm and an aching meniscus from my days spent scrambling around the island's volcanoes. Granada, which sits near the northern shores of Lake Nicaragua, is known as one of the country's prettier towns and whose old colonial architecture is still largely intact. While on the ferry from Ometepe to the mainland, I struck up a conversation with an excitable Aussie woman named Betty. She told me about a hostel in Granada called the Oasis where she was planning on staying, so upon rolling into town I decided to check it out. The Oasis had been converted from a giant colonial residence into a vibrant, yet low-budget, backpacker destination and had a nice, relaxed atmosphere. I decided the hostel's pretty courtyards would be a good place to catch up with my journaling so I booked a dorm bed for a couple of nights. I parked El Rojo inside, along with some other motorcycles, next to a giant, peeling mural of dancing ladies.

After checking in, I had been shown to my quarters, one of four beds in a small room. The Oasis provided a locker for my bag, a personal fan to help with the heat and a power outlet next to my bed. Sharing the room with me was a sweet girl from California and two hulking German guys. I chose the lower bed in a rickety, two-level bunk that shook to the point of collapse when Fritz, my bunkmate, clambered into his upper bunk. Boarding school memories from my childhood flashed into my mind, but I was hopeful that unlike homesick eight-year-olds, grown men rarely wet their beds.

And so a couple of days later, there I was, sitting on the previously mentioned raggedy couch next to a communal kitchen, and feeling a little worse for wear. It was late, and since I wasn't able to sleep, I sat in the courtyard recording a journal entry. The rest of the hostel was asleep, except for a small group of thickly accented, cigarette-smoking Israeli backpackers who busied themselves whipping up a large batch of hummus in the kitchen. I was poking at a tasteless tamale that I had spiced up with some local hot sauce in an attempt to mask its blandness. After a while the Israelis finished preparing their midnight snack. Like other hostels, the Oasis was packed with people of all different ages, travelers from different countries who often delighted in sharing their customs and traditions with other travelers. *But not these Israelis and not this hummus.*

"Good night, man!" one waved to me as the trio headed back to their room, unshared hummus in hand. I returned somewhat bitterly to my cold tamale and journal entry, and set about capturing the details from the day.

It had all started innocently enough. After a solid sleep, I'd ventured out into the breakfast area. One of the perks of the Oasis was that they provided eggs and pancakes in the morning and the dining area was a flurry of activity. I saw Betty across the patio, sitting at a table next to a small pool and surrounded by a bunch of fun-looking characters. I loaded up a large plate and headed over.

"Hey everybody, eggs on me!" When you act like a goofball who already knows everyone it can be remarkably easy to be welcomed into a group of random people.

"Ah, the egg man has arrived!" a young, smiley and attractive American guy replied. "I'm Charlie." Both his hair and his skin possessed the sun-kissed, golden quality of a life dedicated to the beach.

"Dougie, you made it!" Betty cried in an excited shrill. I sat down and smiled. One of the recurring themes of this trip seemed to be that as soon as I felt confident and solid within myself, things would just start to fit together effortlessly. Traveling is an especially good time to practice going with the flow, to witness how our energy levels and external situations influence our mood, and the regularly shifting context consistently offers the opportunity to practice how we act and react.

Besides bubbly Betty and beach bum Charlie the other people at the table included a couple of Canadian guys, my California roommate, who was named Alexis and a Swedish woman named Helga. Stories of their previous night began to emerge, during which a karaoke escapade had ended in an orgy between the two Canadians and Helga, and I greatly admired how everyone was laughing about it all over their eggs and pancakes. After breakfast we continued to lounge around the pool, where we were joined by a mom with her two kids, a boy of four and a girl of six. She was from Minnesota, traveling alone, and appreciated us entertaining her kids while she got to relax. In fact, we were all having so much fun that we decided to go on a day of sightseeing together.

After getting dressed we met back up in the lobby. Charlie and I put the kids on our shoulders and we set off, an impromptu family of ten or so new friends, ranging in age from four to fifty. We walked around the quaint, cobbled streets of Granada, visiting art galleries, climbing up the bell tower of the town's church, and zigzagging through a bustling market where we bought ice creams for the kids and beers for ourselves.

An hour or so later I broke off from the group, jumped on El Rojo and headed out of town, along dusty roads and through farmlands, on my way to check out a series of islands called Las Isletas. These numerous tiny islands had been created during a massive volcanic explosion millennia ago which had left rocky remnants scattered all around a peninsula at the north end of Lake Nicaragua. After getting a little lost when my Bluetooth headset led me to the incorrect destination, I eventually found a bunch of leathery-skinned men loitering around a restaurant next to a small marina of motorboats. There were no other tourists so I decided to haggle with one of them.

After some back and forth with one fellow we settled on a price and set out on a late afternoon boat tour. Las Isletas is home to all sorts of private homes, old forts and rundown structures. I made it back from the boat tour with just enough time to successfully deflect Diego's demands for additional money and to navigate safely back to the Oasis for happy hour.

Back at the hostel the rum was flowing and I soon met back up with my friends from the morning who were already good and sauced-up. During happy hour, I heard murmurings of a party at a place called the Treehouse and noted down some cryptic directions for how to get there. I did my best to rally the breakfast posse but still exhausted from karaoke and the orgy the previous night, besides all once again being plastered, they decided to keep it low-key so I headed out by myself into the warm night air of Grenada.

The Treehouse was in a remote location just outside of town, and accessible only to those who knew the back roads, or as it was in my case, to those who knew of a secret shuttle that left at a certain time from a shady bar that I'd heard about at happy hour. I had a couple of drinks at the bar and soon a group of about ten gringos had gathered and were loaded up into the back of a pickup truck that soon sped off, out of town. I was grateful to have scored the shotgun seat next to the speeding driver and watched as the revelers in the back got their faces slapped and hats knocked off by low hanging jungle vines. Twenty minutes or so later we were dropped at the foot of a rocky forest path. The driver pointed into the forest and said he'd be back in a few hours to pick us up. He then got back in his truck and promptly zoomed away, back down the dark, dirt road from which we'd come. Our initial excitement had given way to a little more apprehension but with little other option the group of us set off into the forest.

After a muddy, jagged, fifteen-minute climb with only sporadic solar-powered lanterns to indicate that we were on the right path, we were grateful to hear voices of merriment and soon emerged into a scene of sparkling revelry. The Treehouse was made up of a series of suspended walkways, hammocks, lofted platforms and janky structures all rigged up and fastened to trees and anchored to rocky outcrops. When we arrived, the party was in full swing and we had no idea that we were actually crashing the wedding reception of a tall Austrian man to a starry eyed, young French woman.

I looked around and my tripper-sense tingled; most of those in attendance were almost certainly on a large amount of psychedelics. To add to the already bizarre scene everyone at the party was dressed in drag. And so it was no surprise that upon our approach to the dance floor we were promptly directed to a large box of various pieces of clothing. I ditched my grey jeans and black T-shirt for a tight, gold miniskirt, thin blouse and flamboyant hat:

"You know it's a good party when getting into drag makes you stand out *less,*" I said to a girl who'd also arrived with me. She laughed as she pulled a glittery item from the box.

After getting a drink at the bar, a smiling fellow in a red velvet bodysuit approached me, his pupils as big as saucers.

"Welcome, beautiful man! I'm Sparkles!" He grinned like a loon. Sparkles was flanked by a giggling girl, both of whom were in their early twenties and obviously high as kites. "Looks like *someone* hasn't been glittered yet!" And that's when I noticed the sheer amount of glitter that surrounded me. It was on glowing faces, on the dance floor, on the surrounding paths and even on the trees. It was like a giant unicorn with irritable bowel syndrome had farted rainbow sprinkles over the entire party; meanwhile, my new friend Sparkles was already heaping a glittery mound into the girl's hands.

"Close your eyes!" Sparkles said. The girl squealed gleefully as she blew the entire pile onto my face and exposed chest. And then, as quickly as they'd appeared Sparkles and his jubilant assistant moved along to the next glitter victim.

After the psytrance DJ *finally* took a break, a variety of nontraditional wedding traditions got underway, including a twerkshop led by a beautifully voluptuous woman whose copious butt movements reverberated throughout the entire suspended platform. This impressive act was followed by a much-anticipated round of penis limbo. One fellow, whose costume was made up of shiny sneakers, a rainbow Afro, sweat bands and a whole bunch of glitter, had tied a piece of ribbon between his penis and a bar stool, under which a line of eager contestants began to limbo. With each round, the naked fellow squatted a little lower as the stool wobbled and the crowd cheered. On the other side of the dance floor I saw Fritz, my German roommate from the Oasis, looking somewhat awkward in a tight, furry vest and silver fishnets. His buddy, who I'd still never actually seen sober, was propped up on the bar, wearing a form-fitting onesie and silver star-shaped sunglasses, so drunk that he was barely able to stand. After watching penis limbo for a little while longer I decided to go explore the rest of the place before witnessing the inevitable penile disaster. I was halfway across a suspension bridge that led away from the dance floor when I heard the stool tumble and the naked man yelp in strained glee, no doubt signaling the end of the penis limbo tournament. The walkway led to a series of tented platforms that were full of beds. At the end of the walkway a few metal steps led up to a platform that was perched over the cliff. Sounds of sex came from the mosquito-net-draped bedroom, moans emanating out into the jungle night. The whole scene at the Treehouse was a puritanical nightmare of excess and debauchery, an unabashed display of hedonism playing out in the treetops. I gotta tell ya, it was pretty great.

A few hours, a bunch of rum and plenty of strange multithreaded conversations later I carefully descended the rocky path just in time to catch the last shuttle home. It started raining as we drove back toward Grenada and I could only imagine how the scene at the Treehouse was unfolding. It was one of those magical nights that had luckily concluded before daylight cast the whole mess into stark reality. It was late when I finally got back to the Oasis, but I was still feeling poetically lyrical from the booze so I settled down in the courtyard to collect my thoughts and attempt to work my way through this awful tamale.

I marveled at how my Grenada experience was so far removed from the high-vibe, hippie-conscious community of Lake Atitlán. It was like all the yoga, meditation, healthy food and cacao ceremonies had been replaced with rum, cigarettes and illicit drug use. Instead of ecstatic dance in the clouds there were now acid weddings in the jungle. I thought about how my external environment had such a powerful influence on my behavior. It felt like just when I got closest to clarity, to deep connection with myself and others, I would hit the *"Let's throw it all out the window"* button and revert to mindlessly debauched behavior that would invariably leave me feeling numb and energetically depleted, *but often with a great story.*

This was an old pattern. *But what's wrong with a little partying now and then? I'd tell myself.* Of course, within a relatively short span of time my balance inevitably tipped from the higher-vibe activities toward excessive food, sex, alcohol and pretty much any other vice I could find. Once the party was really rolling, I would typically get into an increasingly celebratory mood until before you know it, BAM! I'm in drag at a psychedelic wedding watching penis limbo.

I finished up my journal entry, pushed the remnants of the tamale away and pulled my last cigarette from the pack. How much of this celebration, how much of this travel and quest for peak experiences is just another form of escape? *Maybe it was time to rein it in just a little bit?* My plan was to ride up to León in a couple of days where I had heard there was a variety of volcano expeditions, and if I was going to haul a heavy backpack up and down a mountain then I better have a few days of healthy eating. *And no more drinking or smoking for a while, jeez!* I took a long final drag from the cigarette.

The following morning, after the complementary eggs and pancakes, I would say goodbye to my drunken friends and head to a place to the north of Grenada called Hostel Paradiso, which lay on the edge of the Apoyo lagoon. From the photos it looked calm and serene, far away from the big-city distractions. Surely there I would find the rest and relaxation I needed. Well, it turns out I was very wrong about that and the temptations of Nicaragua were just getting started.

21. Sex With The Cosmos

After a sexually barren adolescence followed by largely bungled exploits in my mid-teens, I finally reached college, which provided ample opportunity to catch up on practice. However, it was the arrival of my "dirty thirties" that really heralded the most memorable period, as of yet, of erotic discovery. These have been delightful times indeed. During the past two decades I had been lucky enough to sample a variety of different types of lovers and fantasies. Steamy memories of tattooed emo chicks, unexpected threesomes, exotic belly dancers and Irish bridesmaids all dance through my carnal nostalgia.

After a stint of living in Asia in my early twenties I discovered I was a great fan of oiled-up massages, explored the world of prostitution and even got to experience the unexpected surprise of a Thai ladyboy. So, all in all, if I died tomorrow, I could say that I had had some memorable sexy times. But could I say that I had had sex with *the cosmos*? I hadn't even considered the concept until a few weeks earlier when I'd been talking to Nadia, my Russian tantrika roommate in San Marcos, about the evolution of her sexuality.

"When you are truly connected on a deep and intimate level," Nadia had said, "then you are making love not only to the other person but to the cosmos itself."

"And how exactly do you know that you and the cosmos are getting it on?"

"Oh, you'll know. You'll know when your bodies, hearts and minds meld into one. When the pulse of your sexuality is the pulse of all that is alive. When your breath becomes the expansion of the universe itself. In that moment you are beyond any concept of time, identity. You are one with everything, an infinite being of light."

"Well, that sounds nice." I'd have to keep experimenting.

A few days prior I'd woken up at the Oasis, staggered out of my room loosely draped in a towel, intent on taking a shower. I was feeling soft and pudgy in the face from nights of drinking and hoarse from too many cigarettes. A couple of local guys who were painting a wall looked at me and started laughing. When I got to the bathroom and looked in the mirror I remembered why. My chest and head were covered in glitter, the sparkly remnants of a raucous evening. But I rallied, said my goodbyes and departed from Grenada fueled by free eggs and pancakes.

The drive was smooth, weaving through rural backroads and finally descending along the north side of a dormant volcanic crater lake known as Apoyo Lagoon. It was early afternoon when I pulled into the Paradiso Hostel, which sat right on the water's edge. As I entered, I felt like I'd arrived at a pretty, if somewhat worse-for-wear Mediterranean resort. White walls sprung up from red-tiled patios, small casitas dotted around the place and bright pink bougainvillea wove through lattice walls that framed a restaurant that overlooked the crater lake. The tables were filled with smiling faces, all possessing the same expression: "We have found paradise!" Private rooms were about thirty dollars per night but I decided to settle on a dorm bunk for twelve dollars. The plan was to just take it easy and I didn't need the added temptation of bringing anyone back to my room.

"No need to carry any cash here, everything gets put on your room number," the helpful tan man at the registration desk said. "We have a variety of tours and excursions that leave each day. There are towels and chairs down on the beach and you can get food and drinks down there, too. Enjoy!"

I dropped my belongings, changed into my swimming suit and descended a beautiful path that led to the shore. People were splashing around on floaties and kayaks while others were basking in the sun, and diving off of a platform that was anchored offshore. I was feeling friendly so over the next couple of hours I had social butterflied my way across the beach and out to the diving platform. While tanning my Scottish Italian hide, I struck up a conversation with a rabble of Canadian nurses who'd taken a break from their ER jobs and were all on a week's holiday together.

"Oh, you get used to it," one of them had said. "People come in completely mangled, missing or holding parts of themselves. You see some gnarly stuff. And then you get off, and go grab a bite, have a drink, do the laundry or whatever. I mean it's just a job."

It was early evening by the time I returned to the shore and a tanned woman wearing an orange bikini and golden-tinted shades smiled at me. I recognized her as a Dutch woman from the Oasis. I think her name was Mila. It was typical along the backpacker circuit to repeatedly run into the same people and Mila and I had met during a happy hour. It had been fun, at least until her drunk friend, who had been rather abusive toward my status as an American, vomited on herself and had to be taken care of.

"Hi there," I said.

"Hi! Didn't I meet you at the Oasis?" she asked, pushing her sunglasses up on top of her brown hair, revealing bright green eyes. She was probably around thirty and possessed an attractive air of confidence.

"Yeah, happy hour, I think. How's your friend?" I asked.

"Oh! HA! She's okay. She's not usually such a sloppy, mean drunk."

"Well, I thought she was just delightful," I said sarcastically. She laughed.

"Want to join me for a rum at the bar?" she asked. Oh, how easily the devil appears.

A fun group had gathered at the bar but after a couple of rum and cokes I was finally hitting a wall, and made my excuses, something about going to lie down and read a book.

"Well, that's not as fun as hanging out with us," Mila said, flashing me a flirtatious grin. "It's trivia night tonight. Maybe we could be on the same team."

"I'll try to make it down." Despite her attractiveness and apparent interest in me, my honest intention was to just lie down and read my book.

"Don't be ridiculous. We'll see you later." She shot me another mischievous smile as I turned to go.

I got back to my bunk, messaged my dear mother to tell her I was still alive and pulled out my travel book. I began to read up on León, my next destination, and think about what I wanted to do there. I was in need of some exercise and a good backpacking excursion could be just the thing. León was also an important holdout during the revolution and would no doubt have some good history and museums to check out.

Eventually sounds of laughter and music drifted up from the shore. My imagination turned to Mila's flirty smile. "You really should get some rest," I thought to myself. "But it's still early and you only live once. But you have been drinking a little too much lately. But you'll certainly have some healthy days ahead." And so my internal dialogue played out until one side was victorious; I arrived back at the bar just as trivia night was moving into its second round. Mila beamed when she saw me and waved me over.

"He's on our team." Mila hollered to Santiago, one of the Paradiso's employees, who was leading the game. I was attracted to her bravado. She gestured at a rickety chair next to her as she scooted her chair over. I sat down, sandwiched between flirty Mila and her *delightful* friend.

"Oh, good to see you again!" I said as wholeheartedly as I could muster.

"Oh, hi again, Captain America," her friend said, her tone one of jest mixed with a shot of sheepishness. "Sorry for the other night."

The trivia questions seemed to all have been chosen from my high school years, things I hadn't thought about in ages but the answers just fell out of my head and onto our game card. There were about five teams and soon our team, *The Paradisco Divas*, had climbed up from last place all the way to second with one more round to go. Meanwhile the chair I was sitting on was so structurally challenged that it kept leaning toward Mila, our legs brushing against one another's under the table. This provided a subtle opportunity to flirt, and a good way to test the waters.

"It's not me," I grinned. "It's the chair."

"Uh, huh." She smiled, but didn't recoil. The waters were warm.

The rum flowed. It was easy to be generous when liquor is cheap and the only thing you needed to say to the waiter is your room number. I bought a round for our whole team. To keep it healthy, I thought to myself, I would avoid the coke and just drink my rum with a little soda and lime. And it would probably be my last one anyway.

"MEATLOAF!!!" the Divas yelled in sync, the correct answer to some atrocious song from the 90s. What exactly was it that Meatloaf wouldn't "do" from that song? Did he ever say?

And so, with a final string of correct answers, the Divas took first place. And what prize did the winning team get? A bottle of rum, of course. About twenty-five people had gathered and the entire place was in a celebratory mood. I could feel my inner party animal begin to awaken.

"Okay, everyone, we have a serious question now," the dashing Santiago hollered above the din. People went quiet. "How about a game of Rollick?"

"Yes! And I have no idea what that is!" some drunk person yelled. Everyone laughed.

A group of about twenty or so people pulled some tables and chairs together and the posse was split into two teams. The challenge was to act out a word that you were given on a card. Some people were better at acting, some better at guessing, some people's English wasn't very good but everyone was still having a great time. A while later one of the bartenders came up and talked to Santiago.

"Okay, everyone," Santiago said. "The bar is closing up but they said we can stay. So if you want anything now is a good time to ask them." We ordered twenty bottles of beer and three bottles of rum with mixers. "No problem," the waiter said and went off to get our drinks. Gotta love how things work down here.

The rum continued to flow. There were some jolly drunks, some combative drunks and one melancholy, twenty-year-old girl from France. Well, soon enough even the innocent enough game of Rollick turned competitive. We'd been playing for points and keeping score on a scorecard and suddenly it all started getting more edgy. Even Mila, who was now on the other team and had been making snarky comments about how I was cheating, was getting a little more aggressive. I wanted things to be fun and flirty again; I began thinking about how to weave some social magic.

Our team was winning, but even so Martin, my German teammate, was constantly arguing about something or other. The French girl was looking increasingly glum. My social senses told me that things were going to soon come to a head. How could I help navigate the frenetic energy of this social situation to some sort of grand finale that would make everyone happy, instead of just disintegrating or arguing about points? By now, Santiago was flirting with another member of staff off to the side and of little help in managing the situation, so I decided to take charge. Something in me felt this moment called for something big, and in an instant that something took over my whole being.

"I have an idea!" I exclaimed loudly. The chatter fell silent. I picked up the scorecard, crumpled it up dramatically and threw it over my shoulder.

"But …" Martin started, but I interrupted him and began to outline my plan.

"The warm-up rounds are finished, my friends! We have now come to the ultimate round." I said. I felt my heart begin to beat faster, reminding me of being on stage at school plays. "Welcome to … SUDDEN DEATH!" All eyes were on me. "The first team to ten points wins. Now who's got a coin?"

The other team won the toss and before long it was 8-9 with them in the lead. But in a stunning victory we took the next two rounds with the winning words being "sunset" and "clown," which felt oddly appropriate. I could tell there was still some lingering upset feelings and so in a moment of divine inspiration I summoned the best drunken Southern Baptist minister I could and rose up from the beer- and rum-strewn table.

"My friends!" I rallied. "We are explorers. We have come from distant lands spread all across the globe. To discover new places, new cultures and even new family! We are on-the-ground diplomats for our countries, for our cultures, for our communities!" I felt chills of excitement move around my body. "Can I get a 'Hallelujah!'"

"HALLELUJAH!" the people agreed.

"We have found joy, we have found challenges, indeed we have found each other at this volcanic lagoon. But most importantly my friends, most importantly we have found ourselves. Can I get a 'Praise Be!?!'"

"PRAISE BE!" the crowd clamored. I picked up a damp cocktail napkin, mopped my brow for effect and began waving it around. "So, as this day comes to a close, let's not ask who won, because when I look around this room, I see the truth. The truth, my brothers and sisters, is that we are ALL winners here. Can I get an 'Amen!?'"

"AMEN!" They were hanging on my every word. And now the following wasn't something I would *normally* do but it was still warm, I was rummed up and sweaty from the gameplay and so it seemed appropriate in this instance.

"And at the end of such a blessed day, what is left to be done?" I started unbuttoning my shirt. "What is left to be done but to shed these restrictive clothes?" My shirt fell to the ground and I began to take off my shorts. Eyes were wide. Thankfully I wasn't alone and Martin had begun to take off his clothes, too. "Let us run, my brothers and sisters, let us run toward that gleaming path of moonlight and into the cool water beyond!? WE ARE SAVED!" I turned and ran toward the beach.

As my feet touched the sand I removed my underwear, my pasty butt no doubt glistening in the moonlight. I splashed into the water and dove in. At first I didn't hear anyone joining me, but soon I heard a splash, and then another, and before I knew it there were about a dozen other people splashing around and laughing under the stars.

I swam out to the platform and lay on my back, looking at the Milky Way, laughing at the whole situation, laughing at the sheer unlikeliness of every experience that led to this funny moment, naked on a platform and floating on a volcanic lake in a land far from home. But most of all I was laughing at myself, at my own socially fueled hedonistic behavior, and how humorously weak my willpower could be at times. A flirtatious sunset clown, I laughed to myself.

Speaking of flirtation, what had happened to Mila? This had all been fun, but wouldn't it be even *more* fun with that sassy Dutch flirt? Surely my fantastic performance at both trivia and Rollick, not to mention my inspiring wrap-up as a Southern Baptist minister, had only made her more enamored by my charm and wit? *Surely!* But I looked around and saw no sign of her. Eventually I dove off the platform into the pitch-black water and began swimming back to shore.

As my feet touched the sandy bottom, I saw a curvy silhouette walking toward the water. Was it? Could it be?

"How is it?" a voice said. Mila's voice.

"It's perfect now that you're getting in." She laughed as she waded out to where I was standing.

"You think you're quite the entertainer, don't you?"

"Oh, thank you!" I replied, feigning that I misheard her.

"Well, you are pretty good at games. Even if you cheat a little sometimes." She swam out to where I was, just as another couple of people swam up and we all began chatting and laughing about the night's shenanigans. Mila's body brushed against me, her smooth legs glancing mine. Eventually the conversation petered out and we drifted away from the other couple, finding our own slice of the darkness.

"I'm getting chilly," Mila said.

"Well, we can practice hugging," I joked, and before long Mila and I were in each other's arms, and I felt the warm buzz of arousal move through my body. She stood up, the water lapping at her navel as she slipped out of her bikini top, one of the strings hanging for a moment on a hard nipple, a beam of moonlight making her pert breasts glow in monochrome. We made our way to shallower water and she straddled me. It was exceedingly sexy but not the most comfortable place for romance.

"I have a good idea. How about we go find a nice comfortable spot up on the beach.

"I like that idea," she said, her eyelids lowered and her voice deep and breathy. We walked up onto the beach and I grabbed my shorts, in which I'd optimistically put some "just-in-case" condoms. In my other hand I began to drag a giant beanbag-type thing over to a shadowy nook on the side of the cove. A few people were finishing off the final rum up at the bar but it was unlikely they could see us and I don't think either of us cared that much anyway.

No words were exchanged as we lay down next to each other. It's always so fascinating to me how people's characters evolve as they become aroused. All of Mila's snark was now gone, her hard European armor had been lowered and in this moment she felt completely present with me. She slipped out of her bikini bottoms, revealing a neatly coiffed tuft of pubic hair. She then straddled me and began to tease my growing erection. No words, just hot breathing and electric pulses as communication. I could already feel her slippery wetness so I reached over for a condom and with the most skillful dexterity I could muster I removed it from its packaging, avoiding contact with any sand. Nothing ruins the beachside fun like sand in a vagina. I could feel Mila's hunger as I slipped inside her sweet warmth. *Yoni meet lingam.* I smiled to myself, thinking about the terms that Nadia had used to describe the human genitals. Mila rode on top of me, a perfectly curved silhouette surrounded by a sea of stars. The water lapped at the shore nearby. I felt like I was having sex with a goddess, a Valkyrie on her steed, riding to victory! As I lay there, pleasure receptors firing off all around my body, I kid you not, an honest-to-Buddha shooting star shot right across the sky behind her. I laughed lightly.

"What's funny," she asked, breathing heavily.

"I think I'm having sex with the cosmos!" I grinned. She smiled and groaned even deeper. Afterwards we cuddled and talked about where we were going next. It didn't seem likely that we'd meet up again but neither of us mentioned that fact. Just more practice at living in the moment and not clinging too tightly. Eventually we played treasure hunt for our various items of clothing and headed back to our separate dorms.

The following morning I woke up less groggy than I was expecting but still the prospect of packing up my things and driving the few hours to León seemed thoroughly unattractive. As I approached the reception desk to inform them that I was staying another night I ran into Mila and her friend, who were checking out. The friend shot me a glance that said, "I know what you did!" and Mila smiled. They were heading toward the coast for some surfing adventures. Social media info was ceremoniously exchanged. Goodbyes, I always felt, were best kept short and sweet.

I walked into the restaurant on a cloud, flinging greetings and niceties at the breakfasters.

"Hey, we were just talking about you." It was Charlie from Oasis, and Betty was sitting next to him. "You're one of the most positive people we've ever met."

"Oh, that's sweet to hear first thing in the morning. Thanks, Charlie!"

"We came here because of YOU! It's amazing here," Betty said.

"You guys don't even know! I was going to leave today but I'm going to take it easy and stay another night."

"Great, let's hang."

Later that day, I found myself once again lounging on the floating platform where I met some Belgian guys who loved techno and who were heading to Grenada that afternoon. I told them about the Treehouse, which I said explained the glitter that was still embedded in much of my beard and chest hair. I'd heard that they had

Tuesday techno nights so I gave them all the instructions on how to get there. They were psyched.

On the other side of me was a cool young guy from Michigan, just super chill. His name was Jim and he was heading up to León the following day and also exploring hikes. I told him that I had found a two-day volcano expedition that went to a volcano called El Hoyo. He sounded interested so I said we should trade contact info before we left and maybe go on one together. I also told him that I had some magical treats to share.

I was high on life. A lot of people from the day before had left and I finally was able to catch up on some rest and reading. After dinner I met a group of fun-loving American guys had arrived who were wrapping up a wild bachelor party tour of Nicaragua. Everyone else had gone to bed but I decided to have a little rum, just a taste, to celebrate with these guys. They regaled me with stories of their debauched nights filled with drugs, decadence and strippers. I turned down the cocaine when they offered it to me. Cigars were lit and soon conversations were speedily overlapping each other.

"Are you sure you don't want some coke? It's really good quality."

"What the hell. Why not? It's not every day you get to sample the local delicacies." Apparently a couple of rums and being asked twice was all it took to erode my pathetic willpower. I took the bullet and snorted a bump in each nostril. Sure enough it was good. And strong.

Within a few moments I felt the bitter drip hit the back of my throat reminding me of parties from my early twenties in Los Angeles. Almost instantly my energy became amplified, any lingering body aches evaporated and soon, like the others, I wanted to talk about everything regardless of its actual importance, with great gusto. But it was fun to hear their stories. They were mostly doctors, which I was at first surprised about, but they said that it was pretty typical that doctors party as hard as they work. The groom-to-be was getting married to a spicy Tex-Mex woman who would no doubt be very curious about everything they had done in Nicaragua. This was their last night before heading back to Grenada the following day, back to work, back to their wives. There was something so humorously cliché about it all. Eventually, after the buzz wore off and a joint had been passed around, I was ready to call it a night. I said goodnight to the fellas and retired to my bunk, tossing and turning for an hour until drifting off into a collage of jagged, semi-lucid dreams.

I awoke to another beautiful morning at the Paradiso, immediately wondering how much I had made a loud-mouthed asshole of myself the previous night, another side effect of coke-fueled benders. In the grand scheme of things, I think I had held it mostly together. After breakfast I ran into the bachelor boys who were about to catch a taxi back to Grenada to catch their flight to Wisconsin.

"Hey Dougie!" one of them said. He walked over to me. "Good times last night, man! Damn, we were up 'til sunrise!"

"Haha, I bet! Yeah, thanks for that."

"Well, listen," the one who'd offered me the bullet said in a hushed voice. "Try as we might we didn't even *nearly* finish our cocaine and we didn't want to travel with it, so we hid it under the trash bag in Room 32. So if you want it, you know where it is," he said and smiled. "Have fun, buddy!"

"Oh, thanks!" I said. "Travel safely, guys. Good luck with the wedding!"

While the last thing I wanted was a bag of coke I'm also not one to look a gift horse in the mouth so I took a detour over to Room 32 and sure enough found a large baggie of white powder just where he'd said it was. I pocketed it, returned to the reception and checked out. Two rum-fueled nights, all the delicious meals plus lodging came to under a hundred bucks. I was walking back to my room to pack my bags when I ran into Charlie. I told him about how my night had gone. He laughed.

"Hey, you don't like mushrooms by any chance, do you?" he asked me.

"I love mushrooms! Why?"

"Well, before they left one of those bachelor guys gave me a bag!"

"That IS funny. One of those guys gave ME a bag of cocaine and I'm not sure what I'm going to do with it!"

"I love cocaine! Want to trade?" Charlie asked.

We both laughed as we traded and pocketed our gifts from the American doctors.

"See you when I see you, buddy. Say goodbye to Betty for me," I said. "And do everything I wouldn't do," I said, tapping my nostril. I gave him a hug, and we parted ways.

I returned to my room, packed up my backpack, loaded up El Rojo and headed north to León, away from the volcanic lagoon and the pristine, mischievous shores of the Hostel Paradiso.

22. El Hoyo And The Butterfly

Dogs and chickens were everywhere, kids playing with an upside-down table, potato chip bags littered the roadside and there wasn't another gringo in sight. I was sitting at a small food stall somewhere along the road to León, eating a lunch of BBQ pork, salad, tortillas and chimichurri and sitting on a cheap plastic chair that overlooked a stretch of sugarcane fields.

Interesting side note: A good portion of the Nicaraguan countryside is owned by a liquor company called Flor de Caña, which manufactures rum that is so abundant that you can buy a large bottle for USD$4. This fact obviously did little to help with my temptations and I was worse for wear after my unexpected run-in with Flor de Caña and other vices at the Paradiso. My legs were stiff and cramped from the drive, my jaw ached from the cocaine-fueled teeth-clenching, and overall my body was feeling run down.

My usual buoyant mood was somewhat deflated and something within me felt uneasy. I wondered what I was doing out here, making fleeting friendships, drinking and smoking too many cigarettes and snorting cocaine from random strangers. This didn't really feel like my best self, at least not the self I intended to be. Luckily I knew better than to make sweeping life judgments on days like this and instead to just clamber back onto the wagon with as much grace and as little self-judgment as possible lest I spiral further into the depravity. I would officially limit the booze, throw out the rest of the pack of cigarettes, this time for real, and eat more healthily. And I'd start right after this BBQ pork. Far better to search out the healthier hostels, stick to yoga and stay mostly sober—besides, of course, the occasional psychedelic trip.

Speaking of psychedelics, I was looking forward to the volcano adventure. Before leaving the Paradiso I'd rallied a few others to join the expedition, whom I'd coordinate with upon my arrival in León. I relish the kind of adventures during which I left my regular life, or even my regular planet, behind and jettisoned into an experience that might be bizarre, strenuous and maybe even a little dangerous.

Over the years I'd led groups of psychonauts all over the West Coast of the U.S., to abandoned ghost towns and old mines, to sand dunes by moonlight, to the strange world of the Salton Sea and Slab City, to eclipses on smoky lakes, and countless other exploits. I've personally enjoyed, at least most of the time enjoyed, over one hundred psychedelic experiences from Disneyland to Cirque du Soleil, from countless festivals to wilderness expeditions with a mind swirling in psychedelic compounds. Things sometimes get weird, but never quite as weird as my first time in drag, and way too high on LSD, at the Doo Dah Parade in 2009. But that's a story for another time. Why *do* these things? Isn't life already colorful enough already? All I know is that each time I would return to earth a stronger, more resilient version of myself. Things I may not have wanted to face are revealed in stark clarity. Things that I'm grasping too tightly onto begin to fall away into irrelevance. Restrictions and judgments, be they socially or self-imposed, become loosened. And it's all fun and games until sometimes, just once in a while, I maybe take things a little too far.

After arriving in León, I dropped my things off at Lazybones hostel and walked over to the Quetzaltrekkers office to reserve my spot for the following day's trek. The two-day trip cost sixty-nine dollars for an all-included adventure that featured three volcanoes, as well as sledding down one called Cerro Negro on some sort of makeshift sled. I'd decided to go with a volunteer-run tour outfit as their price was low and they used any proceeds to pay local guides and support local schools. It would soon become apparent that they further lowered costs by cutting some corners here and there. You know, *for the kids!* I had coordinated with Jim, the chill guy from the Paradiso, to meet at their offices the next morning, along with a couple of the others whom I'd roped in to the adventure, including a young

Swedish couple named Hugo and Freja whom I'd befriended at the Treehouse glitter party.

That evening I was planning on finding a gym to have a good workout. Instead I joined the others for pizza. But rather than curse my willpower, I congratulated myself for having water instead of rum, and making it an early night in preparation for the strenuous journey ahead.

The following morning, after parking El Rojo in Lazybones' courtyard and leaving a good portion of my belongings in a locker, I walked over to Quetzaltrekkers with my largely empty backpack containing just a few items I'd need on the hike. I am an experienced hiker and in pretty decent shape, and now that my pack was light I wasn't very concerned. Upon arriving at Quetzaltrekkers however, we were informed that we would be carrying all of the food, water and gear that our group would need for the trip. Apparently the price we paid was not sufficient to hire Sherpas and as we loaded up our packs we exchanged concerned glances. Quetzaltrekkers' tents were old and thus heavier than more modern equipment and the large amount of water added a heavy load.

"My pack is even heavier than when it was full with all my stuff!" Freja exclaimed glumly as we heaved our packs on to the waiting truck. There was some nervous laughter from others in the group.

A handful of others had joined the group just for the day and together we set off down the cobblestone streets toward the outskirts of the city. We arrived, bones well-rattled, at our first stop, the Cerro Negro volcano, which we'd be climbing with smaller packs and makeshift sleds. The plan was that we would strap ourselves to the sled and then hurl ourselves down the side of the volcano. Cerro Negro is a large and steep cinder-cone, its sides comprised of sharp scree, and we were also each given gloves, thick yellow canvas jumpsuits and goggles like the ones you got in science class. As we wove our way up our guide told us stories about people who'd been hurt on its slopes.

"Some years ago, a world-famous mountain biker came here to set a record for the fastest downhill speed. On his third attempt he hit 170 km/hour just before his bike split in two. He broke the record, as well as fifty percent of the bones in his body." There was silence among the hikers. "He was in the hospital for almost a full year. But the funny part of the story is that in the meantime he fell in love with his nurse and they eventually got married. So you never know why things happen."

We kept walking up the rough incline until we reached Cerro Negro's windy summit, where we donned the heavy canvas jumpsuit and gloves. One of the guides directed us to the route where we'd be descending and showed us how to use the sled's steering and brakes, both of which seemed rather ineffective. It was impossible to see the bottom because of the exponential downward curve of the volcano, but one by one we sat faithfully on our sleds and launched into the unknown, quickly gathering speed and disappearing out of the view of the remaining waiting sledders. The whole way down I was aware of the mountain biker story as well as the amount of grit that was being kicked up into my face and under the poor seal of my goggles. A few people fell off their sleds but suffered only minor scrapes and bruises. I'm not too old for this shit yet, but I'm getting close, I thought to myself.

Once we had all descended, we got in the waiting truck and took off toward the entrance of the park, where the overnight trekkers got dropped off. We waved to the day-trippers who zoomed back toward their pools and happy hours while we prepared ourselves for the expedition ahead.

There were ten of us in total, including the guides. Me, chill Jim, the young Swedes, a frenetic Viennese man named Hans, a hopelessly in love German couple and a Swiss guy named Michael, who always wore a fedora. Our local guide, Gonzales, was joined by Dennis, a somewhat awkward fellow who seemed like he'd just graduated from a Boy Scout senior academy. His clothes were clean. He had glasses and a very neat haircut. I couldn't place his accent. At first I thought he might be Dutch. Or maybe Irish? Was there some Canadian twang in there? Well, I wasn't the only one that was curious and it turned out, upon further inquiry, that Dennis was American but years of speech therapy, due to a stuttering impediment as a child, had left him with his peculiar accent.

We loaded up our packs and set out, and it was instantly exhausting. No warm-up whatsoever, we were immediately hit with a steep incline. The guides were ahead, with the eight of us shuffling behind. Unable to speak we breathlessly exchanged looks that said, "Just what the hell have we gotten ourselves into?"

"Come on, you lot, it gets easier after this part!" Dennis said in his chipper tone, once again sounding more like an old Irish man than a twenty-something American.

And so we kept climbing, heaving and sweating and guzzling water. At least with every sip our packs got lighter. One foot in front of the other, trying to keep balance and remember that suffering is only temporary. But Dennis was right and eventually, after a grueling hour the trail leveled out and conversation picked back up.

I already knew Jim was on board for a psychedelic experience, and the Swedes had expressed interest, too. The German couple seemed a little too proper and I was still gently fishing for clues with Hans and Michael before asking them.

"Oh, we have very good drugs in Vienna," Hans told me. He was older, probably in his late-forties, and not in the best shape. His posture indicated a more sedentary life, shoulders hunched forward with a ring of belly fat encircling his midriff. He wore what gangsters call a do-rag, but Hans couldn't have been less gangster. He talked fast, almost like he may already have snorted some cocaine. Or maybe he was naturally just a little manic. He proceeded to tell me about his partying days and how much he loved ecstasy when he was younger. I steered the conversation to psychedelics.

"Why not? I like to get weird!" Hans said. But he said it in such a way that it made me wonder if I'd like him to see him get any more weird.

"What about you, Michael?"

"Oh ya, I used to do all that stuff." He looked up from the path, his fedora shading his eyes. "But I'm not that much fun on psychedelics anymore. These days I tend to go into my head and think about death a lot," Michael said. I would not be giving any drugs to Michael.

I didn't feel that offering any to our guides Dennis or Gonzales was a good idea so I didn't bother inquiring with them. Usually on my wilderness adventures when drugs are involved either everyone is on them or everyone who *isn't* knows that everyone else *is*. This time any trippers would be an unannounced subset of the larger group. Not a big deal, I thought, I'd just keep the dosage reasonable.

Eventually we stopped at a stunning vista to eat some prepackaged baguette sandwiches. I pulled out a crumpled bag of Cheetos, which contained the mushrooms that Charlie had given me.

Jim wasn't feeling great and Freja didn't want any either, so the only person who wanted any besides me was Hugo. Even when totally sober, Hugo had a wide, permanent smile. He was probably twenty years old and had impossibly smooth, blemish-free skin and his eyes possessed a sweet, if slightly naive trust of all things. His black hair was pulled up from his face into a little palm-tree bun at the top of his head. Hugo was a total sweetheart. It turned out that the Cheetos, although somewhat stale, were a pretty fantastic way to consume the typically foul-tasting fungus. I had no idea how to dose the mushrooms so Hugo and I just divided the contents of the bag evenly.

Soon we were back on the trail, and continued along spectacular vistas of lagoons and volcanoes. Open plains studded with tufts of greenery spread out into the distance. An hour and a half went by. At one point I thought I felt something from the mushrooms. Maybe. Was my vision getting a little more crisp? Did my skin feel a little more sensitive? Was I contemplating existence and the meaning of life? Not really, at least not any more than usual. Overall the mushrooms had been a psychedelic bust.

A few hours later we arrived at our campsite that sat in a small bowl on the side of El Hoyo, right below a giant sinkhole that was maybe 100 meters/300 feet wide. El Hoyo, which translates to The Eye, was named for this mysterious feature. It was as if a perfectly circular piece of the mountain had simply vanished into thin air. From the campsite we could see the eye of the mountain gazing down on us. In the other direction the valley spread out as far as the eye could see, a rolling blanket of greens and browns, broken by a handful of lakes, farmland and other volcanoes. It was late afternoon and the light had taken on that sweet golden hue. We set up camp, rested for a while and then walked up the mountain, around the eye, past a smoking fumarole and up to a splendid lookout spot for sunset.

"Did you feel anything?" I asked Hugo as we reached the top.

"Everything felt quite nice," Hugo said, in his sweet accent.

"Does everything usually feel quite nice to you, Hugo?" He was a pretty airy type of guy, after all.

"Yes. Everything *is* usually quite nice," he replied, his smile somehow widening even more than usual.

"Okay, well it sounds like neither of us experienced very much. We'll make up for it tomorrow," I said.

"That sounds nice," Hugo smiled. We watched the sunset paint a path along a string of volcanoes that spread north.

That night the winds picked up but our tents were well staked down and Dennis and Gonzales prepared a giant pot of pasta and veggies. After dinner we toasted marshmallows around the campfire and Hans told us stories about his job as a parole officer back in Vienna until late into the evening.

We were woken up at dawn by Dennis' shrill "Good Morning! Breakfast and coffee are ready, everyone!" I turned to Jim, who I'd shared a tent with.

"Good morning. How are you feeling?"

"Feeling good. Looking forward to some breakfast!"

"How about a little acid appetizer?" I asked.

"Well, there's no time like the present!" he said, so I took the small breath-mint dropper from my backpack.

"Here's to a day of mischief and insight!" I let a drop fall onto each of our fingers.

As I emerged from our tent, I heard Hugo and Freja talking in the tent next to us. Their tent was open so I poked my head in.

"Good morning friends! Who's up for some acid?"

"I am!" Hugo exclaimed.

"I think I'm okay," Freja said. She certainly had seemed like the more sensible one, a fact which I didn't yet know I'd later be grateful for. I gave Hugo his drop and ventured on my merry way, passing Hans who was walking by with a heaping bowl of porridge.

"Hey Hans, want some acid?"

"Ha! Want some acid! Good morning to you too!" He must have thought I was joking because he just carried on walking right past me. It was probably for the best not to dose up this talkative Viennese parole officer anyway.

Striking camp and packing up our packs took a little longer than expected and by the time we were ready I could already feel the effects of the LSD weaving its way through my mind and body. The sun was just emerging from beyond the horizon, washing El Hoyo in a warm glow. Mist was rising up from the ground in the distance. Jim had a peaceful smile on his face. And Hugo was grinning like a total lunatic.

"I can't believe how amazing this is," Hugo said, and already seemed to be tripping pretty hard.

"Alright, everyone ready?" Dennis asked, not really waiting for an answer as he set off down a rocky path along the side of the volcano. *Were we ready?* The plan was pretty simple, to walk down this volcano without falling over, weave through the jungle and arrive at a completely isolated lagoon where we'd have lunch and cool off from the dry heat. The thing about psychedelics though is that no matter how many times I take them they're always a little bit of a surprise. And here we were, three undercover trippers, our confident Freja, and six others who had no idea. Now as I've said before, if you're experienced, especially around people who don't really know you, you can pretty easily get away with it. That is *if you're experienced.* And apparently Hugo was not quite as experienced as he'd led me to believe.

Everything was fine at first. There was a little bit of stumbling, a lot of laughing and we were just moving along. But it was a little while later, when we stopped for a break, that things started to get strange.

"Okay, everyone, water break," Dennis said. "Also, we have some snacks and nuts!" I was sitting on a rock when someone passed me a pack of nuts. The idea of food was not very appetizing so I passed them along. Jim was sitting under a tree, cool and collected, that same chill smile on his face. A pro. And then there was Hugo.

"Hugo, are you alright?" Dennis asked. Hugo was standing in the sun, red-faced, sweating profusely and looking a bit dazed. He'd removed most of his clothes except a small pair of skimpy pink running shorts. "Have you been drinking enough water?" And that's when the reality of the situation hit me. We were in for a long, awkward and possibly dangerous morning. And we had to handle it all without revealing our illegal activities.

"Yeah, water. Water's nice." But he didn't reach for any so I pulled my mind together as best I could, got up and went over to him.

"Heeeey, buddy. How ya doin'?" I asked quietly, putting a hand on his shoulder.

"Nice. Loving this!" It certainly didn't sound like he was *loving this.* Freja stood next to him looking concerned.

"Okay, well the good news is that there's nothing to worry about," I said calmly. "We're here for you. Just remember to breathe and drink water."

"Oh, I love you guys," he gushed.

"Thanks Hugo, we love you, too. We're just chilling. Nowhere to go."

"Oh, we're ready to go?" Hugo said, suddenly all amped up. "I didn't know everyone was waiting for me. I'm ready!"

"No, no one's waiting for you, we're all just chilling …"

But it was too late. He had already picked up his pack and began to take off down the path, his palm tree of hair bobbing as he went. Holy shit. Dennis was watching, no words came out of his mouth but his face said, "Ummm, what's happening, chaps?"

"Oh, Hugo's just super excited to get to that lagoon!" I said before Dennis could mumble anything. "We're going to get a head start!" I grabbed my pack and set off after him, watching as he stumbled on some loose rocks up ahead.

"Hey, slow down there, buddy. No rush," I said as I caught up to him.

"Oh, yes, so nice! I'm loving this." Balance and muscular control can start acting a little funny on psychedelics and Hugo was as frenetic as he was unsteady. I tried to change the subject.

"Isn't all this nature so beautiful?" I asked him.

"So beautiful! I can't believe it."

"Seriously, we're so lucky to be here. It's a safe and magical place."

"So magical!"

I wanted to keep him lucid and present in his body. I scrambled for things to talk about.

"So what's your favorite animal?" In retrospect this was perhaps not the best question and his brow furrowed deeply.

"Animals, animals …" I was losing him.

"Well, what do you think of these butterflies?" Choosing a simpler question as a few butterflies fluttered by.

"I love butterflies!" And with that he started to remove his pack, apparently intent on following them off the path and into the jungle. Hugo, in his bright pink runner's shorts, was barely hanging on to the thread of reality.

"Okay," I exclaimed with renewed authority. "We're keeping our packs on right now, Hugo!" Thankfully he registered my command and slipped back into his shoulder straps.

"Can you imagine how good that lagoon will feel when we jump in?" I said, attempting to offer a tangible and enticing goal in order to keep him on the path.

"Oh, the lagoon! We need to get there!" Perfect, it was the promise of a cool lagoon that would keep this bizarre trip moving along.

We had slowed down enough so that the others were catching up, presenting another problem, interacting with non-trippers. This was going to take some skilled social fabric-weaving. Right before Dennis caught up to us, I laughed out loud at nothing and patted Hugo on the shoulder, hoping to lessen any perceived tension.

"Is everything okay?" Dennis asked.

"Oh yes, we're just looking at butterflies!" I said.

"Good. Okay. Just let me know if you guys need anything." If Dennis thought something was going on, he certainly didn't show it. Or maybe he was just nervous and grateful that someone else was handling this situation. Freja returned to Hugo's side and was giving him some water. As long as he didn't get heatstroke or break anything, we were going to get through this. People were still looking at him nervously so I thought the best way to redirect attention from Hugo was to be even more bizarre and outspoken than he was being.

"You all are so great!" I exclaimed to the rest of the group. "What a beautiful day!" And it seemed to be working, the group's tension already felt lighter.

"Is something going on?" Michael quietly asked as we continued down the path. I decided to share what we had for breakfast along with our coffee and porridge. "HA! I thought Hugo was acting strange!"

"Okay, well, keep it quiet. I don't want the tour guides finding out." Not that I knew what would happen if they did. But I was feeling a little anxious about finding out what happens to people who are caught giving acid to tourists on the sides of volcanoes in Nicaragua. "Let's just make sure to give him lots of love."

The following three hours were a mix of awkwardness and hilarity. Any time Hugo said anything too strange I countered with something even weirder to throw the others off the scent. Meanwhile those that knew what was going on with Hugo helped keep him hydrated and on the path. All the while, Jim maintained the same chill look on his face. As we descended into a volcanic crater we were met with the vision of a pristine lagoon. We hiked along its edge to a small beach, which was completely devoid of human activity. The sun was high in the sky, it was hot and the breeze made the surface of the water look like someone had scattered diamonds across a pane of glass.

Hugo took off, running the rest of the way down the trail, stripping off his pack, shoes and socks before running into the water. He plunged in, submerging his entire body. By this point we were all watching as a terrible thought passed my mind: please God, I hope he knows how to swim! A few seconds passed, and then a few more. I don't think I was breathing. And then he emerged, bursting above the surface, both hands in the air:

"SO NICE!" Hugo yelled, sounding victorious. I breathed and everyone laughed.

I was next into the lake, and as I submerged my hot head into the cool water I felt the relief wash over me. Soon everyone was in the water, splashing around, laughing and revitalized. Gonzales set about making burritos for lunch and the trippers all finally had their appetites back.

"I love you guys so much!" Hugo said to the entire group, more lucidly this time, in between bites of his second burrito. Everyone laughed, still probably confused but at least relieved. The great eye of El Hoyo was visible from the lake. It had been watching all along, following our journey for the entire day, like a parent or teacher who suspected that something mischievous was going on but didn't have the proof. But we'd fuckin' gotten away with it! Over the peaks, through the jungle and besides some scrapes everyone was still mostly intact from our adventure *within* the adventure.

As we packed up to go, Hans approached me, wagging up to me like an eager Labrador. "Hey, what was going on back there with you guys?" So I told him.

"I knew something was going on with you guys!" he exclaimed.

"Well, I tried to offer you some at breakfast!" I laughed.

"HA! You were serious!?" He smiled for a moment. "Well, do you have any more?"

"Nope, all out, I'm afraid." I wasn't about to give anyone else any more acid on this expedition, especially not Hans. Things didn't need to get any weirder.

We left the lagoon, hiking up the steep side of the crater but at least our packs were lighter, free of food and the majority of our water reserves. We trekked down a few miles of dusty roads, passing only a local guy who was going somewhere with his cow, until we came to a roadside rest stop. We were a bunch of filthy, smiling backpackers drinking Gatorade and laughing about the whole experience.

Eventually an old yellow school bus pulled up and we piled on. There were chickens in baskets and lots of sweaty people crammed in every nook. I inserted myself on a seat between a fat man and a small potted tree that was apparently being taken somewhere to be planted. Two hot hours and two crammed buses later we were dropped at the far end of León, having to walk another thirty minutes through much more squalid areas of town than I'd seen before. Street vendors, puddles of fetid water, and a feeling of general poverty filled my senses. It was certainly a challenging reentry and not a very enjoyable final portion of the trip, but after all, corners had to be cut if Quetzaltrekkers wanted to charge sixty-nine dollars for two days and still have some money left over to help the local kids. I was especially glad that the LSD had mostly worn off by that point and also that I hadn't given Hans any because this would have been a hellish psychedelic experience for even the most experienced tripper.

By the time we got back to Quetzaltrekkers everyone except Dennis and Gonzales knew about the LSD, and as far as I know they never found out the full story. We had journeyed through the eye of the volcano and returned stronger, more resilient versions of ourselves. Welcome to the oft challenging, and always memorable world of exposure therapy!

23. Recovery At El Transito

Unlike other beach towns I'd visited so far, El Transito, which occupies a tiny stretch on the west coast of Nicaragua just west of Managua, is raw and undeveloped. Nicaragua doesn't yet have a coastal road so after leaving the backbone of the Pan-American Highway, getting to each beach town offers its own separate adventure, most of the time down miles of gravelly, wash boarded roads. There's a plan in the works for the construction of a coastal road which would help open up the country's beach communities to more development and increased tourist access. For now, many beaches are visited only by a small number of travelers, surfers chasing the perfect wave, adventure-seeking hitchhikers or bipolar writer types looking for some goddamn peace and quiet. It had been a week of hedonic delight and I figured that the little town would surely provide just the transition I needed, for real this time.

El Transito was my first stop on the five hundred-mile, return journey south, back toward San Juan del Sur, where I planned to drop my motorcycle and continue on a short hop into Costa Rica before flying back home—back to a home that I hoped would still be there. After I'd checked into my hostel, I found a hammock to relax in to recover from the bumpy ride. I was feeling slightly melancholy. Perhaps it was that I was nearing the end of my trip. Perhaps it was the little pieces of my heart that I'd be leaving here, strewn among new friends and around this beautiful land. Or perhaps it was just the lingering effects of the rum working its way out of my system. Where Guatemala had been healthy and heart-centered, Nicaragua had been more devilishly tempting and sensually decadent. Everyone always said that I got my character from my Italian grandfather—"Party Joe," they called him—who was always either hosting a party or at the center of it. So hey, it's in my blood, *what do you all expect!?*

Cultural and genetic excuses aside, this trip was helping me see how I struggled with addiction. Throughout my life I'd looked to escape from my reality and my feelings with whatever I could get my hands on. I knew myself and knew how I could stumble so keeping myself in check was constantly on my mind. And for good reason, I knew plenty of people who'd fallen off the wagon. When I was young, I remember my dad drinking a lot. After my parents had divorced my mom had had an alcoholic boyfriend who struggled with addiction. One vacation I came home to find a dozen empty Johnnie Walker bottles hidden in my bed. He was never violent or mean, just sad. As an adult I'd seen so many people lose their way with drugs and alcohol. They weren't just born like that; choice after poor choice compounded until they just could no longer keep it together. It was scary how often that happened.

Finding that balance has been an elusive part of my life's mission, which I've found with varying degrees of success. There's something so delectable about twisting together the unexpected, from heartfelt ceremonies and the raw vegan brightness of ecstatic dances, to drug-fueled treehouse parties and debauched sexual escapades, the thrill of exploring the edges. I try to balance, I really do. So why is it that in my quest to find healthy romance do I usually only find romance with naughty Airbnb hostesses and Dutch party girls? Is it something unresolved within myself? Something lingering just outside of my perception? They say you attract what you put out, your similar vibration. Well, apparently I still have a party-going, naughty-girl thing to get out of my system before I can find my bright-eyed, salubrious lover. Shit. Do I need to be more authentic? More disciplined? Do I have problems with intimacy? How am I feeling about my self-worth? Hmmm, maybe I am still trying to escape from something within myself and hence attracting others who are in the same boat. That's probably all true. Maybe I would work best with someone as dynamic and intrigued by human diversity as myself. A mostly vegetarian but *occasionally* rum-drinking, molecule-popping yoga type? I decided to take a break from my relentless self-analysis and head over to a sunset yoga class on the beach, to breathe and clear my head.

Later that evening I was lying in a hammock and enjoying a fresh juice while collecting my thoughts. Before leaving León I had visited the Museo de la Revolución, where I learned what a crucial hub the city had been during the Nicaraguan revolution back in the '50s through the late '70s. We'd been shown around the colorful building by Francisco, who'd been recruited as a Sandinista soldier when he was fifteen. He took us up to the rickety roof of the museum, where we enjoyed a 360 view of the town all while avoiding falling through gaping holes into the museum below. It was inspiring to hear him talk about their hard-won cultural victory and the possibility of transforming old ways of thinking into something new. So often forces of greed and fear of change threaten to close their grip on humanity, and so often people rise up proving that our humanity cannot be so easily extinguished. So how had the civil war unfolded in Nicaragua? Francisco hadn't spoken the best English so my understanding was a little spotty and I decided to do some more research.

The United States, intent on controlling land in Nicaragua, had been fighting in the region from as far back as the 1800s, invading the country no less than eight times, overthrowing and installing successive governments. This brutal history spawned a rebellion that would change the course of Nicaragua. Augusto César Sandino was a Nicaraguan revolutionary and leader of the rebellion against the U.S. military occupation of Nicaragua between 1927 and 1933. Sandino eventually met his end when he was assassinated in 1934 by the National Guard forces of U.S.-backed General Anastasio Somoza García. García went on to seize power in a coup d'état two years later which marked the beginning of the Somoza family dictatorship that lasted for forty-three years. However, Sandino's legacy lived on in the formation of the Sandinista ideals that stood for sovereignty, independence, democracy and social justice.

García used his power to accumulate extraordinary wealth at the expense of the peasantry but it was years later, during the leadership of García's second son, Anastasio Somoza Debayle, that marked the most violent period of oppression. Debayle was so barbaric that he was even known to go so far as to throw his enemies into nearby volcanoes, which of course only further galvanized his opponents. The rising opposition to the Somoza regime in the 1960s and 1970s was led by the Sandinista National Liberation Front

(FSLN), which was a coalition of students, intellectuals and farm workers led by a committee of nine military "commandantés," including later president Daniel Ortega.

The Sandinista Revolution, as it came to be called, grew into an all-out conflict with the FSLN, gathering support from international governments such as Cuba and Costa Rica. The U.S. continued to fund the Somoza regime until it eventually withdrew official support after the publicized execution of an American war correspondent. With few supporters left the revolution against Somoza's oppressive dictatorial regime was successful and the Sandinistas took charge, offering a new promise of peace and democracy for the impoverished and war-torn country. But just as the country began to rebuild old tensions began to reemerge. The U.S., fearful of a Communist-backed government so close to home and concerned how Nicaragua's successful revolution might influence other countries, further ravaged the country by attempting to overthrow the Sandinista government with the help of Reagan's new Contra force, partly made up of the remnants of Somoza's National Guard. Not having the funds or weapons needed to defend themselves, the Sandinistas turned to the U.S.S.R. for help, which further aggravated the situation.

Nicaragua was once again at war for its freedom. Both sides turned to brutal tactics, including executions of peasant leaders by the Contras and the conscription of boy soldiers by the Sandinistas. Our guide at the museum, Francisco, had been one of these soldiers. By 1985 the Reagan administration had imposed a crippling embargo on the country, instantly strangling the country's access to fuel and fertilizers while decimating profits from their restricted exports. Both sides were struggling, with the Sandinistas in disarray and the Contras losing support from their war-criminal behavior. And then I hit a familiar piece of research that I'd read about in Guatemala. In 1986 the U.S. Congress banned Reagan from using any further U.S. dollars to fund the conflict so he had U.S. officials quietly sell weapons to Iran in exchange for the release of U.S. hostages and millions of dollars. This scheme, which I'd read about before, was known as the Iran-Contra affair, and continued to covertly fund the Contras in Nicaragua until eventually its discovery and dissolution led to Contras demise. The public perception of the Sandinistas' leadership, led by Daniel Ortega, had also suffered so much that they lost the resulting democratic election, honorably conceding to a new president. Mrs. Violeta Chamorro won the election on 25 February 1990, becoming the first elected female head of state in the Americas. President Reagan, meanwhile, survived the entire scandal by claiming he was "having some trouble remembering that." Goddammit, people.

I swung gently in the hammock, trying in vain to imagine how it would feel to be part of that history. To fight for something you believe in so deeply that you lay your life on the line. What would we lay our lives on the line for these days? Or are we too distracted by the eighth season of whatever show we're watching and thrilled by all the new ways that our pizza can be stuffed with more cheese and meat to really even care? Everywhere you look right now the majority or people are distracting themselves in whatever way they can. Sometimes they distract themselves in relatively harmless ways. Addiction to social media, games and entertainment, and even seemingly "productive" activities like work are favored over doing "nothing," as if *doing nothing* is always such a bad thing. Other distractions can be more destructive, for example, excessive food or alcohol, and dangerous drug use, most recently illustrated by the exploding rates of opiate addiction. Unfortunately, when enough people are distracted and kept in fear they can begin to be easily manipulated and democracy itself begins to suffer. Has our culture become so complacent that we'd rather not even bother to think about these things? Perhaps we're too paralyzed by fear from the news media or too distracted how many likes our last social media post got? I know I've been guilty of these things but if we become too lethargic, too disempowered and too distracted can we really hope to retain any influence over *who* controls *us*?

The world is electing despots. Nationalism is on the rise. Old walls are being rebuilt and all the while our ravaged environment is having trouble supporting us. Even the most hopeful outlooks indicate that things will get worse before they got better. So how are you preparing for it? As Francisco explained, there's so many roles to fill in revolutions, ways to create new things outside of the existing structure, some transforming it from within through legislation while others working outside to subvert it. Inevitably the majority of citizens are just along for the ride, opinionated but motionless until conflict is on their doorstep, at which point, unable to take care of themselves they hand their power to whoever promises to protect them.

I thought about the slew of expats that were settling down here in Nicaragua, from the bustling streets of San Juan del Sur, to the charming jungly nooks of Ometepe and the remote beach communities like El Transito, buying up property and developing it. In many ways it smacked of that same type of neo-Colonialism I'd thought so much about before. Or perhaps it represented a welcome evolution? Some of the worst of our kind had come in and messed things up pretty badly. We'd told these people how to live and got them dependent on fertilizer-based farming and plastic bottled water, numbed them out on brain-clogging processed food, all while blaring televisions promoted the joys of a Mickey Mouse existence. Well, maybe now some of the best of us can return to make amends, to see this country as more than just an untapped consumer market and help heal the misery that our predecessors caused.

Am I fooling myself? Is coming down here with our knowledge, skills and funds even helpful? Can it be done in a culturally respectful way? Can we build sustainable projects and improve the lives of locals with our actions, while still allowing them their sovereignty? Or should the U.S. stop trying to mansplain everything to everyone and just let people get on with their lives? Well, that's a good question and I don't have the answer right now, I thought. But I do know that Aunt Jemima, Betty Crocker and the rest of those bastards should burn in an especially searing, high-fructose corn syrup hell for their crimes against nutrition.

And yet at the same time we're living in an age of magic. Abundant, cheap or even free energy, promising AI and robotic developments, decentralized currencies outside of the heavy-handed control of the financial giants, biotech that can heal so much suffering. All hold such promise and also such shadow. Like everything, since the dawn of the universe itself when matter and antimatter waged their epic battle, life has hung in an unlikely and precarious balance. Surely that tiny bit of matter that survived represents the equally tiny sliver of hope, an ineffable source of energy upon which our cosmos is built, and this love will win out in the end. *Surely!?* It's a humbling realization when the solution might take centuries and yet you only have a regular human lifespan.

As Francisco told us about the importance that self-reliant communities played in the revolution it reminded me of some of the basic tenets of permaculture: Paying attention to what is working,

working to be as self-sufficient as possible as the old paradigm withers on the vine. The era of western control lingers on as a strained empire. There will be blood. There will be collapse. And yet, there will be great successes, too. So let's figure out what we're reliant on, how we can best prepare for tough times, build community connection and support, acknowledge what we can change, accept what we can't and grab a seat for the best show on Earth.

I switched from the battle going on inside my head to the battle going on outside my head as I hopped onto the Wi-Fi and called into the weekly Manzanita conference call. The turmoil was continuing and we were no closer to any financial solution. To make matters even more challenging, Wave 2, led by Stoic Joel and his girlfriend, was now requesting that Earth Mama Angela's onerous boyfriend leave the property. Angela said if he had to leave, she would too, so the rest of Wave 1, standing in solidarity with her, had rejected the offer of a loan from Wave 2. Once again, we were at a standstill.

"Well, we have another offer," Joel said. I was not privy to what this was. "Since Wave 1 won't accept our offer that would allow them to stay at Manzanita, Wave 2 is offering to buy them out of the project." The words hung in the air. Wave 1, the pro-beaver faction, the earliest members who'd heard about and started this whole project, were now being asked if they'd accept an offer that would mean their departure.

Gabe, somewhat flustered at first but speaking on behalf of Wave 1, said that they'd have to consider it. Or course this was a little bit sad for all of us and furthermore didn't completely solve our problems, since if Wave 1 accepted, Wave 2 would no longer have any remaining funds to settle the original loan with the previous owners and hence risk foreclosure. I stayed on the call with Joel after the rest of the members left to get his thoughts.

"So, this is the best option, huh?" I asked.

"Yeah, I mean, obviously defaulting on the loan and losing the property is terrible for everyone and an undesirable outcome, but we feel that if we can get free from Wave 1 then the rest will figure itself out. But we want you to stay. In fact, we need you to stay."

"Oh, that's nice of you to say."

"Yeah, we love you. And we can't afford to buy you out, too," Joel replied. Joel told me that this move was also supported by the previous owners who'd been witnessing the whole shit show and he felt confident that they might even cut us a little slack with the loan deadline.

"Man, I wish I was there," I said. I even partially meant it.

"Be glad you're not," Joel said. "And anyway, there's not much more you could do if you were."

When the call was finally over I took a deep breath, trying to remain optimistic and to see these unexpected developments as new opportunities. I knew that in general when I'm too busy thinking about how things *aren't* working the way that I'd planned then I'm not noticing how many things *are* working, and how sometimes they're working even better. Well, wasn't that a good lesson for any person, any group of people, to learn? Of course, not everyone probably felt that way. I felt bad for Gabe and Angela. I even felt bad for her rabble rouser of a boyfriend. Everyone had gone into this project with grand hopes and now a decision was on the table that would affect us all in ways we hadn't imagined. At least at this point the emotional flare-ups had mostly subsided and it was coming down to the final negotiations of a business deal. Note to any future community builder: create the vision, find the people, design the legal and financial framework together and then find and purchase the property. Do it the other way around and you might just have a revolution on your hands. And so the saga continued ...

24. The Dictator And The Seagull

If there's anything weirder than being all alone in a hotel, it's being alone in a totally dark hotel, with no electricity and no hotel staff anywhere to be found. No, I wasn't trespassing, I'd just come to La Boquita, a seaside village, at the exact wrong time of year. I was once again lounging in a hammock overlooking the water, this time in total darkness. But let me back up a little.

I'd woken up at the crack of dawn in my previous hammock at El Transito and hauled my introspective lump of humanity to a final yoga class. After packing up I headed south toward an apparently vibrant eco-community called Apapachoa located halfway between El Transito and La Boquita. I was attracted to the place by pictures that I'd seen online, featuring colorful buildings, workshops and lush gardens.

El Rojo's clutch pedal had become so unreliable that now it was almost impossible to get the bike into first gear, but besides the occasional ill-timed stall I was mostly making it work. I took a side road away from the Pan-American Highway and after traversing some arid lowlands I was soon weaving up a hilly mountain road that led into misty jungle terrain. Eventually my Bluetooth earpiece informed me that I should turn onto an unmarked dirt road and I was soon winding along a ridgeline with steep drop offs on either side.

I knew I'd really gotten into the groove of traveling because I'd stopped feeling the need to share my experience on social media. I also knew that the jungle that lay below this mountainous road was the exact kind of place that could swallow up me and my motorcycle completely. Maybe I should have told someone where I was going?

On the other hand, what a mysterious demise that would be! "Did you hear, Dougie got lost in Central America! He was riding a motorcycle in the jungle and then no one ever saw him again!" And yet it was often in moments like these, with the possibility of death cozied up on either side of me, that I felt my most alive. Ever since I was young I never really wanted to grow old and frail, I wanted to go on adventures and bring back tales of what I found, so there'd always been something enticing about going out in a story like that; dangerous situations were at least *story worthy, and to* live a story-worthy life, well, that's the life for me! I made a note to discuss this with my therapist.

The rains had carved deep ruts in the road and chickens, children and horse-drawn carts would occasionally appear out of nowhere, offering no indication of their next erratic movement. This whole detour to Apapachoa was a gamble. I hadn't been able to contact the community so instead chose to wing it and see what happened if I just showed up. If no one was there or I wasn't welcome I would just have to turn around.

"You have arrived," the GPS informed me. And as often happens in these remote areas, my cached GPS had helpfully led me to a turn in the road with no driveway nor clue of what I was actually looking for, so I pulled over to figure things out. The jungle valley stretched into the distance as far as the eye could see. Besides some patches that had been carved out to create steep terraced farming, the jungle looked largely untouched and impassable. I looked at the map on my cell phone's screen, I was a blue dot in a vast roadless patch of green.

I opted to keep exploring and a few minutes further up the road I arrived at a tiny village comprised of just a handful of homes and a sparsely stocked store. After inquiring with some locals, most of whom were living in extreme poverty, I was directed to a large gate that surrounded an amazingly colorful building. Brightly painted Apapachoa stood in stark contrast from the lush greenery and muddy browns surrounding it. There were no signs of other humans but I honked my horn anyway and waited. A few minutes later an elderly, Spanish-speaking lady appeared who, after some initial confusion, showed me in. I parked my mud-covered motorcycle and was led down a path until we came upon two young, English-speaking women. They were incredibly excited to have a visitor and I could understand why, the entire place was completely vacant. One of them, a French woman called Claudine, happily offered to give me a tour and tell me more about the project. Her friend, a local woman named Sofia, joined us while the older woman went back to her duties.

We started with the house. Each room overlooked the jungle below and was more colorful than the last. Claudine had arrived a week or two earlier to what she thought was going to be a vibrant community. But when she arrived it was all a little different than she expected. Apapachoa was going through a big community transition so she'd unexpectedly assumed the role of caretaker and invited her friend to keep her company. Finding these two women living at this vacant compound in the Nicaraguan jungle only added to this trip feeling like an odd dream. They led me to the top of the house, which provided a 360 view with hardly any other house in sight. Further up the hill was a very large expanse of flat concrete, with raised edges, all angled downhill. For a moment I wondered what it was for, until with almost perfect timing a deluge arrived at Apapachoa. I soon surmised that these flat concrete surfaces were intended to catch the rain and divert it into large reservoirs further downhill below the house.

When I asked what the purpose of gathering all this rainwater was Claudine told me that this had been a coffee plantation and since then the place had gone through a pretty fascinating journey. And so I learned, in a bizarre twist of timing, that Apapachoa had in fact been the old summer refuge of the barbaric General Anastasio Somoza Debayle before he was overthrown and stripped of his property. I was walking in the same footprints of the sociopathic tyrant that I'd just learned all about in León.

Sometime after the revolution Apapachoa had been purchased and transformed into a community and retreat center for meditation, yoga, permaculture and more. And it really was a perfect use for it. Within an hour of Managua and with views of undisturbed jungle it could be an amazing venue. And there was something beautifully poetic about ousting a tyrannical dictator and transmuting an object of his greed into a healing retreat center and permaculture community. But of course, as sometimes happens with these types of community projects, the benevolent energy of the founders eventually waned and now Apapachoa stood largely vacant while they found a director of programming who could breathe new life into the project.

"It's a funny time for your visit," said Sofia. "Do you know what today is in Mayan culture?"

"Is it … the day of charming unexpected strangers visiting your life?" I joked.

"Close!!" she laughed. "It's the day of arrival, of a seed sprouting. Power through physical existence."

"Maybe that's why you visited!" Claudine exclaimed.

"Well, I hope I don't disappoint you."

I had a lot more questions but being new to the scene they didn't know much more than the basics and besides it was getting late and I still wanted to get to La Boquita by nightfall. We drank coffee and ate avocado on toast in the kitchen until the storm had passed, after which we returned to the parking lot just in time to find a mischievous puppy who'd managed to steal my grey fedora, which I was carrying in a plastic bag attached to my backpack. The meddling little mutt was making good progress on destroying the brim. Claudine scolded the puppy, who ran off, tail between its legs.

"Oh, I'm sorry!" Claudine said.

"No problem, it gives it more character," I said, wiping off the puppy saliva, placing the hat back into the plastic bag and reattaching it to my backpack.

I expressed gratitude to the women for taking me on the tour and said my goodbyes. They waved from the gates as I rode away, back down the winding mountain road, riding the edges of rain clouds. Another community and another totally different type of struggle, I thought to myself as I descended into the warmer temperatures of the valley below. The road soon smoothed out and the ride to La Boquita was perfectly timed to catch the sun as it was setting over the Pacific.

I didn't see one other tourist as I entered the small town. Not even one other *local* tourist. The place was deserted aside from a few locals who swiveled their heads as I passed by. The street was lined with closed restaurants and empty hotels. Eventually I came to the end of the road, a turnaround at an arcade amusement area, also deserted. I circled back, stopping at a hotel that seemed to be under renovation, but at least I'd seen another human milling about the entrance gate.

The man, who looked like he'd been painting a wall, was finishing up work for the day, and I managed to convey to him that I was looking for lodging. He told me that everything in town was closed but to wait here for a little while and he'd find someone, and walked off down the road. A short while later an older man emerged from one of the side streets that led away from the ocean. He approached me and after a brief interchange he said he could give me a room for the night. We haggled for a while and eventually agreed on a price whereupon he unlocked the gate and brought me through the deserted hotel to an empty room. And I mean totally empty.

"Cama?" I said, remembering the word for "bed."

"Si, claro!" the man said, gesturing me to follow him. We went into another room which was full of propped-up beds. He began dragging it into the room so I helped.

"Esparas …" he said and disappeared into yet another room, this time reappearing with some linens and towels, which he dropped on the bed. After my deluxe suite was ready, I asked him where I could find some dinner. He said he'd find out and sauntered off downstairs, out of the hotel and up the side street from where he'd come. I was grateful for the hot shower and was just toweling off when all the lights went off. So I went out on to the porch, sank into the hammock and gently swung in the darkness, laughing at this ridiculous La Boquita experience. Just when I thought that I was going to have a dark, hungry night ahead of me I heard the gate clank open and shortly after that the man appeared on the porch and said something I didn't understand about the electricity. He then told me he'd found some food nearby and told me to follow him. We left the hotel and he locked the gate behind us. He told me, largely with hand gestures, that when I came back I should just climb the fence to get back in. Okay, seemed manageable enough.

We walked down the street, cutting into some back alleys and eventually emerging into a small square where kids were kicking a plastic bottle around. He brought me over to a solitary street vendor, said something quickly in Spanish and then shook my hand and left. The street vendor smiled and set out a small white plastic chair for me to sit on. It was really a kid's chair and I sat on it a little awkwardly. A short while later he handed me a heaping plate of something mysterious. The strange meal was comprised of chunks of beef piled on top of a bed of plantain chips. It felt like something a kid who was left alone at home would make out of whatever he could find in the kitchen. But I was appreciative and sat on the kid's chair and gratefully ate my kid's meal. To wash the meal down he gave me a plastic bag full of brown liquid that had a straw coming out of the top.

I was grateful to discover that it was chocolate milk, but even more delicious. It tasted like real cacao, not that processed Nestlé junk. After I was finished, I paid the food vendor USD$2.25 and made my way back to the hotel, through the deserted streets, before hopping the fence and walking up to my room.

The hotel's electricity was still out but luckily I had a small battery pack to charge up my phone and headset for the following day's adventure. My next stop would be the beach town of Playa Gigante, stopping at a place along the way called Popoyo, which apparently was what neo-hippies call a "high-vibe vortex." It was only 9 p.m. but without much else to distract me I made it an early night, crawled into bed and soon fell asleep in my large, dark and completely empty hotel.

When I woke up there was still no one around. I showered and climbed back over the gate of the hotel, loaded up El Rojo and rode south to the end of the road to see if I could find some coffee. A short while later I arrived at a small fishing village at the end of the road but after a somewhat befuddled interaction with a wide-eyed fisherman, I decided to just continue on to El Gigante and find some coffee and something to eat along the way.

I headed east toward the Pan-American Highway. It was a beautiful stretch of road, thirty kilometers of tree-lined curves, punctuated only by one horse-drawn buggy, a startled pig that seemed to be on its own adventure, and finally a committee of vultures that were gorging on some roadkill. I was going fast and the vultures, just as surprised as me, took flight with one coming so close to my head that I had to duck out of its way. It had been so close that I saw the details of its feathers in slow motion and remnants of carrion glistening on its bloody beak.

When I got back to the Pan-American Highway, I took a right and continued south over hilly terrain, my fists clenched tight onto the handlebars to counteract the ferocious crosswinds. I was hungry and critically in need of coffee by the time I arrived at a small bustling town called Jinotega. I quickly got turned around and asked a tanned man in a cowboy hat for directions to a cafe. He pointed me toward the town center where I discovered an out-of-place American-themed diner called Terry's. I drank coffee and ate an American-sized Western omelet served with gallo pinto, the local dish of rice and beans. Besides a couple of Nicaraguan guys who were cursing at a game of football on TV it was a relaxed atmosphere so I caught up on some emails and journaling before finding my way out of town and continuing south.

Initially I had been intent on finding a cafe called the El Gato Negro, where I was told by a stoned backpacker there were great brownies, but despite searching I never found the cafe nor its fabled brownies; such is the reality when you get your intel from stoned backpackers. Just before I got to El Gigante I decided to take a detour to the surfing and yoga town of Popoyo. It didn't seem too out of the way because on my map it looked like there was a short coastal segment of road that would connect with the road to El Gigante, my destination for the evening. Frenzied chickens and their chicks scattered as I wove down the dirt road toward Popoyo.

The landscape had become dry, with dusty roads flanked by golden fields studded with the occasional green tree. It reminded me of the chaparral landscapes of southern Oregon where I lived. I passed by a school and suddenly hundreds of school kids in white shirts and blue trousers and skirts swarmed the road; kids getting on buses, kids getting on bikes, and kids getting on parents. I managed to slowly weave through the throng, bumping and skidding on the loose gravel as El Rojo popped in and out of gear. By the time I got through the chaos, I noticed that my backpack was sagging. I pulled aside and discovered that my remaining bungee was on its last legs, but luckily the backpack, and the fluttering pink plastic bag that contained my puppy chewed fedora, were still hanging on. I did my best to reattach the bag and a short while later I found a local ferretería where I could pick up some new bungees. The store was open but there was no one anywhere to be seen. I estimated that the pack of bungees would have cost about USD$1 and left it on the counter. I went back outside, reattached my bag and continued on my way to Popoyo.

Before long I was sitting at the cute and clean Café au Lait where I finally celebrated with the brownie that I so deserved after the five-hour ride on dirt roads. After my brownie, and a brief conversation with a couple of tanning German ladies by the pool, I took a ride up to a place called Magnificent Rock Popoyo, a spectacular restaurant that jutted out over the ocean. It served healthy food and sat below a yoga studio that overlooked a sweeping view of the bay. As if it wasn't already delightful enough, the entire town of Popoyo seemed to be populated by cute, friendly yoginis who seemed only too eager to listen to my motorcycle stories. Despite my impulses I pulled myself away and continued south to El Gigante where I'd booked a room for a night at a place called the Camino del Gigante Bay.

Now rather than go back the way I'd come and drive a bunch more distance, I decided to take the beach route over to the next access road to the south. I was warned by the friendly owner of Magnificent Rock Popoyo that the beach route was a little sandy. As I approached the sandy stretch of road, I decided that it looked doable enough so picked up some speed; I hit the sand and El Rojo lurched but kept moving, and kept moving for a moment longer until I tried to take a slight turn, upon which my front wheel dug into the sand and I promptly flew from the bike, as did my bag. I got up from the soft sand, my body unscathed but ego a little bruised due to a few smiling onlookers. I tossed my backpack on my shoulders and got back on the bike, but to no avail. Try as I might, El Rojo was just not powerful enough to compete with the sand with me on its back so I had to unmount and for the next few hundred yards, delicately throttle it in first gear with me by huffing by its side, quietly cursing my ineptitude. I finally made it to the paved road, reattached my backpack and wove through some small beach villages until I cut back out onto the main road.

From there a stunning, curvy road led me to the sandy little town of El Gigante. I soon found my hostel and as I checked in, I solemnly noted, especially after just departing the maiden-rich lands of Popoyo, that the lounge area was mostly comprised of men, bearded men who were just as excited to me as I was to see them. It didn't matter. My plan for El Gigante was to rest and catch up with some online stuff. Dorm beds were ten dollars but I decided to splurge and spend an extra ten dollars for my own space. Captain Ahab's bunk, as my room was called, was furnished like a ship's cabin, with an anchor, a ship's wheel and some other thematic touches including a solitary book of Moby Dick on a dusty shelf. There was a fan pointed at a double bed shrouded in a mosquito net that looked like it had seen better days.

I changed into my bathing suit and headed down to the beach for a cerveza and a jump in the ocean. I instantly felt refreshed as the dust of the Nicaraguan highways washed off my skin and drifted out to sea, taking any lingering stress along with it. A while later I was in a hammock, enjoying another cerveza when a strong-looking woman who I'd noticed earlier buzzing around the reception approached me and asked me if I wanted a massage. It was inexpensive and I had a nice buzz going so why the hell not? I noticed that I had a new email with the subject "Manzanita Wave 1 Buy Out Decision" and I felt like getting the massage first would make reading whatever it said more tolerable. I was led upstairs to a massage table, instructed to disrobe and lie face down. Rosaria was even more strong than she looked and before long I was a supple puddle of human under her skillful hands. After the massage I ate some fish tacos and decided I was amply prepared for whatever the conversation back home would bring. I logged on to the Wi-Fi and pulled up the email. Wave 1 had agreed to the buyout offer.

I know, it's kind of complicated, so let me summarize: A beaver prompted a community meltdown, which erupted into a multitude of other problems. In an attempt to resolve a key issue with equity allotment Wave 1, formerly known as the *pro-beaver* group, had been offered a loan by Wave 2, formerly known as the beaver-hesitant group, that would allow them to remain on the project. Wave 1 hadn't accepted this offer so Wave 2's previous loan offer was replaced with a buyout offer which Wave 1 had now accepted. Like Joel had said, there wasn't enough money to buy me out too, so even if I had wanted to bail, which part of me certainly did, I didn't really have too much of a choice. Furthermore, upon reading the rest of the email, I found that the equalization strategy that would balance out everyone's original investments, meant that I would now be expected to pay a little more into the project, which I felt was fair since I'd at least received a cabin that had a roof on it; such was the cost of my diplomatic bi-partisanship. The Wave 1 Manzanita members had put so much time and energy into the project to make it happen and now they were leaving. I felt sad so I sent an email to Gabe and the rest of Wave 1 expressing as much.

The drama had been temporarily stalled, but the remaining members, who we referred to as Wave 3 and which included me, now had another significant problem on our hands. We needed to come up with a way to pay off a two hundred thousand-dollar loan that was due in just a few weeks. The fact that I might not be returning to Manzanita was still a very real possibility, so we all set off to find the funds; but first, I set off to find a beer.

The following morning, after sleeping off the beers and Manzanita discussion, I woke up to the sound of sea birds and laughing people, and a smell of coffee and baked goods emanating up from the kitchen below. And in that moment, I realized that I wouldn't be leaving today. It was my last planned stop before returning to San Juan del Sur and I still had the bike booked for a few days, so there was no immediate rush.

After a fruit salad and coffee, I loaded up my day pack and walked south along the beach toward a tall, rocky peninsula. I found a trail that led up into the jungly terrain and before long crested the summit, surrounded only by snarled trees and cacti that had been weathered by the elements. There were striking views in all directions. Even though it was the dry season it was easy to tell how vibrant this place must be during its wet season, which would soon get underway in April. As I sat on top of the rocky peninsula I looked back at the coast. Cliffs dropped off in every direction, cutting down hundreds of feet to the water. I turned to face the ocean and laid down with my face poking off the edge of the cliff, watching the waves crash against the rocks below.

I thought about the trip and how much had happened over the last couple of months, all the colorful characters I'd met and experiences that I'd stumbled into. When we come out to these places, we are scattering pieces of ourselves along the way, co-creating memories with other transient souls who in turn share pieces of life's puzzle with us. Different ways of living than we're used to. Different ways of being.

Every time we travel, we have the opportunity to return as someone new. Just as we decide *where* we want to travel to and *how* we want to interact along the way, so too can we decide how we want to *return*. This process doesn't just happen naturally. As we return to our old lives there can be a tendency for us to mold back into the selves that the world knew before we left. To best integrate our experience, we must be intentional about how we return or we run the risk of falling back into old patterns and behaviors. To take full advantage of our journey, it helps us to think about how we want to return and to set ourselves up for success. Who was I when I left? Who do I want to be when I return? How does the world that I'm returning to support, or challenge, this new version of myself?

What a beautiful realization. Does this transformation even need to end when I return home? Perhaps I can treat my entire life like a journey from which I'm constantly returning? A journey that presents me with a constant opportunity for new beginnings. Maybe the return is even *more* important than the trip itself. The art of living life itself as an iterative design process.

"The fountain of perpetual freshness!" I said out loud and laughed to myself.

My thoughts spiraled like the wisps of clouds that extended into the stratosphere above my head and I felt some lingering shame about my recent behavior. I'd deviated far from my personal health routine. I'd traded yoga and meditation for nights of romance and decadent temptations of the senses. And as delicious as they all had been, I knew that without prioritizing my mind, body and spirit connection I ran the risk of getting lost in temptation and then everything would seem less fulfilling. In the past when I felt on top of the world, I tended to over-consume, eat, drink and live to excess. Then I would lose track of myself, stumble and begin to self-destruct. It had happened so many times that I was now perpetually course-correcting to avoid it. But it was getting easier. I was noticing the patterns more quickly. I would stumble, notice the patterns, climb. Stumble, notice the patterns, climb. And as long as we're stumbling *upward,* right?

Travel has a way to bring it all to the surface, our emotions and reactions appearing in quick succession, and if we're aware, if we observe these patterns with enough acuity we can begin to consider if we really want to keep them, tweak them or cast them aside altogether. I noticed that when I start moving around too much, being too busy, my healthy routine tends to fall apart. And without a healthy routine, when the storm clouds of emotion gather, I revert to old vices and behaviors. To counter this, it helps to surround myself with characters I want to emulate, and to be in places where healthy options and activities are easy to find. Staying in these places for slightly longer portions of time helps me develop a good routine. The goal of finding a good routine was that in time I can replace my less healthy behaviors with more healthy habits and learn how to navigate myself smoothly through any circumstance. I imagined what my therapist would say. Probably something about my inner critic being a real drill sergeant asshole.

I thought back to San Marcos, where my inner grandmother had told me not to be too hard on myself. Why *was* I so hard on myself? Why did I hold myself to such high ideals? This constant quest to be the most bright-eyed, sober human surrounded by healthy folks and mindful activities? Did all that really get me more in touch with myself and others? Because judging from the last week or two it seemed like when I drank and let loose, I met all sorts of people, got into memorable mischief and even got laid. Twice! So, which was the true me? Which was the more "connected" me?

I took a moment to smile at the hilarity of it all. The game, the struggle. I vowed to love myself all along the rocky path. Not just the side of myself that shined when everything was glowing, but to love that side of myself made of shadow and despair. To let my darkness rise, free of judgment, to learn any lessons it holds, feel what it wants me to feel and then to observe it as it falls away, echoes of an old self that might no longer be necessary. Seagulls, pelicans and dragonflies all swirled around my abused fedora, riding gusts of salty air that promised to keep them aloft just as long as they continued to adjust to the ever-changing patterns of the wind. The wind carries no emotion, just an opportunity for change, to practice acceptance and to take action.

As I descended back down toward the Camino del Gigante Bay I felt that familiar catharsis that humans often feel when returning from something large and challenging. The struggle and the *return*. While I might not be exactly sure how things were going to work out at Manzanita, I felt more confident than ever that the right thing was going to happen. Along the way I had tried to keep the bigger picture in mind and hadn't allowed myself to be absorbed into anyone's particular drama. I hadn't felt it necessary to push an agenda nor allow myself to get trampled. In my experience, the more that I seem to go with the flow of how things *want* to be, the more things seem to work out exactly as they should. I was certain that in time everyone involved would see why it had to happen the way it did.

I was proud of myself for remaining flexible. The world doesn't need more dictators. Like a seagull I would continue to adjust to whatever winds came my way. Soon I'd be returning to my small cabin in the woods where I could read books, find time to write and continue to practice a well-balanced lifestyle. Well, at least that was the plan.

25. Want To Do Some Dougie?

"Well, I thought you'd forgotten about your mother," my mother said, as usual half-joking, and half giving me her trademark jab of Italian guilt.

"Never!" I laughed. "I just wanted to let you know that I'm back from my motorcycle trip."

"You never told me you were on a motorcycle trip!"

"Oh, I'm pretty sure I did! Well, just a little jaunt." Even if I had mentioned the trip I hadn't really told her much about it, learning over the years that sometimes it was better to tell her about things that might worry her *after* they were over.

"Well, thank God you're safe," she said. "I hear it's very dangerous down there. You know, the world just isn't as safe as it used to be. Just read the news, people are going crazy and attacking each other everywhere."

"Actually, Mom, it's really pretty safe down here. A lot of what you hear about amounts to just a few crazy people. And there's crazy people everywhere."

"Well, that's true. And God knows, when your time's up, it's up. And at the end of the day," one of her most frequently used phrases, "I've learned that you kids do what you want. What do I know? I'm only your mother." She feigned the poor mama routine with finesse but it was just an act. And then, in a technique formed through years of trial and error, I replied:

"Thanks so much for your support, Mom, I feel your love and I am safe and happy." After that reassurance I steered the conversation toward more creative terrain. We talked about her recent writing projects and her paintings, how she was still playing the piano despite her arthritis and which galleries she'd recently visited in San Francisco, where she lived, and before long the whole interaction was nothing but good vibes.

"Well, I'm so happy to hear from you, my dear son. You sound fantastic. I can hear it in the tone of your voice," she said, notably calmer by this point.

"Thanks for everything, Mom," I continued buttering her up a little. "I know my life is a little different than the lawyer-slash-tennis-club son that you might have hoped for."

"Oh, forget all that. I'm proud of you. And all that society stuff can be SO boring anyway," she replied. "Well, I'm going to tell your sisters that I'm not worried about you at all." This was yet another magical evolution in our relationship, a reality that had seemed completely impossible just a few years earlier. Even my sisters couldn't even believe how I'd managed to maintain my "golden boy" status for as long as I had. In truth, the more I learned to love and soothe myself out of my own frenzies, the more I could practice with others, not least of all my sweet, and occasionally prone to drama, Italian mama.

"Love you, Mom."

"Ciao, bello!" she replied with her usual sign off.

I was lying on a fantastically comfortable bed in the middle of a bohemian-chic room in the heart of San Juan del Sur. The walls, window trim and other details had that sort of distressed effect in which deeper layers of old paint, in this case pastel blues, yellows and pinks, peek through worn-away areas. The furniture was all secondhand, but tastefully chosen, a bed with carved posts, an old trunk at the foot of the bed, a child's pram with dolls in it, and a rocking chair. Swaying gently above the bed was a dreamcatcher, plants hung from the ceiling, shelves were full of books in different languages and a variety of animal artwork adorned the walls. I'd found the room on Airbnb, which was an activity as convenient as it was full of regret. Why? Well, it just so happens that I went to RISD with the founders of Airbnb and we'd talked about the project in its earliest days. "You're already kind of living the life, traveling and working from all over the place. Maybe there's a way you could get involved?" Brian, one of the founders had said. "No thanks," I replied, busy with my own projects in Los Angeles. "But good luck with that!" And once again I forced myself to smile over my life as a dot-com millionaire that wasn't meant to be.

It turned out that the room was above a surf shop and its French owner had given me a key to the front door, so after he closed up shop I had the whole place to myself.

Yesterday's ride from El Gigante had been smooth. Initially I had thought that I'd found a shortcut but the road quickly became rough and littered with piles of concrete and construction materials. Finally I backtracked and pulled over to ask a couple of schoolgirls who were waiting for a bus if this was the road that went to San Juan del Sur. I strung together the best sentence I could.

"Hola, señoritas. Este camino arribar a San Juan del Sur?"

They giggled and replied in perfect English that the road that I was heading down didn't yet exist. It was under construction, apparently part of the yet-to-be-constructed coastal road. Faced with either trusting digital maps or giggling schoolgirls, I decided to go with the latter.

After hitting town and checking into the Airbnb, I found a local yoga studio where I'd taken a soothing Yin class. Afterwards I went grocery shopping and ate a large plate of fruit before dragging my weary bones into bed. Even the seasonal winds of San Juan Del Sur, which were still going strong and threatened to tear the surf shop's rattling tin roof clean off, didn't prevent me from falling into a deep, dreamless sleep.

When I finally woke up the wind had died down and had been replaced by the blaring sound of the local juice seller, who was relentlessly yelling to the world that he had fresh "Jugo! Jugo! Jugo!" I blinked my initial annoyance aside, threw on some clothes and ventured down into the surf shop where a group of young kids were renting surf gear. The street outside was buzzing with cars and scooters, swerving around the juice seller who continued his monotonous, and seemingly unacknowledged wail: "Jugo! Jugo! Jugo!"

"And no one ever wants his damn juice," Patrick, the French owner shook his head. He brought me a cappuccino and offered to make some pancakes. As I sat there drinking a world-class cappuccino and eating a pile of the most American of pancakes, I took in the scene and smiled. Once your senses adjust to it there is something fascinating about living right smack in the middle of the unrestricted cacophony of an urban center in a developing country.

After breakfast I mounted El Rojo one last time and rode over to El Gringo's motorcycle rental shop, where I got back my deposit and told the tattooed owner about the clutch. He hopped on, changed gears a few times and swore.

"You rode it the whole way like this? Good job, mate!"

I simmered a little bit but decided to not make a big deal of it. I said a final goodbye to El Rojo, thinking back to all the miles we'd covered together, along dusty roads, aboard choppy ferries, through the jungles and over the mountains, spreading mischief as we went. Shitty clutch and all, El Rojo had brought us home, body and bike intact. As the owner wheeled the motorcycle away, I thought about how many adventurers had found him before me, and how many more still would, flexing their freedom and stoking their destiny by way of the janky metal beast.

To celebrate my return, I decided to spend the day sipping watermelon slushies and catching up on some writing at a resort up the hill named Pelican Eyes. Bizarre name aside it was a stunning place, crisscrossed by paths that led to a string of infinity pools with spectacular views of the bay.

After enjoying an explosively crimson sunset I headed back down the hill and treated myself to a delicious dinner at a restaurant called Nica Thai, which served typical Thai recipes with a tropical twist, like passion fruit-infused hot sauce. For dessert they served a fruit called a sapodilla that tastes like caramel and has a large black seed in its center.

Over dinner I began plotting my route to Costa Rica, from where I'd fly home in just over a week. My original plan had been to get down there in time for a big festival called Envision and end the trip with a bang. But I didn't have tickets to the festival and felt like I might have already had enough bangs. I decided to give up on making any decisions and just get down there and go with the flow. First and foremost my immediate plan was to wrap up my Nicaragua travels with a weekend of fun in San Juan del Sur. Freja, the Swedish girl from El Hoyo, had messaged me a few days earlier and told me that she and Hugo were in town and might be going to something called Sunday Funday, which was taking place the following day. So in a pattern you should by now be familiar with, while I *aspire* to choose healthy and mindful activities, I also find it's important to acknowledge the side of me that aspires to take part in an all-day, skimpily dressed party that shuttles people in rickety pickup trucks between pools all over town. After all, how can one experience the full clarity of one's own brightness without dabbling in the shadowy alleys of intoxication and excess from time to time? Ah, the smooth logic that I use to convince myself.

As I was finishing up dinner, I met a German woman called Kate who was picking up a to-go order. She was in her early forties and had curly blonde hair. She was attractive, although years of smoking, judging from her greyed complexion and the yellowed skin between her index and middle fingers, had drained her vibrancy and made her look older than she probably was. But she was fun, a freelance writer working her way through Central America and sending stories back home to a German magazine. She was also planning to go to Sunday Funday the next day so we decided to meet up and roll over to the starting point together.

After saying goodbye to Kate, I was making my way back to the surf shop when I heard someone yell my name.

"Dougie! Yo, Dougie!" I'd turned and it was that beautiful beach bum, Charlie, sitting outside a bar and waving me over. Next to him was the always bubbly Betty. "Good to see you, buddy!" he exclaimed.

"Oh yeah! How have you guys been?"

"Oh man," his voice got quieter. "That stuff you gave us! The past week has been awesome! We call it *Dougie*. Like, 'Hey Betty, want to do a little *Dougie*?'" He was talking about the cocaine that I'd traded him for the mushrooms back at the Paradiso. They both looked at each other and started laughing.

"Well, I hope you've been sharing it!" I said.

"Oh, I've been sharing it …" he paused. "With her!" He pointed at Betty and they laughed again.

"Well, we didn't do ALL of it. We still have a little left," she smirked. "Want a bump?"

"I'm good, thanks, Betty." Look at me, setting boundaries. "So, what are you guys doing here?"

"We're just here for a few days, enjoying the last of our vacation." He took a swig from a bottle that he had hidden in a brown paper bag. He noticed that I noticed. "The drinks in this place are expensive so I bought some rum at the store. Want some?" He passed me the bag. I took it from him and took a good swig. A nightcap, if you will.

"So, what have you been up to?" Betty asked.

I told them about León and El Hoyo. They laughed at the vision of Hugo in his pink running shorts, thinking he was a butterfly. Then I told them about the journey back south.

"Wow, you've had some adventures! We've just been mostly drunk or high since we last saw you." And I didn't doubt it.

"I remember being your age. Enjoy it while you can!" I laughed. "These days I just don't bounce back so quickly."

"Yeah right, Dougie, like you're so old! We heard you described as a legend at the Paradiso. Apparently you do a great American preacher impression!"

"A wise man picks his battles … *wisely*!" I said, conjuring my best regal bravado. "Speaking of which, what are you guys up to tomorrow? Are you going to Sunday Funday?"

"We might crash it. Or we'll probably just do the same as we did today. Surfing, rum … and maybe the last of the *Dougie*." They laughed. Betty told me excitedly that tonight she was excited to try something new.

"I'm going to snort a line off of Charlie's penis!" she clapped.

"Well, I wish you the best of luck with that. Don't forget to take some pictures." I smiled. We shot the shit for a little while longer and then I said goodnight and headed back to the surf shop, which had closed for the day. I unlocked the front door, made my way through to the back of the shop and upstairs to my room.

As I lay on my bed and looked up at the dreamcatcher, I thought about how people live and how they spend their lives. In less than four decades I'd experienced a lot. I'd seen how the wealthy live, on sprawling estates, private planes and yachts, their time filled with enough fancy meals that even lobster and filet mignon could become a bore. I'd witnessed life in very poor countries while traveling through rural Asia and India, and found that all in all, once people's basic human needs are met, there was little variance in baseline happiness between the rich and the poor. If anything, the rich often seemed *less* happy. Maybe by creating our own little kingdoms we disconnect ourselves from others and then think that by making more money and filling this hole with things, we might find happiness. But satisfaction seems to be a constantly moving target and the danger is that the more we have, the more we need to feel content. Perhaps those with a lot to lose feel an additional stress not felt by those who already possess very little?

I'd never been one to chase the golden ticket. First of all, as I mentioned earlier, I'm not convinced that more money is synonymous with more happiness. Besides, having to maintain such a complicated life, relentlessly powering away just to get our next bump of happiness just isn't that attractive to me. I'd rather be satisfied without so much complexity because *at the end of the day*, as my mother is so fond of saying, once all the bells and whistles have quieted, after the cars and homes have been amassed, we're still left with ourselves. And are we okay with that?

Don't get me wrong, I enjoy the finer things. Fancy foods, grand hotels, the opera. Okay, maybe not the opera, but I think that's partly an age thing. And yet I can still enjoy the simpler pleasures like hiking in nature, riding a bike and traveling on a tight budget. If I was staying at the Hilton I probably wouldn't be interacting with all these questionable characters or living above a surf shop and eating instant pancakes offered to me by a charming French expat. Maybe life isn't best lived in just one style, or even in one place, but in a mixture of complementary combinations. When we have everything it's easy to take things for granted, while the time spent without certain things can make us appreciate them that much more. Currently I found it greatly enjoyable to live simply and frugally in an off-the-grid cabin in the woods of Oregon and then to visit friends in town to experience the luxury of flushing toilets, light switches, central air-conditioning and entertainment on demand. Perhaps it's this fusion of different ways of living, a twisting together of the unexpected, that makes for a content existence?

Do I have it all? No way. Are there things I'd love to have? Sure. But for now, I'm feeling creatively fulfilled, healthy, and kicking back in a unique and colorful setting, feeling inspired. And I'm feeling pretty damn happy about that.

26. Dark Water Light

It's curious how much I think about death. Seriously, it tends to pop out of nowhere. I might be driving close to the edge of a cliff, hanging off on a ski gondola or as I was, in this case, just lying on a bed in a quirky room above a surf shop in a foreign country. In these moments I ask myself: *"How would I feel if it all ended right now?"* I don't know why, maybe it's just a way to gauge my current level of life satisfaction. It's less dark and depressing than it sounds and more of a conceptual pastime. In other words, it's less *"Woe is me! I can't deal with this cruel world anymore!"* and more *"You know what? How nice would it be to not have to deal with this cruel world anymore!"*

Since I was a child I have felt awe at the idea of returning to where I came from. I imagined that death would probably feel similar to how I felt before birth. In other words, total egoic nothingness. I remember being in my Transformers pajamas at a family dinner party when I was six years old and asking my mother's elderly friend how old she was.

"Well, I just turned eighty-five last month, young man," she said, to my amazement.

"You must have been so patient to reach that age!" I exclaimed.

"Oh, it goes faster than you'd think," she'd replied, her wrinkled face smiling down on mine as I was sternly reprimanded by my mother for asking such a rude question.

But my fascination with death only grew. As the years went by I watched people cry at funerals, family pets get buried and my remaining grandparents pass on and yet I never felt very emotional about any of these things. Perhaps I was bestowed with a larger perspective. Or maybe I'd shut off a certain side of myself as a result of one early trauma or another. Most probably it was a mix of the two. Even at that young age the world seemed like a pretty harsh place and death seemed to offer a pretty happy alternative. They are finally free from this chaos! I would think to myself. We should be celebrating for them!

More than thirty years later and not much has changed. What would it look like if we celebrated death instead of mourning it? Instead of thinking about our loss, thinking about our loved one's great return to that giant pool of energy from which we all came. The notion of living forever makes no sense to me; I guess I've just never been that attached to the human experience. Rather than share these opinions I would instead usually attempt to conjure some emotional response lest I seem like some sort of insensitive bastard.

As an adult I have seen glimpses of the infinite through meditation, drugs and dreams, moments in which I came into contact with Source, God, or whatever else you want to call it. And it felt truly blissful. Waves of reassurance wash over me each time the doors to the great Home are thrown open and my perception expands into the bright light. Yet each time the same doors would inevitably slam shut as I was forced to return to this depressingly limited filter of human perception and all the petty shit that goes along with it—okay, and I guess all the love, connection and puppies that come along with this tiny little slice of the human timescale too. But when all is said and done the disappointment is just as fleeting as the puppies.

I'd thought about suicide many times before but usually got too hung up on the details to actually consider following through with it. I mean, how would I do it without leaving a big mess and traumatizing those I leave behind? I had thought about hanging myself, but I'd feel too bad for whoever found me. *No one* wants to find someone swinging from a rafter. Overdosing on drugs seemed like a nauseating and unreliable strategy. Razor blade in the tub? Hell no. I've never been a cutter and get far too woozy at the sight of blood. Maybe I could drive off a cliff or make it look like a paragliding accident or something? Yeah, falling into a chasm and leaving behind no one who really cares enough to look for you seemed the most convenient option. But god dammit, I still had people who cared about me and would probably be pretty traumatized so I was back to square one. On the flip side, people who survive suicide attempts often talk about their newfound gratitude for life. Perhaps there's a way to get to the latter without having to do the former? In time, even when I felt my least hopeful, the storm clouds would eventually pass and the dark fantasies would fade away.

But suicide aside, why is there so much stigma and fear surrounding death anyway? Besides any pain experienced *during* the process of dying death itself must be incredibly peaceful. How lovely it must be to shrug off these earthly anchors and just fold back into the infinite? And yet most people seem so attached to their fleeting role as a human, clinging onto their mortality like their lives depended on it. And why? Maybe it's our fear of the unknown? Maybe it's the fiery pits of some imagined damnation? Maybe we don't want to lose the fragile lives that our egos have built or are terrified of being separated from our loved ones. Occasionally, like this morning lying on my bed, this whole life thing just seemed like a pointless game, a game in which we are all just doing our best to kill time until the time inevitably kills us.

Okaaaaaaay, buddddy ... let's rewind a little bit because it seems like Sunday Funday had been less fun than I'd been expecting.

To be honest I didn't know *what* I expected but the reality was hundreds of day-glow kids who were getting wasted and dancing to shitty techno that was blaring from shittier speakers. I'd arrived with Kate, the German woman who I'd met the night before, but while she seemed to be having fun I couldn't help but feel somewhat out of place. So I'd hit the rum, intent on slowing my mind down for just long enough to stem the pangs of self-loathing.

A couple of pools and more than a few rums later we'd made our way to a hostel called Tiger Palace. The rum had temporarily replaced my depression with extroversion and I'd found a fun group of people that were hanging out near the DJ booth on the dance floor. The rum was actually making the music seem better. I went to get some more drinks.

The bartender was dancing like a lunatic and even when I finally got his attention he could barely maintain eye contact. He finally worked out how to mix my rum and colas and placed the drinks in front of me.

"That's 50 Cordobas." He slurred, so I gave him a 100 Cordoba bill. He spent a good amount of time rifling through the cash drawer, eventually handing me 150 Cordobas in return. I tried to explain his mistake over the loud music him but he gave me a fist bump and went back to dancing, so I left a 50 Cordoba tip and returned to the dance floor with the drinks and my original 100 Cordoba bill.

As I walked by the pool a grinning young man skipped drippily up to me.

"Dougie!" It was Hugo, everyone's favorite Swedish butterfly, still wearing his colorful pink running shorts. "Oh man! I love you, man!"

"Hugo! Good to see you, buddy. How are things?"

"Everything is amazing!" As usual, he was ecstatic. He told me about how great the El Hoyo experience had been for him and how grateful he was. "You really changed my life, man!"

"Glad to hear it! It was definitely a memorable adventure," I laughed. A moment later we were joined by Freja, who looked as radiant as always, a quiet yin to Hugo's yang.

"Should I cannonball?" Hugo asked, but before either of us could answer he flung himself into the water, splashing a bunch of upset-looking bystanders. I was still carrying two drinks and Kate, who I'd bought one for, was nowhere to be found so I offered one to Freja.

"Nothing weird in it, is there?" Freja asked, smiling.

"Just some soda, rum, and a little acid." Her eyes widened. "Citric acid, you know, from a lime. Sheesh, Freja! Who do you think I am?" We both laughed.

"You know, that El Hoyo experience. I think it was just what Hugo needed. He hasn't shut up about it," she said. "A weight feels like it was lifted from him."

"Well, I'm glad to hear that, I thought we'd lost him for a moment there."

"Yeah! We all did!" She giggled. "Well, thank you. We're heading back to Sweden this week and he has all sorts of new ideas for his future." She told me that she and Hugo had been friends for a while, but something had changed since El Hoyo. They appreciated each other more. "I know he's a little crazy. But he makes me remember that it isn't all so serious, you know? This life can also be light and fun." We watched Hugo splash around in the water with a giant inflatable beach ball. She smiled. "Want to jump in?"

"I think I'm good for now."

"Okay, see you later!" She downed the rest of her drink and followed Hugo's example, cannonballing into the water next to him.

After sunset the increasingly raucous, day-glow-streaked partygoers were loaded into a motorcade of rusted pickup trucks that proceeded to parade through town as they smoked cigarettes and did bumps of cocaine, whooping and hollering as they went. I was up front and asked the driver what the locals thought of the Sunday Funday lunatics.

"They're used to it. And it brings in tourism money," he replied. The trucks dropped their drunken cargo at a beachfront bar called Lit, the last stop on the Sunday Funday tour. Before long the dance floor was a serious freak fest, and a fusion of reggaeton, hip-hop and dubstep washed over the sandy, sweaty, inebriated crowd. Kate, who'd confided in me on the ride over her fetish for tall, long haired Latin men was now surrounded by three of them who were gyrating their hips and thrusting at her, much to her drunken delight. As for me, my rum high was giving way to a broody low. Where there'd been laughter I now felt a wave disgust for the scene, the swarming mass of drunken humans who'd traded their inhibitions for any opportunity for meaningful connection. Whoa! I could be such a judgmental asshole sometimes! Was I judging them or really judging myself, rejecting myself in some way? Because everyone else seemed to be having a great time! Yeah, I was the one with the problem, I thought. As I considered the shittiness of everything and how much everyone sucked, I realized it was time to take my cranky ass home to bed. I never said goodbye to Kate.

I returned to the surf shop where I sat in the café portion of the shop and sulked. The furniture was made out of old wooden pallets and a hat hung on the wall, bordered by a blue frame. The doldrums of the rum made the whole place feel more contrived. I was feeling overstimulated, and knew what I really needed was to avoid any more adventures, and find some time for quiet reflection away from all the activity. I took stock of my situation.

I had met a young woman at the Tiger Palace who said she had a rental car and had mentioned that she might be driving to the Nicaragua-Costa Rica border in a couple of days and might be able to give me a ride. So I decided that rather than try to stumble into Costa Rica hungover the following morning I would stick around for another night and hitch a ride with her the next day if possible. Some days earlier my old friend Davis back in Oregon had given me the contact info of a guy who ran a community down in Costa Rica, so before heading to bed I sent him a message to see if he'd be around.

I woke up hungover and hating myself, naked on top of the sheets and with the taste of rum still on my breath. My mind was filled with resentment and regret. This wasn't even about last night. I mean, maybe something had triggered it but these feelings of not belonging, of not being good enough, seemed to come from a deeper place within myself. As I lay there, thinking about death again I began to talk myself down from the edge. I reminded myself that maybe I was in a shitty mood right now but in general I had been feeling pretty damn content. Although it might feel like a world away I noted that most of the time I felt love and compassion for myself and others. In fact, I'm generally a pretty damn happy person. Yes, I still have shadowy days, days when the darkness creeps in, feelings of regret and rejection and other old demons appear, if only to remind me that I'm never going to be completely free of them. Days like today. During these times I imagine all the decisions that I might have made differently. Surely this is a completely normal human tendency? I reasoned with myself. We all mess things up, that's part of life. We all feel the effects of rejection, even if only from that original trauma when we were each pushed out from the warm embrace of the womb into this cold, bright and loud world.

Luckily my dwellings on death are relatively short affairs and I have a few things that help me navigate the storm clouds of thoughts and feelings back toward the light. Before long I was coaxing myself to remember that this world also has cuddle puddles and baby animals. These are the times I might even pull up those emergency adorable Instagram accounts until I feel my frown relax and heart soften. I acknowledge all the things that are actually working and that everything isn't completely falling apart.

I sat up on the bed and did a short gratitude meditation, reminding myself of the things that I have rather than focusing on the things I don't. By the end of the meditation I reaffirmed that I am safe and I am still breathing, and the feeling of impending doom had begun to subside. Rather than focusing on my eventual return to the infinite

I contemplated the gift of the present moment, grateful for this brief and improbable little slice of time in which we can be creators of experience for ourselves and others. It is a practice of grace to sit with and accept all these sensations as they arise and to inevitably watch them morph, dissolve and pass on by. It's another day, and there's no rush to return to Source just yet. For those that don't understand depression, this is what the process into and through it can feel like.

Downstairs, over another delicious cappuccino, I caught up on communications. I decided to skip the social media, which could sometimes add to my depression, and instead send some messages to distant loved ones, reminding myself of all the people who I care for and who care for me. Whether they reply or not didn't so much matter, it was the act of sending the messages that I found had the cathartic effect, and any response I got was just a bonus. Healthy eating is the next thing. I chose the fruit platter over the pancakes and after breakfast I returned to my room and recorded a voice journal. Recording my thoughts always felt like a poor man's version of talk therapy and by the end of it I would often find myself laughing. Voice journaling also helps me observe the state of my inner voice. Is it friendly and supportive? Would I want to be friends with this person or is he an asshole? If so, how can I change that? My inner voice should be my confidant, my best friend. We can all keep a variety of types of friends inside us, a diverse and wise council to call upon whenever we need. Now I can even conjure my own inner grandma whenever I needed. She was my most recent addition to the council, a sweet old lady with a calm and soothing voice.

"Oh, my dear boy, don't be so hard on yourself. You don't have to figure it all out right now," her loving voice might say. "Maybe make it a self-care day my love, and treat yourself to something nice."

I showered, got dressed and headed over to a late-morning yoga class. After that I found a gym, went to get a haircut and by sunset I was enjoying a delicious meal back up at Pelican Eyes.

"I am a unique and special fucking snowflake, dammit," I said out loud as I watched the sunset from the edge of the infinity pool. I was back on top, back in the light and things were going to be okay. I got out of the pool, dried off and went to the bar to pay my bill. While I waited I checked my phone. And right on cue, like a nod from the universe itself, I had two new messages. The girl with the rental car,

Amy, was leaving for the border the following morning and said she had a spot for me, and the owner of the community in Costa Rica, an American guy named Chris, had invited me to come stay. His place was called the Living Library, which he described as a holistic wellness community and retreat center, set in the jungle near the town of Tinamaste. As a bonus Chris said he had a motorcycle that I could use to get around the area. So, it was settled, I'd end the trip in a calm and healthy way by spending some quiet final days in the jungle and on the beaches of Costa Rica before catching my flight home.

A couple of years ago I had learned that the name "Douglas" was derived from the Gaelic, meaning "Dark Water", which felt like it summed up a good portion of my life. My darkness was a side I kept hidden from people, even from myself, by any means possible. To share my darkness was to admit the suffering, the pain, the rejection. But these feelings were real and in time I learned that hiding them didn't resolve them. And so I'd begun to share a more fully realized version of myself with others. While there were certainly some friends who were made uncomfortable by my newfound expression of feelings, to my surprise I discovered that many other friends appreciated me even more. And in turn this authenticity invited them to open up to me, thus creating a deeper connection between us.

To soften up the "Dark Water" I'd started going by "Dougie," a diminutive which seemed to get a smile out of most people. Some years later, after that particularly powerful yoga teacher-training experience in Thailand I had decided to return home with the last name "Lux," Latin for "light." And so Dougie Lux was born, intended not as a static character but as an inspiration, a journey, a state of being and becoming. Dougie Lux is my lighthouse in the storm, and an aspirational call to action. He the best version of myself, a masterpiece in progress.

"Dark Water Light," I reminded myself as I walked down the hill to the surf shop. I felt renewed. With relative gracefulness I had visited my shadowy underworld and emerged back into the light. With each journey into my depths I gain a deeper understanding of who I am and how I work. And just when I think I've figured it all out, old patterns appear to challenge me, but each time I am more equipped to face them. As I entered the empty surf shop my inner grandma made an appearance.

"Behold the great cosmic onion skin, sweet boy," she said. "And after all the tears are shed, after all the sorrow is felt, what else is there to do but laugh?" Or course, she was right. What else is there to do but to cry and heal and laugh as we peel back the layers of our own humanity, stumbling along on this unpredictable path of our human experience.

27. Welcome To The Jungle

As planned, I met Amy out front of the surf shop the following morning. She was short, in her early twenties and wore a bright blue tank top over an orange bikini. Her knock-off Ray Bans were pushed up on top of her head, keeping her hair out of her face. Amy had pulled up in a muddy, economy-size rental car. She'd already picked up Ron, another American backpacker who was also intent on getting across the border. The surf shop owner bid me farewell and sent me on my way with a cappuccino in a paper cup and a napkin full of pancakes. I squeezed into the back, crammed between the backpacks, Ron's front seat and a dirty window. But spirits were high as we set off toward the Pan-American Highway, and then southbound toward Costa Rica.

Before long, Ron, who was writing a travel piece about budget travelling in Central America, was jabbering on about various things. He was tall, barely squeezing into the cramped front seat, and had dreadlocks that were wrapped up neatly at the top of his head. He spoke decent Spanish and had gotten wind of some early stirrings of political unrest in Nicaragua.

"I don't know, I mean my source was a waiter serving me breakfast yesterday morning," he said. "But he was saying something about the government threatening the elderly or some shit like that. Not physically, of course, something to do with money or taxes. Anyway, it seems like a good time to get out of town and head into Costa Rica."

Ah, Costa Rica, the land of lush green jungles and progressive environmental practices. A fabled land of peaceful people who'd decided to dissolve their military and redirect its funding toward improving the lives of people, plants and wildlife. Also, Costa Rica was apparently a haven for New Age gringos and property investors who were still riding a wave of foreign investment that had begun many years earlier. The country prided itself on the intact ecosystems of its protected interior, boasting innumerable wildlife refuges, zip lines through cloud forests, and countless permaculture communities, yoga retreats and other opportunities for eco-tourism.

After a short drive we arrived at the border where the typical scene of border-crossing chaos was playing out. Money exchangers, yelling bus drivers, old ladies selling churros, and young kids hocking phone chargers were all weaving between a mix of local and gringo passengers, the latter of which were looking at phones, maps and each other in various states of confusion.

After a brief and heated volley with the rental car rep over the filthy state of the car, Ron was able to calm him down and Amy gave him some extra cash as a tip. We got our passports stamped and then proceeded to find our transport. Amy and Ron were headed to Tamarindo Beach and I was trying to get to Tinamaste so I thanked them, said goodbye, and they soon disappeared into the bustling crowd. Tinamaste is the closest town to the Envision Festival which I was still considering attending, so I began looking around for someone who might know how to get there; I spotted a tattooed gringo with giant earlobe plugs. I bet he's going to the festival, I thought, so I approached him and discovered that my intuition was correct and he informed me of the correct route. The first stop would be in the capital of San Jose, where I would be able to catch a connection to Tinamaste. His bus was full but after some further exploration I managed to get the last spot on another bus that was departing soon afterward.

Besides myself and a couple of other gringos the rest of those waiting in line were locals, and before long we were all jostled into the TransNica bus. After an inordinate amount of time going nowhere the bus eventually crossed the border, upon which we exited to get our passports stamped. In line I struck up a conversation with the other gringos, one whom was English and the other Irish. They were on their way to a meditation retreat.

"Meditation tourism is the next big thing," Nigel the Englishman said. "I guess you could say we come out here so we can go in there." He tapped his skull and laughed.

"It's all about being in the flow, like," said his Irish friend.

It was the perfect conversation because by this point that's exactly how I was feeling. This was fortunate since while I didn't know it at the time the rest of the day would require me to flex my flow-maintaining abilities. At passport control I saw a young fellow whom I'd met briefly at the El Pital chocolate factory on Ometepe a couple of weeks earlier. He was headed down to perform fire-spinning at Envision so I told him that I might see him there.

The roads of Costa Rica felt notably different from the roads of Nicaragua. While certainly beautiful and lush I couldn't help but feel a slight adverse reaction toward the sudden reappearance of American brands. Home Depots and McDonald's sprung out of the jungle like gleaming corporate monuments, edifices of Western capitalism. Still, even from the bus I could see why so many people think this place is magical and why "pura vida," was the catchphrase of the country; the term, loosely translated as "pure life" and could be used in greetings or farewells as well as a way to express gratitude and appreciation.

After consulting a map on my phone, I found what seemed like a shortcut through a town called Dominical, which meant that I wouldn't have to go all the way to San Jose. I thought it might save me some time so at a rest stop I approached the bus driver, pointed on the map and strung together some words. He said he could drop me off at a place where I could find a bus for Dominical. A couple of hours later the bus driver hollered at me and ground the bus to a halt. I said goodbye to the gringos, slung my pack over my shoulder and exited the bus. And no sooner had the bus pulled off in a cloud of dust than I realized this wasn't actually a bus stop but a gas station. I was a little confused, so made my way over to a local man who was filling up his tank.

"Donde esta el autobus para arribar in Dominical?" I asked. He just shook his head and then turned and yelled out something to the gas station attendant. The two exchanged some words and arm gestures. Apparently there *had* been a bus but it had left moments before I arrived.

"It's not here. I can take you. Vamanos," the first man said. Unsure of any other option I threw my bag in his trunk, hopped in the passenger seat and we took off. Before long we pulled up to a roadside bus stop just as a solitary bus was pulling out. The man honked twice and the red lights of the bus's brakes illuminated. "Your bus," he said, smiling. I thanked him, gave him a handful of Nicaraguan Cordobas, grabbed my bag and hopped on the waiting bus. The bus was packed with only standing room left and it wasn't even going to Dominical, it was headed to Quepos, and after some initial confusion the driver told me I could connect in Quepos to Dominical. From there I'd look for a way to Tinamaste and then on to my last stop, the Living Library. In the meantime, at least I was going in the right direction.

I hadn't heard anything from Chris since the previous day. His last message had provided an address followed by some cryptic arrival instructions which included a string of sign posts and turns to a community called Fuente Verde. He'd also apologized as it now looked like he wasn't going to be around. Apparently he had been asked to lead some type of jungle ceremony but a few of his people were on site and I was still welcome to stay. So I'd asked for a few clarifying details but hadn't yet gotten a response. Hopefully it was enough information to get me there.

I soon realized that my shortcut idea had been a terrible one. While the route appeared shorter on the map the bus I was on made numerous stops, and by the time we arrived in Quepos I had missed my connecting bus to Dominical. A local guy who'd been on the bus with me had heard my discussion with the driver and said he could find me a ride. He made a call and then told me his friend could take me for USD$100. I told him no thanks. He relayed the info to his friend and came back with USD$80. It still seemed too steep so I decided to walk over to a taxi stand. The taxi driver told me USD$60. I said I'd think about it at which point he offered "USD$50, I take you right now!" Dominical really wasn't that far and the price still seemed high so I decided to walk around the cute little town of Quepos and stop for some shrimp ceviche and a beer while I figured things out. I still hadn't gotten any response from Chris and was contemplating my next move when I remembered that I'd heard Uber worked in Costa Rica. I brought up the app and sure enough there was one nearby car and it gave me an estimated cost of USD$40 to take me directly to the address that Chris had provided. I paid my bill and hailed the ride, content with my resourcefulness. I also smiled at my own contradictions, lamenting Home Depot but praising Uber. How personal convenience shapes our ideals! After all, I'm sure if I was building a house I'd be psyched to have Home Depot nearby.

Oscar, my Uber driver, was a wannabe tough guy, sporting a tight shirt and tribal tattoos, while he drove around in a Prius that was bumping popular 80s tunes. Sweet Dreams by Eurythmics was my departure anthem as we left Quepos, bound for the Living Library.

"Sweet dreams are made of this
Who am I to disagree?
I travel the world
And the seven seas
Everybody's looking for something ..."

As it turned out, Oscar was a real sweetheart. He told me about his kids and life growing up in Costa Rica, which sounded peaceful and idyllic. By this point I'd been travelling for more than twelve hours, fueled mostly by cold pancakes, a few plantain chips and the remnants of a bag of nuts that I'd bought on the bus. We drove through Dominical and then Tinamaste, stopping at a small market along the way so I could buy some groceries, and then turned inland, traveling away from the coastal towns and up a steep, curvy road into the jungle.

The sky was dark by the time Oscar, following his phone's map, turned onto a small dirt road. We wove down through increasingly thick jungle, eventually stopping when his map indicated that we'd arrived at the address Chris had provided. And of course, there was nothing there. No residence, not even a driveway, just a thick wall of impenetrable jungle. Oscar looked at me. I looked at Oscar. I suggested that maybe we should keep going a little further. We drove for a while but soon decided that maybe we should turn around and look again. As we drove up the road we spotted a turnout that we'd previously missed marked with a small sign that read "Fuente Verde." This was the marker we were looking for and Oscar made the turn, driving deeper into the jungle. The road became progressively bumpier as Oscar navigated his Prius along the twists and turns while avoiding potholes. The next clue Chris had given me was to look for a Rainbow Fish sign. I wasn't sure if he had meant to look for the words or an image of said fish but we never saw either. The only sign we saw was for a place called Summertime House so we pulled into the driveway to ask for help. A young fellow who was tending a pretty garden offered us some vague directions and we were soon back on our way.

A few more turns and signposts later we arrived in front of a beautiful earthen house. The walls had been molded into organic curves, studded with small glass portholes of different colors and the roof was made of red clay shingles. As we pulled up, a tall, tanned goddess appeared at the door, her golden skin radiated with an inner glow. Pura vida, indeed!

"Is this Fuente Verde?" I asked, poking my head out the window.

"Yes, it is," she said. I heard laughter coming from inside the door. This must be the community house, I thought, so assumed the Living Library must be somewhere nearby.

"Excellent!" I looked at Oscar. "This is it!" By the time I got my backpack out of the car the goddess had disappeared back inside. I thanked Oscar again and he drove off. As I approached the front door a bronzed older man with short-cropped, salt-and-pepper hair opened it.

"Hello, may I help you?"

"Oh hi, yes. I'm Dougie, a guest of Chris," I said, overflowing with gratitude that I'd arrived.

"There's no Chris here," he said. My short-lived elation sputtered out like a stalled engine.

"Oh, that's strange. This is Fuente Verde, right?"

"Well, yes, this whole neighborhood is Fuente Verde. Our home is called 'Be Here Now.' *Where are you meant to be?*" he replied, apparently missing the humor of his non sequitur.

"I'm staying with Chris at a place called the Living Library."

"Hmmm, well I'm not sure what that is but you look tired, why don't you come in?" My frustration was nearing a breaking point but the man was so kind and soft-spoken that I felt put at ease. I entered the spacious, open-air living room and lay my bag near the door. The home was neat, cream canvas-and-wood couches on top of red tile, candles burning, bathing the place in a soft warm light.

There was a group of about seven people, ranging in age from thirty to sixty, of various shades of tan. "This is Dougie, everyone. He's a little lost," he said as he waved at me. "We're just about to eat dinner, would you like to join us?"

"Thank you, that's very generous!"

After getting cleaned up in their bathroom I emerged back into the kitchen area, was offered a stool and served a delicious-looking plate of Mediterranean food.

I was grateful for the dinner and after some sleuthing the good news was that I wasn't that far away. The Living Library was a fifteen-minute walk into the jungle. I struck up a conversation with the tall woman whom I'd first seen at the door and asked her how she liked living in Costa Rica.

"Oh, I love it. But I love all of my experiences. They're all perfect and each shows me the path that I'm meant to be on." Each of my questions were met with a similar response and it was a little weird. I don't know if it was because I was tired, but her tone was a little too "peaceful" and her "everything-is-perfect" routine made me wonder if there was a little spiritual bypassing going on. Someone had told me that the gringos of Costa Rica could sometimes exude an air of pretension and maybe this was what they were talking about. It was getting late and the whole discussion was getting a little woo-woo for my liking but I was an uninvited guest, and they'd been nice enough, so it was time to say my goodbyes and be on my way. The older man walked me out and pointed down the road, into the dark jungle.

"Just head that way and you should find it. It's right at the end of the path."

As I walked into the jungle I realized that there was a good chance I wouldn't find it. The man had mentioned some clues to watch out for but I immediately felt lost. At least I had my tent and sleeping bag if things came down to it, I thought. Fortunately the moon, which had just crested the adjacent hills, was almost full and illuminated my path. Loud insects cut through the darkness on either side of me and I was aware of the quiet flapping sounds of bats as they swooped for unwitting moths and other nocturnal tidbits.

I passed a few unlit structures until I eventually came to the end of the road where it transitioned into impassable jungle. I returned the way I'd come until I got to the last structure that I'd passed. It was only around 10 p.m. but the place was totally dark. As I got closer I called out. Nothing. I called out again and a light on the second floor of the open-air building flicked on.

"Hello?" a voice called out.

"Hello, is this the Living Library?" I called back.

"Yes," came the response.

"I'm Dougie, a guest of Chris."

"Oh, yes. One moment," the faceless voice replied. Sweet moon goddess of the jungle, I'd finally arrived.

After a brief intro I was led by a sleepy Raphael, the caretaker of the Living Library, through the kitchen to a room full of books and crystals; there were no walls, just screens to keep the insects out. "Chris is not here, and he might not be back for a few days, but he said that you were welcome to sleep here." I thanked Raphael and he crept off back to bed. The room was musty, that smell of old books, maybe with a hint of wet dog, but I was appreciative to have finally found my destination, and a place to lie down after the day's adventure.

Before going to bed I went back into the kitchen, which was open on all sides to nature. It had a rustic table in the center, made from a large slab of wood that was scarred with knife marks from years of chopping. On one of the walls hung a large print. I recognized it; it was a replication of a painting by Mark Henson called The New Pioneers. In the center of the panoramic image stood a traveler with a backpack and a lamp. He was standing on a tree-lined ridgetop with steep drops descending on either side. On the left side an apocalyptic scene was unfolding. The ground was littered with dead bodies and car wrecks, while tanks patrolled the wreckage and helicopters flew above burning buildings. A few other refugees were ascending the incline, away from the madness, toward the traveler. The right side of the image descended into a lush valley where colorfully clothed people were making their way over a clear, flowing stream toward a neatly terraced landscape of bountiful gardens beyond. Geometric structures stood on the shore of a sunset-washed bay. In the distance, away from the shore, sat a group of people enjoying a meal together.

Returning to my room I dusted off the old futon and checked the sheets for any unwanted critters. When satisfied I lay down, turned off the lights, and fell asleep to the sound of the jungle, journeying into a dream realm of shadow and light.

28. Full Moon Loons

Sunshine. Insects. And people laughing nearby. At first, as my eyes blinked open and fell upon the unfamiliar room, I forgot where I was. And then the adventures of the previous day fell back into place. I got out of bed, threw on some shorts and a tank top and strolled out into the kitchen. Raphael was chatting and laughing with a pretty, young woman in her mid-twenties who was chopping up some vegetables. Another fellow was making coffee. Everyone was exceptionally tanned and healthy looking.

"Good morning, everyone!" I said.

"Good morning, Dougie. How did you sleep?" Raphael asked.

"Oh great, thank you. What a peaceful place to wake up in," I replied, my gaze turning to the other man. "Hi, I'm Dougie."

"Hi, I'm David," the other fellow said. "And this Jessica." He introduced the young woman, who I intuited was his girlfriend.

I offered up the groceries I brought for the breakfast preparations and before long we'd prepared a feast. Jessica had wrangled some clean forks and plates and began to arrange a delicious spread of scrambled eggs mixed with veggies, refried beans, local cheese and fresh bread.

We were just sitting down to breakfast when we heard the sound of a loud engine emanating from the jungle path that led up to the house. The sputtering sound grew louder until finally it was upon us, as a tanned and shirtless young kid zigzagged a janky-looking motorcycle right up the hill to where we were eating. After skidding to a halt, the kid, who couldn't have been more than eighteen years old, hopped off and approached the table.

"Well, it's not so great but it works," he laughed. "There's no first gear and the brakes are pretty weak, but it's usable!"

In that moment, I realized two things. First, that this was the motorcycle that Chris had offered to loan me. The second thing that I realized was that there was no way in hell that I'd be driving this mechanical death trap around the muddy and gravelly roads of rural Costa Rica. But I expressed my gratitude to him for bringing it over and we invited the kid, who had introduced himself as Luca, to join us for breakfast.

As we ate, I felt my entire nervous system begin to settle. I learned that there were around five or so people staying at the Living Library at any one point, all guests of Chris, the absent owner of the property. This is a community structure that I like to refer to as a "benevolent dictatorship."

Maybe that's a little sharp, but it gets the idea across. Someone owns the land and people can come and work on it, often in exchange for meals and a place to crash. Occasionally more advanced models offer long-term residents a share in the actual ownership as an acknowledgement for their sweat equity, but this was rarely the case. There are lots of benefits to the structure of benevolent dictatorship, most notably that meetings and agreements are far simpler than having to deal with group decision making. Obviously it was in the owner's best interest that people were generally in agreement with his or her decisions, but it wasn't mandatory and if a resident didn't like the arrangement then they were free to leave at any time. And that is also the precise reason these sorts of community structures, ones with a shot-calling leader and without ways to work toward ownership, don't tend to attract long-term residents. Over time most hard-working people tend to become a little resentful of the time and energy that they put into these projects without receiving any actual ownership.

But overall things at the Living Library were pretty sweet. Chris seemed like a good guy and the place was a beautiful work in progress. I spent the morning helping with a few projects around the place, some sapling planting, garden-bed weeding and the reparation and painting of a fence. My overstimulated vibes from San Juan del Sur and the challenging trip down began to melt away.

Luca, who by now I had learned was quite the free spirit, had decided to stick around and after lunch offered to take me to some waterfalls and crystal pools back near the Summertime House. I hadn't been able to tell in the darkness but the neighborhood of Fuente Verde was truly spectacular. It stretched from the steep cliffs that rose up behind the Living Library and down a gentle incline until it met a thick jungle that descended back down to the coast. Along the way we passed a handful of other properties, nestled between shady trees and rich vegetation. Luca told me that there were many other private residences and small communities in the village of Fuente Verde, and that together they formed some sort of membership model that cared for the land. Chickens clucked around earthen structures in which handmade mosaic signs and glass bottles had been inlaid, while water catchment systems and other telltale signs of permaculture design were visible in various states of functionality. It was a little hippie version of the Garden of Eden and it was feeling increasingly likely that I'd blow off the whole plan of getting to the Envision festival and just chill out right here for my remaining days.

Luca was a smiling beacon of joy, a billboard for the hopeful and exuberant youth of the world. He was born and raised in Costa Rica and had left his more conservative home life when he was sixteen to explore the country. His English was very good, with a large vocabulary and only a small, charming Spanish accent. As we walked he told me about his life, of working on land projects, of sleeping in the jungle, literally sleeping in the jungle like a modern-day Mowgli, where he foraged for food and communed with nature.

"Imagine how animals see the world, completely free of ego. Our perception is just one style, you know?" He had the playfulness of a child, but the wisdom of an old soul. We'd come to a small, magical waterfall and were lying on some nearby rocks.

"In every moment we can decide, with our thoughts, our words and our actions, which story we want to create." His words echoed many of my own sentiments, the only difference being that mine had taken many more years to crystallize.

I enjoyed listening to him, how he described the forest of trees that he envisions planting in his mind, trees of love and compassion, and humility and respect. Sowing seeds of intention, watering the saplings and caring for their well-being. "We create every moment with every thought we have, you know? If we don't take care of what we plant, what we think, we can create crazy things." Luca gave me a little more hope for the future of humanity.

After returning from the waterfall I spent the rest of the afternoon lounging, reading and catching up on some communications, disturbed only by some parrots and Jessica when she asked me if I wanted any tea. Meanwhile back at Manzanita, Wave 1 had officially signed the buyout agreement from Wave 2 and would sell back their shares of the property to the others, along with an additional portion rewarded to them for their early sweat equity. It obviously wasn't the outcome that any of us had originally intended but at least everyone seemed to be handling things like mature adults. Neither Teddy Bear Gabe nor any of the others had answered my consolatory email so I assumed they must be feeling pretty disappointed. It kind of felt like a breakup. And just like a breakup there's often nothing that you can do or say to fix the hurt, it just takes time. As for the rest of us, we still weren't free of the original loan but like Stoic Joel had expected, the previous owners, feeling sensitive to our situation, offered to give us an extension, which bought us a little more time to work it out. Meanwhile we all continued to look for the extra funds.

At sunset we gathered to enjoy a bottle of wine that Raphael had found while Jessica and David made a veggie stew and quinoa. Luca, who didn't really have anywhere else to be, apparently, made some mango salsa. We all enjoyed dinner together and then for dessert I offered a bar of local dark chocolate that I'd purchased at the market the previous day. *Was that really only yesterday?* This was a different world.

It was going to be a full moon the following night so I suggested we come up with some sort of ceremony. I don't consider myself especially woo-woo, but my time in Oregon living in an off-the-grid cabin, chopping firewood and reading by oil lamp had made me acutely more aware of the seasons and cycles of nature. The effects of the moon at Manzanita were especially obvious, as when it was full I could walk around the property without a flashlight, but when it was new the entire place was plunged into such darkness that all I could make out was the struggling static of my low-light vision.

Spending the last year around Oregon hippies meant that I had inadvertently immersed myself in countless ceremonies for every new moon, full moon, solstice, equinox, eclipse and any other cosmic event. Unlike new moons, which were apparently the time for setting intentions, my witchy friends spoke of the full moon as a time for release: "Release what is holding you back, what is no longer serving you. Release the tight grip on plans and expectations."

Before coming to Oregon I'd spent most of my life around scientists, techies and entrepreneurs who talked about the laws of physics, publishing scientific research, mining large data sets and getting their first round of startup funding. I remember once sitting on the Eureka sand dunes of Death Valley with a few of my most scientifically intelligent friends on a heavy dose of acid while they tried to calculate the amount of grains of sand that we were sitting on, give or take an order of magnitude. More recently, conversations in my immediate sphere seemed to revolve around energy work and chakra alignment with the odd chem-trailing, anti-vaccination, conspiratorial rant by some crunchy character in a hot spring. Anyway, hippie-inspired or not, any opportunity for release is probably a good thing in our emotionally constipated culture, so why not have a full moon ceremony?

"Maybe we could have a morning intention setting!" Luca smiled.

"We could have a full moon drum session," Raphael offered.

"Yes! And a big fire," David said. Jessica seemed to support this idea, as well as offering a special dinner recipe that she'd been wanting to try. And then it was time for my own offer.

"Well, it just so happens," I said with a mischievous smile, "that I have a large amount of extremely fine LSD and I would be happy to share it with anyone who'd like some."

"No!" Luca squealed with delight.

"YES!" I replied. And much to my own delight everyone seemed to be on board for a trippy day of full moon celebrations. As the dinner candle burned down we talked about life back at home, future travel plans and where we still wanted to go. Eventually David and Jessica went to bed while Luca, true to his word, took a blanket and walked off down the path and into the jungle.

"Does he always sleep in the jungle?" I asked Raphael.

"With Luca, you never know," Raphael said. "Sometimes we call him Mowgli." I laughed and told him I'd thought the same exact thing. Long hair, toned and tan, he looked like he'd swung right out of some Costa Rican live-action version of *The Jungle Book*.

Raphael and I finished up the wine and talked about ideas for future community projects until I grew sleepy and retired to bed, lulled into slumber by the rhythmic pulse of the jungle soundtrack.

I awoke from dreams filled with talking animals and after a light breakfast of fruit and tea, excited for our day, we gathered around a newly planted avocado tree. Luca had torn some paper from a sketchbook and cut it up into five pieces. He asked each of us to write an intention for the day on a piece of paper, after which we buried them, one by one, in the dirt around the base of the tree. As we each took turns burying our piece of paper I offered a drop of acid from the breath mint vial onto each extended tongue. Raphael, David and Luca accepted, but Jessica, who had never tried it before and who was too nervous, decided to abstain. I acknowledged her for taking on the important role of babysitter, as before long it was very possible that she'd be dealing with four grown men acting ridiculous and running around like little children. Feeling comfortable in our peaceful setting, and realizing that I wouldn't have to be as responsible for everyone's survival as I had been on El Hoyo, I decided to take a double dose. The two tiny yet infinitely potent minty-fresh drops, which promised an afternoon of interdimensional delights, quickly disappeared down my throat.

We left the avocado tree and everyone seemed to go about their regular activities. Raphael tended to some plants. David and Jessica cleaned up in the kitchen while Luca sat in the garden and strummed on a small, beat-up ukulele. I did some laundry and decided to take a shower, almost forgetting that I'd even taken anything until mid-shower, when I became increasingly aware of my skin's sensations and distracted by some mossy rocks and sparkly trinkets that formed a small altar inside the enclosure. I must have stayed in there for some time because when I emerged things had evolved into a humorous scene. David and Raphael were over by the slackline, doing their best to maintain balance, each time thwarted by the unbalancing effects of the drug as Jessica sat in the shade and laughed at them. Luca meanwhile had moved to a position over by a particularly colorful bed of tropical flowers with whom he now seemed to be engaged in a lively conversation.

Like I've said before, LSD can have this funny effect where even if you've done it a hundred times, it can still surprise you. While I might remember it *theoretically*, each time it hits I'm still like: "Oh yeah, *that's right!* Acid! Whoa! Okay, well I guess I've got at least eight hours of this now!" I was feeling a little unsettled, as can happen to anyone on LSD but especially to those with a tendency toward bipolarity and other psychological anomalies, but nothing I hadn't dealt with before. Everyone seemed to be entertaining themselves so I decided to go for a walk. I grabbed my phone to take some photos and a small microphone which I'd picked up back in the U.S. so I could record interviews and such. And now I had a sudden urge to interview the jungle.

I walked down the path, toward the base of the steep cliffs where the road ended. I came to a small stream that descended from the greenery and turned to look back in the direction from which I'd come. The views across the valley made me feel like my tear ducts had been replaced with liquid sugar dispensers. The foliage everywhere was breathing gently, waving at me, their edges distorting the surrounding air like heat shimmering off a hot road. LSD play tricks with depth perception, hence the classic, and useful, tripper's adage: "Cars are real, fire burns and if you think you can fly, try taking off from the ground first." The entire scene was now shifting between 2D, 3D and a dimension that went beyond my visual field and seemed to incorporate my other sensory faculty. It was like Vincent Van Gogh had come to the tropics and directed an animated movie just for me. My breath was no longer limited to just my lungs, as air seemed to enter and leave my body through every pore and every cell. Proprioception, the awareness of my body in space, was equally subject to manipulation and I felt both larger and more transparent than usual. I had wandered into the shade of the jungle where it was surprisingly cool and dark and I set up the microphone and began recording.

"If the entire universe is expanding in every direction, and I'm part of the universe, does that mean I am expanding, too?" I asked the jungle. "Surely it's not just the space between matter but the space within matter itself that is expanding. Hmmm." The jungle's answer was a relentless buzz of insect sounds, punctuated with birds and the periodic shriek of a monkey. Occasionally one member of the insect orchestra would abruptly stop, possibly to mate, eat food or just to take a break from its incessant musical endeavor, only to start up again moments later. I soon became silent myself, content to let the jungle share its wisdom with me in its own unique language.

As the tiny molecule lit up my body I decided to lead myself through a DIY yoga set. My muscles felt alive, strong yet supple. Any lingering pains faded away as my awareness moved from my outer environment and travelled inside my body, feeling where the breath touched, where better alignment was needed. An indistinguishable amount of time passed. And then, my foot was burning.

I looked down to discover that I'd inadvertently tree-posed right on top of a red ant mound and the vexed little fuckers were understandably pissed off about the whole situation. With my moment of peace broken I decided to head home. To my surprise when I got back to the Living Library everyone else had vanished. There was a note on the kitchen table, scrawled and decorated with all sorts of cartoon figures and flowers, probably by Luca, saying that they'd all gone to waterfalls. Content to finally have some time to myself I made my way up to the second floor of the main house, where a hammock was strung up amid prayer flags and a seemingly excessive amount of laundry lines. The perch looked out over the jungle canopy and provided a delicious amount of texture for my greedy eyeballs to indulge in. The laundry lines, which were strung in every direction, provided irregular windows, iridescent gossamer panes that framed the green and blue world beyond. Is this how babies see the world? I mean, just look at their little faces and compare them with the face of your average tripper. *Almost totally identical.*

I closed my eyes but my inner landscape was just as detailed. I took some breaths, suddenly fully aware of my place between the present moment and the infinite. I tried to gather my thoughts. I felt like I was an onlooker to my own story. Our lives, these stories that we tell ourselves of who we are in reflection of who we're not, of who we've become as a result of what we've been through, of what we've done, of what we'd had done to us, and how we had reacted to all of it. All around the world there was a huge surge in blame and finger-pointing going on. Immigration vs. nationalism, rich vs. poor, intellectual elite vs. the blue-collar class. People everywhere were pissed off at what had been done to them and wanted to point at someone else, anyone else, as the cause of their suffering. Meanwhile, those in control were leveraging our fears to further control us, all with a vague promise of increasing our safety and security.

But in reality, for the majority of people, it's the safest time to live that there's ever been. Medical advances have wiped out diseases, minimized infant mortality, led to longer lifespans, and given freedom to countless less-abled people who in times past might otherwise have not survived. Our halls of science and technology are decked with great achievement and promise a future in which we'll be able to live with more free time to do what we want. What we're able to do with our time and choosing how we want to live is more within reach to more people than ever before. *Isn't it?*

Utopian futurists imagine a world where all the mundane jobs are done by robots, we live longer and healthier lives, and everyone is provided with a universal basic income. If this happened would the results give us more freedom? Or would we all just become busier-than-ever little consumers? Why was it that with each development that offered us more freedom the more we figured out how to stress ourselves out? *What was that all about?*

My mind drifted to the darker side of this proposition and the necessity for capitalism to continue to grow by any means possible. The idea of the sharp divide between the rich and the poor, the masses who have no clear way out of debt, *what of them??* The brightest things possible and the murkiest muck of our humanity were all coming to the surface at an increasingly rapid rate. Platforms for sharing knowledge had become platforms that spread hate and devices that offered to connect us with each other had evolved into shiny little bricks of addiction.

Not a day goes by without a scandal of governmental corruption, discovery of some church's massive kiddie-fiddling cover-up, another horrific school shooting, hackers influencing elections and foreign agents taking down each other's infrastructure, kids being separated from their parents at borders, #metoo, #blacklivesmatter, #insertyourgriefhere, and another day of downright depressing news from our oceanographers and climatologists. The world seems to be locked in a dance of shadow and light.

So, what story do we want to focus on? And what can we do about most of that stuff, anyway? If you can help change it, change it, if not, is it really worth the amount of time you spend worrying about it? Is it worth the fear it instills in us? Probably not. As usual I came back to the wisdom of my permaculture teacher who had only given us five minutes to acknowledge the problems and used the rest of the class to explore solutions.

I still had hope for a world in which our technology could be better integrated with nature, created by those who were inspired by their love for what's possible rather than by their fears and insecurities. Everything we create is infused with the *quality* of the energy we put into it, and our story, at its deepest level, is the operating system that we run on. So, if we analyze our inner OS we can upgrade it with patches, security fixes and new features. When properly tuned, our values, mission and outlook have the capability to transmute blame into compassion, misfortune into opportunity, and miscommunication into understanding. It's all about the *story* we tell ourselves.

In permaculture they talk about the home as Zone 0, the first place to establish security, and I don't know if I have a better idea for where to start with humans than by establishing our own security first. By developing our personal Zone 0, we create a place of sovereignty where no one can *make* us feel anything, and by doing so we can assume responsibility for our own actions and emotions. This personal sovereignty should be a basic human right and helping others achieve it for themselves is indeed a noble way to spend a life.

My thoughts were racing, ideas barely being completed before the next ones took flight. Part of me wants to support radical self-reliance, a life in which we are sovereign beings, not dependent on external resources for our own well-being. But unless we're 100 percent off-grid, independent individuals then this is not realistic. We're social beings, so striking a balance between independence and dependence, call it *interdependence*, is probably the answer. As much as possible, we should be coming to the table, be it as individuals, communities or even nations, and in every setting from romantic, professional or social, with a full cup, with something to offer or at least as self-reliant as possible. Learning how to do more than simply extract value, but to *create* value, is one of the things that we're able to do as humans. It's *regenerative* living. When we sort out our own shit and are unhindered by the baggage and blame that we've left behind, we can work together to do great things, not just scramble to get our basic needs met. A desire to find this, to learn how to be this, is what had led me to Manzanita; this is what our community was fighting for.

I thought about the communities that I'd visited. About how they worked and how they didn't. About how they learned from the past and worked to improve on it. In a well-designed community you don't have to make or do all the things, we can work together to make sure each other's basic needs are met. We can look at our world like a machine with inputs and outputs and consider how to be as efficient a loop as possible, to create a clean-running system that if anything produces *more* energy and raw material for life than it consumes. It's a design problem, really, an opportunity to iterate, tweak and refine. Let us aspire to allow our own inner biology to guide us toward finding balance in our outer biology. We are still a young culture, irresponsible cosmic adolescents, who shouldn't be beaten into submission but handled with stern yet loving action so that we might learn how to coexist and to mature into the adult phase of our species.

Some cling to the hope that a technology will emerge, some super-wise, morally objective AI that helps us through it, or perhaps a limitless, free energy source that disrupts the status quo into oblivion. Who knows, maybe some semi-benevolent aliens will descend in massive warships and tell us that if we don't clean up our act in the next ten years then they're going to come back, harvest us for alien food and take our planet for themselves. And who could blame them? After all we're doing a pretty terrible job with the place.

Do we really need something so major to evolve? Short of any complete disruption, scaling transformation seems incredibly challenging. In the anonymity of large groups, humans get lazy and sociopathic tendencies begin to emerge; people flush crazy weird shit down the toilet, can't figure out how to sort their recycling and need all of their cucumbers individually wrapped in plastic. How had everything come to this? Wasn't there a time when we lived in balance? Maybe, but once this nasty little parasite of the human ego was spawned, convincing us of our separateness from each other and the natural world, that balance was never to be reconciled again.

Seriously though, what's it going to take for humanity to make the changes we need? We invented things like religion as a means to try to make us good people but we had screwed that up pretty much every time. Guilt never works, we can see that pretty clearly. Accountability is a finite resource. Punitive laws and incentives can work pretty well. If only transformation could be made easy, fun, sexy and profitable, what progress we would make! Does it *have* to take a massive catastrophe before we pay attention? Thousand-year floods, blizzard cyclones, megafires and plagues of insects, fungi, and new antibiotic-resistant super diseases are appearing with increasing regularity on the planet. *Why is it necessary for us to suffer so much before we take hold of our own transformation?*

Big thoughts happening here in the hammock, I laughed. Maybe it's all unfolding exactly as it should and is just my limited human timescale that is making it seem like more of a mess than it really is. And maybe that's just some great spiritual bypassing talking. We have the ability to experience what it means to be fully human, to create beauty and maximize the quality of life for ourselves and as many other beings, animal, mineral and goddamn vegetable, as possible. We have the power to live in a generative way in which we give back to the environment that supports us. We can hunt and gather experience and come back to share what we find with others. Sounds like a good way to live a life to me. And maybe, if we ever do reach our full potential, if we can ever step into the vastness of our creativity, we will be worthy to spread out across the cosmos. In the meantime, let's just have some humility for the infinite, keep enjoying the fact that we're little more than receptors that the universe created as a way to observe itself, *and just keep making art.*

Speaking of art, my entire visual field was a splendid canvas of vibrant expression. I smiled at this enjoyably unexpected psychedelic retreat and was grateful to Chris and the community for welcoming me in. I had flowed right into my own transformational Costa Rican getaway, beautifully aware of the dance between assertive action and open reception that had brought me here.

I wasn't aware of the time but it felt like late afternoon and probably at least a handful of hours since we launched off the planet at that fateful avocado tree. My antsiness had since subsided and I was calm within myself, lying in this hammock, exploring my thoughts, watching as my hopes and fears played out on the stage of my mind, bringing myself back to center when either direction got too demanding. Know when to assert. Know when to surrender. This is the balance of life.

I had managed to capture a good amount of my jumbled thoughts as audio journals when, just as the sun was setting, a posse of giggling lunatics swaggered down the jungle path, hooting and hollering my name.

"Dougieeeee."

"Woohee!"

"Welcome back, space travelers!" I hollered from the hammock. "How were your adventures?"

"So fine!!" Luca wailed. "And you?

"I'm pretty sure I left the planet for a while!" I replied. "I'm not sure I completely solved humanity's struggles but I definitely made some progress."

"Well, looking forward to hearing that!" David said. "Let's make some dinner!"

We gathered around the kitchen table and caught each other up about the day's adventures over hand-rolled cigarettes. Jessica led the dinner charge, David and Raphael carefully chopped vegetables, Luca played the ukulele and I tried to convey even the tiniest sliver of my past few hours, before giving up the futile task and joining Luca in singing some Beatles songs instead.

After a spectacular dinner of shakshuka, veggies grown in the garden and homemade tortillas, we brought the wine down to the fire pit and David started a fire just as the moon appeared above the steep cliffs. I had brought down five little pieces of paper and pens, and instructed everyone to write something that they wanted to release. When they were finished I invited them to place the pieces into the fire. I wrote, "CONTROL," and watched it burn to ashes.

"Can I read something I wrote earlier?" I asked. Everyone seemed eager to hear so I pulled up some notes I'd scribbled on my phone while high as a kite in the hammock.

"Ahem," I said, feigning coughing, as if something very serious was about to happen.

"The full moon is here to remind us of the importance of letting go. To take a breath, to calm our assertive ways and to allow ourselves to listen, and to surrender to what wants to naturally emerge. May we not be an impediment to that." I continued, "May we be clear channels of love, acceptance, compassion, and of all that is good and honorable in this world. May we collectively learn how to embody these values and to creatively express what it means to be human. May we heal ourselves and heal the world. May we work toward the light while we explore and transmute our shadows. May we deeply live in this vibration." I let the pause hang. "And may we not take ourselves too goddamn seriously."

"Haha! Aho!" Luca said.

"Aho!" everyone joined in.

The fire dwindled and people eventually took turns bowing out and heading to bed. I was the last one to retire and as I walked back up to the kitchen, a distraught young woman appeared from the jungle, lugging a backpack, totally lost and wondering where the Be Here Now house was. How humorous, she was lost at *our* place looking for *her* place, while just the other night I had been lost at *that* place looking for *this* place! I was still pretty awake so I offered to help her get over there. Twenty minutes later I'd sent her on her way and heard lots of cheerful greetings as she entered the home. I walked back to the Living Library under the light of the full moon, curled up on the old futon surrounded by books, crystals and that wet dog smell, and slept for a long, long time.

29. Dominical And The Gift

I was on the beach, lying in the shade of some palm trees, and I had two things on my mind. The first was a beautiful female silhouette in front of me, which actually made me forget what the second thing was. She was facing the ocean, framed by palm trees with the cresting waves of the Pacific as a backdrop. It was my last night in Costa Rica and there was obviously only one way to end it. I would go up and talk to this dreamy young lady. She'd think I was charming and funny, so I'd invite her out for a delicious dinner. She'd accept the invitation. My conversation would be witty, insightful with just the right amount of flirtation, not too heavy, not too subtle. She'd laugh and we'd leave the restaurant, arm in arm, stopping at a beachside night club. We'd enjoy a few drinks and after a while I'd offer to take her back to my place.

"As long as you can promise to behave yourself," I'd say. She'd laugh again and with a smile she'd tell me sarcastically, "Oh, I promise," as she gave me a wink.

My time at the Living Library had been so rejuvenating that I had decided to ditch my plans to attend the Envision festival and just stay there for a few more days. Finally, this morning, feeling totally refreshed, I said goodbye to Raphael and the rest of the community, asked them to relay my gratitude to Chris, whom I'd never actually met, and hitched a ride out of the jungle, down to a beach town called Dominical. I had dropped my bags at a small, tucked-away hotel, got into a bathing suit and strolled down the palm-tree-lined beach. I found a nice spot and jumped in the ocean, which was warm. Not to sound like an ungrateful dick but the ocean was actually a little *too* warm to be refreshing from the heat and humidity, so I got out and bought a cold soda from a guy with a cooler.

And so here I was, sitting in the shade of some palm trees and drinking a cold soda when I saw the formerly mentioned, alluring silhouette. The final night of my Central American expedition would be filled with magical tropical lust and a decadent amount of coconut oil. I was feeling confident and revitalized so I got out of the hammock and strolled over to her to begin my conquest.

"How's your surfing?" I asked casually as I idled up next to her.

"Pretty good, actually." Her eyes moved from the water to glance at me briefly. She was taller than she'd seemed from where I'd been, taller than me, in fact, and confident to match. Her blonde hair blew gently in the breeze. Her nose and cheeks were rosy with a light sunburn. "I was surfing all day yesterday and caught some big ones. I'm just taking the day off."

"Yeah, me, too," I blatantly lied for no apparent reason.

"You surf, too?" she asked, her feminine powers of intuition possibly sensing my dishonesty.

"I've been known to hit the waves. Yesterday was gnarly." I feigned surfer machismo with my gaze locked on the ocean.

"'Gnarly.' Do people still say that?" she asked.

"Oh totally. So you're German?" I asked, changing the subject rather ungracefully.

"Swiss, actually. But from the German-speaking part."

"I love Germans," I smiled. "But I'm a big fan of fondue, chocolate and yodeling, so the Swiss aren't all that bad."

"Well, I love Canadians," she said.

"Actually, I'm from the States."

"Oh, I know you are." She looked back at the waves. "But I'm a big fan of hamburgers, milkshakes and Country music so Americans aren't all that bad." We both started laughing.

It was fun and easy. Her name was Lila. She was athletic, easygoing and adventurous. I told her I was lying about being a good surfer and she told me she already knew I was. She was just coming from the Envision festival so I got to hear all about it through some of her stories. There was fire-dancing, art, music, all those fun festival things, all set in a tropical paradise. She'd stayed the previous night with a guy she'd met at Envision, but he'd started acting a little aggressive so she'd decided to just camp on the beach, and I helped her set up a tent near some other wandering-nomad types, just down the road from my hotel. We went for a smoothie and watched the sunset together.

Lila thought I was charming and funny so I invited her out to dinner. She accepted the invitation. My conversation was witty, insightful with just the right amount of flirtation, not too heavy, not too subtle. She laughed and we left the restaurant, arm in arm, stopping at a beach side night club. We enjoyed a few drinks and after a while I offered to take her back to my place.

"As long as you promise to behave yourself," I said. She laughed again and with a smile told me sarcastically, "Oh, sure, and maybe we can invite the guy from last night, too." I laughed too, casually brushing off her rejection I walked her back to her tent, which she zipped closed along with any hopes of fulfilling my final fantasy. My last night in Costa Rica would *not* be filled with magical tropical lust or a decadent amount of coconut oil. At least not applied to my body by anyone other than me. And you know what's almost as good as an attractive lady being attracted to me? An attractive lady blatantly rejecting me and me not feeling totally bummed out about it. Behold the power of personal growth!

On my final morning I woke up in a bright, clean room. The linens were crisp and pillows soft and cool. A light breeze, the smell of toast and the sounds of tropical birds all wafted in through my open window. I ordered some room service, a big platter of eggs, bacon and fruit, which arrived arranged in the shape of a smiley face. The eggs sat at the top like a blond toupee. After breakfast, I enjoyed a long, hot shower. I smiled to myself. After weeks of roughing it I felt a renewed gratitude for such simple luxuries.

Humans get spoiled so easily, I thought. Something we just thought was great a moment ago, we now take for granted or just cast aside while we look for our next fix. We work hard for material goods and when we finally obtain them we feel great … but often only for a short while. Soon we find ourselves wanting something else, convinced that we'll finally be satisfied once we get it. And we are, for a while, until we need the next thing. And so on. Left unchecked our lives can become increasingly consumed by this cycle, requiring larger and more complex things for us to reach that same high. Psychologists refer to this behavior as the hedonic treadmill. I don't think the answer is for us all to renounce all material possessions and live out our lives as monks and nuns. So, what's my solution? I like to be happy with simplicity and then treat myself to decadence. I live in a cabin most of the time but when I vacation I like a big-screen TV and a hot tub. And then back to simplicity, and so the cycle continues, prompting me to find gratitude for even the tiniest things in life. Light switches and hot water on demand … *oh my, the luxury!*

After the shower I packed up, left my bag behind the front desk and decided to take a walk around town to kill some time. I had one important mission to do today before catching the early afternoon bus to the San Juan airport. So I grabbed a smoothie, which was *not* the mission, and got a little lost, eventually veering onto a path next to a river that led to the ocean. I assumed there would be a way to cross but after some time I realized there was no way to get to the side of the river where my hotel was, except by wading through it. The river was deeper than expected and my feet sank into the sand as the water came up to my waist. As I looked for a way up the opposite bank I noticed a small path. I emerged from the water and walked up the path, which led right into the back of a restaurant where a drug deal was obviously taking place. There was a golf ball-sized bag of what appeared to be cocaine on the table and a couple of men sitting on either side who were just as surprised as I was about the situation. Characters in this bizarre scene: me, a puffy faced Westerner, and a red-eyed local.

"Hey fellas!" I said as cheerily and calmly as I could muster. "I got lost and ended up in the river. Sorry to disturb you!"

"Okay. No problem," the Westerner said. He sounded American. I was grateful as things suddenly became more relaxed. "Where are you from?"

"From Oregon," I said. "How about you?"

"Rhode Island," he said, and set about placing a small amount of powder on the tables and carving it up into three neat lines.

"Oh, I went to school there. RISD. Good memories." It was always good to find some common ground in uncomfortable situations.

The local guy, who still seemed a little tense, said something to the American, who then turned to me.

"Juan here wants to know if you want to buy some cocaine." He snorted a line, passing the rolled-up twenty-dollar bill to the local guy.

"You know, I had a big night the other night and I think I need a little break." It was both the truth and an opportunity to establish some more common ground to relieve any final tension. Juan took his turn. "Actually I'm on my way back to my hotel and then to San Juan to catch a flight."

"Well, more for me then," the American smiled, and snorted up the third line.

I stroked the small object in my pocket, considered it for a moment but then decided against it. Not the right scene and not the right characters. So we talked for a little while longer before I excused myself, finding my way through the empty restaurant and out onto a street that led back to the beach.

A bunch of vendors had set up booths selling everything from wire-wrapped pendants to leatherwork and all sorts of other arts and crafts. Yes, this was a much more appropriate scene to find the person I was looking for. Just beyond the vendors there was a shady area, surrounded by palm trees, and in the center there was a bench facing the ocean. And on that bench was a young man, early twenties maybe, scribbling in his journal and wearing a colorful pair of pants. I looked at the guy and fingered the object. He would do nicely.

"Well, hello there, good sir," I said as I took a seat on the bench, calling up memories from that conversation atop the San Pedro volcano.

He looked up, his concentration broken. "Oh, hello," he replied in a soft accent, possibly Dutch.

"Sorry to disturb you. I couldn't be sure from a distance, but now ..." I paused. "Yep, you look like the kind of guy who likes a good adventure."

"How can you tell?" he smiled.

"I have a keen sense for these things. First I find that writers often are adventurous souls." I pointed to his journal.

"Well, that's true," he smiled.

"And if the journal wasn't enough to convince me, those are some cool pants." This made him laugh.

"Thanks, I got them at Envision."

"Good find," I replied. "What are you writing about?"

“Just notes from my experience. I’m going to write a book about my trip.”

“Ah, fantastic. How long are you travelling for?”

“As long as I can until my money runs out, I guess. How about you?”

“Actually, I’m heading home today, gotta get back to work.” I put my hand in my pocket and rolled the small object around in my fingers.

“Oh, that’s too bad. What do you do?” he asked. I turned my gaze out to the ocean, which I hoped would add mystery to my next line:

"Let's just say I work for a certain government agency that is involved, and has been involved in some pretty awful stuff both at home and abroad."

"That sounds like a terrible job."

"Absolutely terrible. You can’t even imagine," I replied. I was now enjoying the ruse.

"Why are you working for them then?"

“You gotta infiltrate. And then assimilate. Open their minds and let curiosity do the rest.”

“Well, it must be nice to be on holiday from that job,” he said.

“For my holidays I like to come to places like this and spread the good cheer. Us Yankees are not all bad. Spark a little benevolent mischief. Maybe shake up a few travelers, a few locals, take ‘em out, you know, blow their minds. Give them a new perspective. An experience they won't forget."

“That sounds like fun.”

"Oh, it is,” I said, looking back out to the waves. “Or maybe I'm just totally fucking with you and I’m just a guy from Oregon who lives in a cabin and comes to Costa Rica to explore intentional communities." He looked up at me and I looked back at him with a mischievous look. He put his pen down, a curious smile on his youthful face. "Yep, you're the one," I finally said, withdrawing the small object from my pocket and keeping it concealed in my hand. "I have something for you." I put my hand up to his ear and then brought my fist down in front of me. I slowly rotated my fist, uncurled my fingers and in my palm was a small object.

"Breath freshener?"

"Yep. But a drop of this particular breath mint will do more than just freshen your breath. It'll freshen your mind." I paused and lowered my voice. "This is about forty doses of some of the finest LSD known to man. I can't tell you how I got it but I can tell you that it's research-grade quality."

"Ha! Well, I was definitely not expecting that! Very nice offer but I don't think I should be buying acid from some guy I just met on the beach."

"Oh, I'm not selling it. It's a gift." The tiny bottle was barely bigger than the tip of a pinky finger. It sat in my hand. "I don't need it anymore. I think you should have it."

"Well, I wouldn't want you traveling back home with this so, what can I say?" he asked.

"How about 'Thank You'?"

"Thank you!"

"Don't mention it." He looked around and when he was satisfied nobody was watching he picked up the bottle out of my hand and pocketed it quickly. "Well, my friend, I gotta go," I said. "I need to catch my bus."

"What's your name by the way?" he asked.

"It's Loki." I smiled.

"I'm Sander. Nice to meet you, Loki." We shook hands and I got up to go.

"Now don't do anything I wouldn't do out there, Sander." Which left things wide, wide open for the young Dutch man.

"I can't promise anything," he replied.

"That-a-boy!" I grinned. I took in the scene one last time and walked away from the beach.

30. Always Coming Home

"Hygge," the Danish call it. The meaning is best translated as *"a mood of coziness and comfort with feelings of wellness and contentment,"* and there is some serious hygge going on right now.

I'm sipping tea from an asymmetrical clay mug and sitting in a beaten-up armchair. Clues in the cushion creases indicate that the chair used to be blue but is now more of a mottled grey, further devolving to a threadbare beige atop the armrests. Despite being late March there is a light dusting of snow spread across the valley that is framed by the large windows. A fire crackles away in an old wood-burning stove, the radiant hearth at the center of the small cabin. The Manzanita community had survived its trial by fire; we were a few members shorter, a little bruised from the whole experience but otherwise still standing. I'd been home for a month and it felt good.

From this old armchair I'd begun writing a book about my trip to Central America. While it wouldn't be the first book I started writing, I pledged to myself that it would damn well be the first one that I actually finished. Writing is one of those things that I completely lose myself in. I lose track of time. I became fully immersed for hours on end, pulling away only long enough to eat, drink and relieve myself. A whole day might go by and yet it would never seem like a wasted day. Note to any creative types: these are all good indications of a creative outlet worth cultivating. And yet I'd never taken writing to be anything more than a hobby.

Over the last few weeks, I'd developed a healthy routine. Daily meditation, yoga, journaling and a stable diet became the norm. I hadn't been smoking and had been moderate with my alcohol. I felt grounded, stable and was realigning with myself, and in doing so I felt confident that the rest of life could just figure itself out around me. As I've said before, people, places and experiences all affect our brains and it helps to learn how to dose ourselves accordingly. You want to be healthy? Hang with healthy friends and consider where and how you live. If Los Angeles had been my amphetamine, the wilderness of Oregon was my valium, and it had a great way of chilling me right the fuck out.

Being in the wilderness had always felt more natural to me than being cooped up in the city. Life in the quiet of the forest reminded me how food, alcohol, substances, and even socially accepted activities like work, could all become distractions when pursued out of balance. Literally anything, even going to the gym or relentlessly reading books can be done to excess, becoming their own forms of escape. None of these distractions can ever completely fulfill our desire for deeper connection. That connection we seek might look very different from person to person, but finding it for yourself is no less important. For me the deeper connection I needed could not be found in more people, more experiences, more sexual conquest or more sensory input; oddly enough, moving to an off-the-grid cabin in the woods, away from all my familiar friends and distractions, was exactly what I needed to discover that deeper connection with myself. In moving out here, I discovered a deeper connection to my creativity, my intuition, and my self-reliance. When those things feel aligned, then and only then can I connect as deeply as I want to with others. Only when I can take care of myself may I bring a full cup to my other relationships. It might not have been the gentlest process, but have I told you recently about my penchant for exposure therapy?

Things at Manzanita were finally settling down. Wave 1 had packed up and moved off the land and although some heaviness still lingered around our unrealized collective dream, the whole place felt lighter. I still hadn't spoken to Gabe but I was confident I'd run into him sooner or later and we'd get to hug it out. As for the loan, at the final hour the remaining members, AKA Wave 3, had managed to pay off our remaining debt with the former owners by convincing a local credit union that a bunch of oddballs sharing a property in the wilderness was a stable enough business plan to warrant another, more favorable, multi-year loan, buying us some time to figure it all out. We could breathe again. Manzanita would live to fight another day.

Despite some signs of PTSD in some of the more sensitive remaining members, the community meetings had become calm and productive. The conversation had taken on a markedly different tone, from a relentless resolving of internal disagreements to the more productive territory of structural improvements and future aspirations. We had a business meeting every week to talk about finances and make important decisions, and they were going pretty smoothly. From the beginning of the project we decided upon a supermajority voting model rather than the consensus model, the latter of which can stall decision making, especially in the long term when some people inevitably become crotchetier as they age. So far, so good.

Every Friday morning we gathered in the community room for a resident's council, during which we'd talk about how we were doing, air any emotions or grievances, share successes and gratitudes, and then get our hands dirty for a few hours in a work project. And there were a lot of projects to keep us busy; clearing out old junk from the barn, fixing leaky pipes or demolishing some old death trap of a structure. In the evenings we'd have occasional potlucks and movie nights. The tenseness was mostly gone, the community finally felt friendly and easygoing.

"You guys actually did pretty well," one of our friends from a neighboring community said to us after the dust had settled. "What Manzanita went through in a year, it took our community *five* years to go through." And it was true, while we lost some members along the way, to our credit we had created a structure that had been strong enough to sustain some damage and still stay afloat.

Living in a community is its own kind of trip. I'd left the city a year and a half earlier and pledged a commitment of time and savings to an experience that offers both great reward and great pain in the ass. Communal living provides a continual opportunity to learn about communication, when and how to assert your opinion, and when to just shut up and listen for what naturally wants to emerge. It can, emphasis on the *can*, be a beautiful way to practice patience and watch as collective wisdom unfolds, inspiring ideas and shaping solutions, as we balance our own desires with the desires of others, and with the desires of the land itself.

As I wrap up my tale, maybe you're thinking that starry-eyed community dwellers are just suckers for punishment? Maybe we all share some deeply rooted trauma that keeps us trying to resolve it collectively? Or maybe we were that much closer to realizing the value of deep connection? Well, we had all chosen this community experiment in the wilderness. It wasn't like we were next-door neighbors in the suburbs, this was real wilderness: I'm talking mountain lions, ticks and satellite Internet. And life on the land presents *endless* lessons of ways to work with nature, instead of against it, to align with its timeline instead of trying to impose our own expectations upon it. Manzanita is a long-term, community project in which the characters are as unpredictable as the environment, setting the stage for all sorts of unexpected comical twists and turns along the way.

Who needs television? This whole Manzanita experience felt like a transformational workshop had been twisted up with a reality TV show in which a bunch of unprepared city folk decide to move to the wilderness to start an alternative community. But sometimes it takes a leap of collective faith, a wild ride into the communal unknown, if only as a step toward the noble goals of mutual understanding and respect; and there's rarely a dull episode of this show.

My trip to Central America had driven home this lesson even more deeply: To go with the flow and not against it. It was humorous to me that no matter how the different communities I'd visited were structured, each faced its own struggles as ideals clashed with reality. Yet the exact same reasons why people say, "Oh, I could never do that!" might just be the exact reasons why maybe they *should.* As we learn to communicate better with others, so do we with ourselves. Only through reflection in others can our shadows, the edgy and shameful aspects of our characters, come to light. To feel as unencumbered as we can possibly be, free to reach toward our highest potential while supporting and being supported by others as we do so, this was the promise of community. At least that was the idea.

If it sounds like a lot of work that's because it is, but learning to relate with others is some of the best work we can do as humans. This style of living isn't for everyone, and nor should it be. There are plenty of meaningful ways to live a life, plenty of roles to play and we should do what rings true for us as individuals. But the truth is that many of us have been sold an out-of-date dream, to claim our own slice of the pie while we can, to become ruler of our own little kingdoms, where we don't have to deal with anyone's crap and no one has to deal with ours. And yet for many of us, once we get there, something doesn't feel quite right. All of these shiny possessions and entertaining distractions aren't leaving us feeling fully satisfied. These are the short-lived, hollow highs of experiential twinkies. This is a gap that only a deeper connection can fill, a deeper connection to ourselves, others and the planet that supports us.

Many people are experiencing a shared vision, perhaps fueled by a longing for aspects of our tribal roots in which deeper collaboration and connection were integral. Perhaps this is a false nostalgia for a peaceful past that never was. *Nevertheless, we can still yearn for something that has yet to be realized.* The desire to be part of a tribe, one in which we can learn to live peacefully and interdependently with each other, is perhaps a vital and missing piece of the human experience. Perhaps our intuition tells us that it is within this style of interaction where we can discover the deep connection we crave. I thought back to the highs and lows of my trip; when I judge myself harshly for getting too wasted, having shallow relationships or experiences, it was because I intuitively knew that those activities were not bringing me closer to this connection, and my soul itself was upset.

So what have we learned at Manzanita? Sheesh, okay, I'll try to sum it up. First of all, the order of action should be considered carefully. We had found a property, found the people to invest in it, and then tried to agree upon the mission. Instead we should have started with the mission. Next, remember when you are entering a business partnership that it should be considered as carefully as a marriage. How well do you really know the person? If the answer is that you just met them, be careful! Also, each person should fully explore the meanings of the words that are to contractually bind them. Is your shared vision *actually* shared? Or does each party have a slightly different understanding of the meaning? Take your time and explore the fine details; is it a fair deal for everyone? How is sweat-equity investment valued in relation to hard financial investment? Read contracts that you sign. Don't let people rush you. To avoid the need for legal proceedings there should be an agreed-upon method of conflict resolution, or what the more sensitive and progressive communities call "tension revelation." This means more than just inviting a long-haired hippie on a guitar to lead you through songs about togetherness; real and agreed-upon techniques to resolve differences are needed. Luckily for us, the formation of a landholding LLC, and subsequent creation of a decently airtight operating agreement was the one thing that kept Manzanita from completely unravelling. Well, those are a few things for any idealistic dreamer to ponder before jumping into the wild world of community living.

Anyway, bringing it back to my personal story: I wouldn't change any of it. I have met myself out here in nature, living in an off-the-grid cabin in a community that is dedicated to making it work and it took me to go away for a while to realize it. Life isn't always joyful; in fact, sometimes it's fucking awful, but through each challenge I emerge stronger and more resilient. Through each obstacle I know myself a little better. The break that my journey had given me had reaffirmed this, because even when untethered I still long to belong. And to belong doesn't just happen, it takes work, it takes grit. At Manzanita I feel the connection I long for. I'm part of a group of humans working on a project that will be around for years to come, building a strong foundation that is not completely dependent on any one of us, thus ensuring a better chance of the community's resilience and longevity.

Alright, that's enough of all that community chitchat. It's almost the end of my tale and you are probably wondering whatever happened to that meddling bastard, the beaver. Ah, good old *Castor canadensis*, the North American beaver and buck-toothed instigator of this entire saga. Well, after all the heated discussions, after all the clandestine attempts to sabotage its musky den and rock it off the property with heavy metal music, after all the trials and tribulations that its mere presence prompted, after all of that, one day, right around the time that Wave 1 was moving out, the furry little prankster packed up his things and left Manzanita on its own accord. Like some trickster spirit animal sent to shake things up, the beaver had done his work, and now was no doubt moving on to the next unsuspecting community that didn't even know they needed him.

I'd finished my writing for the day and was walking down the tree-lined driveway to collect the mail when I passed the large grove of poison oak that had caused me so much grief. I nodded at it respectfully, acknowledging how far I'd come from that first winter. At that exact time a message left a phone somewhere in Central America and pinged over to a wireless cell tower where it was converted into electrical signals. From there it was sent through data cables and transformed into microwaves which were shot into space, redirected through a satellite and then beamed back to Earth. It was finally processed through my router, turned into a Wi-Fi signal and popped up as a notification on the small device which was conveniently located in my pocket.

"Hey! How have you been?" the message read. It was from Stella, my beautiful, German, *Tomb Raider* fantasy girl from Guatemala. Memories of our time together, high on acid in the crystal waters of Semuc Champey, felt like a distant dream. "I decided to head to Honduras since Nicaragua is on the verge of civil war," the message continued. And it was true: soon after I'd left the president had continued to threaten old people's pensions, prompting huge protests and civil unrest. The open roads had been barricaded. Hostels and restaurants had closed and tourists had fled San Juan del Sur in droves. Tania, my French Airbnb lover, had left with her family, as had some of the other families that I'd met down in San Juan del Sur. I'd heard on Facebook that the tattooed fellow who'd rented me El Rojo had closed up shop and fled for Costa Rica, and I hadn't yet heard anything from steely eyed Gaia from InanItah or the women at Apapachoa. Living at the intersection of opportunity and the unknown is the gamble that all pioneering expats take.

A second message from Stella pinged my phone: "I loved our time in Rio Dulce, Dougie. I would love to see you again and maybe go on some more adventures. Maybe I'll come visit Oregon sometime?" My heart fluttered as I finished reading it. I imagined how sweet that could be. And if it stayed in the realm of the imagination, that was fine, too. I felt delightfully unattached to any outcome.

"Just let me know when. I'll be here!" I replied, sliding the device back into my pocket. I'd returned home. Not just to Manzanita but to myself, and there was no place else I'd rather be.

Epilogue

The sun rose on the vernal equinox as a group of humans looked over their community, spread out far across the fertile valley below.

"Sweet Earth Mother, times are good!" one member of the group said.

And indeed, times *were* good. They looked at everything they'd built over the years, everything they'd grown, every man-hour of labor poured lovingly into this small slice of the planet. Solar panels glinted from tops of cabins and a plume of smoke curled from the top of the schoolhouse. The springtime lambs were bouncing in the pasture and chickens clucked and scratched in the yard. The creek that emerged from higher up the valley had slowly been nurtured and brought back to life, gurgling through the landscape. The hillside forests all the way up to and over the ridgetops had been thinned for fire remediation and a good diversity of remaining trees created a rich habitat for wildlife. The surrounding valleys held neighbors with whom they traded cheese, milk, meat and bread and they rarely needed to go into town for much. They felt proud. And they felt humble, for not everyone had made it this far.

The earlier part of the new millennium had paved the way for a series of cataclysmic events, both socially and environmentally, creating a deadly feedback loop. Some cities made it through, while others, being more dependent on distant and dwindling resources, fared less well. Many people starved and many more suffered. Unchecked climate change had led to a series of unprecedented and disastrous storms, fires and floods that further ravaged the already weakened environment. As climate refugees poured into surviving areas it created population tension, prompting waves of nationalistic fervor. Red-faced demagogues took hold of many governments. Walls were built and internment camps resurrected. Meanwhile, unable to deal with the sheer weight of the chaos, the militaries of the global superpowers became extended beyond their control and eventually began to fall apart, splintering into more localized factions. Power grabs and tribal tactics followed and people struggled to get access to clean water and other resources. Civil unrest became the new normal around many parts of the globe.

But day-to-day life went on in many places and not everyone was affected as badly. Some were lucky enough to live in less overpopulated areas and of course the uber-wealthy had long prepared for such outcomes, hoarding resources and continuing to throw lavish banquets in their compounds. Over time though, many of the elite fled to islands and otherwise inaccessible hideouts, including vast floating compounds that roamed the acidified oceans in search of remaining resources. For those that had no choice but to remain, most were overextended debt slaves, locked in a system that provided just enough income to afford fleeting distractions until they died of exhaustion or malnourishment, still indebted to the end of their days. Many years later, even after the old financial institutions had mostly crumbled, these people had no idea how to care for themselves, and many cities became graveyards.

Throughout the Great Unravelling, the more intuitive and resourceful people had the best chance of survival. They moved to strategic areas, some staying solitary while others banded together, hunting and foraging for what they could find until discovering some untapped water source or land they could tend, carving out lives far away from the unfolding chaos. In time, others returned to the land to live more closely to their roots, cleaning up waterways and sustaining themselves through environmentally regenerative farming practices and time-tested permaculture techniques.

Over the following century many millions died and many more millions had been displaced but in time a balance began to reemerge. A few cities even managed to flourish during this period, in particular those that were favorably positioned for climate change and in close proximity to resources such as water, arable soil and trade routes. These self-sustaining cities became beacons for what was possible in the new world, full of gardens, clean energy and governed by a style of social democracy that emerged from the ashes of the old paradigm. They produced everything they needed locally and interfaced with the surrounding rural communities, through trade and a generally shared renewed respect for the environment. It became a new world where the labor of a farmer or teacher was equally as valued as the labor of a doctor or an engineer. Education catered to different forms of creativity, holding emotional intelligence above all else. Technology worked *for* people instead of the other way around and culture came to value well-being for all sentient creatures as one of the most important pillars of an evolved culture. The Great Rebuilding became a time of human flourishing in which every individual was encouraged to express their own unique nature and creativity as they continued toward the top of that noble pyramid, toward the lofty goal of self-actualization and beyond.

The group had gathered around the old medicine wheel at the top of the land. Their predecessors had moved to this valley five generations earlier and leveraged their communal power to turn their dreams into reality. Their collective leadership directed the focus of dozens of community members for over a century toward a unified vision, ensuring the health of the land and of its people. This was their divine ability. And they were grateful for each other. They had learned to live in balance with nature and themselves. In this interdependence they found security. In this togetherness they found meaning.

"Ah, yes," one of the group spoke to the breeze. "What better way could there be to spend a life?" Times were indeed pretty damn good for the community of Manzanita.

But then of course, nothing lasts forever.

THE END

ABOUT THE AUTHOR

Dougie Lux is the alter ego of experience designer Douglas Campbell, cofounder of the Los Angeles event series MindshareLA and tech collective Syyn Labs. After a yoga course in southeast Asia left him questioning his existence, Douglas returned to the United States and began a three-year identity experiment; he changed his name to Dougie Lux, left his flashy life in Southern California behind, and moved up to a wilderness community in Southern Oregon, where he learned carpentry and started restoring an old, off-the-grid cabin. In his proudest achievement, Dougie finally settled down enough to write a book. *The Motorcycle & The Molecule* is a novel about his journey to Oregon and subsequent explorations of Central America during the winter of 2018.

Douglas Campbell lives on as an experience designer and event producer on the West Coast of the United States; Dougie Lux continues to explore his untapped capabilities while getting away with things that Douglas Campbell might never admit to doing.

ACKNOWLEDGMENTS

To my editors, Eric Trueheart and Deirdre Stoelzle, my cover artist Lindsay Carron and my crowdfunding supporters who helped me raise enough money to fund the first run of prints, THANK YOU! Also, I'd like to give special thanks to the folks at Trillium, as well as Dave Zaboski, Robin Harlan, Grace Chevarose, Helix Wolfson, Davis Galligan, Dustin Boyer, Andrew McGregor, Daniellow Ribiat, Zane Cooper & Rosie Arancibia, Mark & Jana Roemer, Martin Ball, Mitch Kirsch, Victoria Campbell, Sissy St. John and last but not least the always dynamic and ever-inspiring Selina Gould who stuck with me through all of the shadows and light that come along with the writing process ... *so much gratitude!*

If you enjoyed this book, please consider leaving a review on Amazon or Goodreads. You can follow @DougieLux on Facebook and Instagram and join my newsletter for more adventures at www.DougieLux.com.

"Everything will be okay in the end. If it's not okay, it's not the end."

— John Lennon

*

Made in the USA
Monee, IL
25 March 2020